Introduction to QUANTUM MECHANICS

Introduction to QUANTUM MECHANICS

by

ROBERT H. DICKE
Princeton University

and

JAMES P. WITTKE
R.C.A. Laboratories
Princeton, New Jersey

ADDISON-WESLEY PUBLISHING COMPANY, INC.

READING, MASSACHUSETTS, U.S.A.

LONDON, ENGLAND

Printed in the United States of America

Library of Congress Catalog Card No. 60-11852

Second printing—August, 1961

PREFACE

At present, quantum mechanics provides us with the best model we have of the physical world and, in particular, of the submicroscopic world of the atom. This book is an introduction to the physical concepts and mathematical formulations of nonrelativistic quantum mechanics. To get the most profit from this book, a familiarity with basic undergraduate-level physics, including atomic physics, electromagnetism, and classical mechanics, is required. A knowledge of differential and integral calculus, and some familiarity with differential equations, is also needed.

The decision to limit the text to nonrelativistic quantum mechanics enabled us to explore the basic concepts of quantum mechanics carefully while avoiding both the complications and unsatisfactory aspects of field theory. It is our firm belief that these complications should be met only after an understanding of, and physical feeling for, nonrelativistic quantum mechanics has been acquired.

This text is designed primarily for an introductory course in quantum mechanics at the first-year graduate level, but the first portion is also suitable for a senior-level course. This text can be divided into three sections. In the first section, the first three chapters, we point out the inadequacy of classical concepts to explain many atomic-scale phenomena and suggest how the basic concepts of classical mechanics must be altered to explain experimental observations. The reasonableness of a wave-mechanical theory of particle behavior is shown, and it is seen how classically anomalous behavior, such as quantization of energy and angular momentum and the "tunneling through" a potential barrier by a particle, can result from a formalism which inherently gives both a wave and a particle aspect to the entity that classically would be considered as a particle.

The second section of the book, Chapters 4 through 10, starts with two chapters which lay the groundwork for the more formal, postulational approach to quantum mechanics which follows. We then place Schrödinger wave mechanics on a more defined and rigorous basis, and we use it to discuss such basic aspects of mechanics as measurement, angular momentum, and the behavior of a particle in a spherically symmetric force field.

These first two sections, in which the emphasis is on a grasp of the fundamental principles and their mathematical formulation, with a minimum of the involved mathematical manipulations that so often obscure the physics of the matter, therefore form an introduction to the subject on a level that a well-prepared undergraduate can handle. This part of the book thus is suitable for use in an undergraduate course. It provides sufficient breadth and depth both to familiarize the reader with the basic ideas and mathematical expression of quantum mechanics and to form the basis for deeper understanding later. We believe that it is desirable to present quantum mechanics at an advanced undergraduate level, whenever possible, for three reasons. First, quantum mechanics is such a basic tool of modern physics that its use should be acquired as early as is feasible. Second, the quantum-mechanical picture of the world is in many ways so foreign to everyday concepts as codified in classical mechanics that considerable time is required to develop that familiarity which permits a truly thorough grasp of the full significance of the concepts. Finally, every year finds more in the way of ideas and techniques crowding their way into the graduate curriculum. Clearly, this new material can be accommodated only by discarding old material or introducing new material earlier in the course of study.

The third section of the book, comprising the last eight chapters, represents a considerable broadening of the viewpoint and of the scope of the problems that can be handled. We introduce alternative representations and geometrical interpretations of the formalism and discuss methods of transforming from one representation to another. Canonical transformations and their relation to transformations of the representation are treated. Approximation methods are developed which permit a tremendous expansion in the number of problems which can be handled with some assurance; these are then applied to important classes of problems, such as scattering and problems concerning the interaction of an atom with strong (classical) electromagnetic fields. Throughout the text, emphasis is given to algebraic techniques, and their power and elegance are clearly shown.

Of special importance is the last chapter, dealing with quantum-statistical mechanics. Here we develop the techniques that are playing an ever-increasing role in modern physics. Until now, these have, in general, been neglected in texts on quantum theory.

To avoid possible misleading impressions, all curves in this book have been carefully computed and plotted.

For the reader who likes to broaden his understanding of the subject by seeing how it developed, not in the hindsight of present-day knowledge but as it appeared to those on the forefront of this developing branch of physics, the first chapter gives references to many of the key papers in the development of the basic viewpoints and concepts of quantum mechanics.

Exercises are given at the ends of most chapters. They further illustrate various aspects and consequences of the quantum-mechanical picture of nature and give a quantitative "feel" for certain aspects of nature, and develop a working capability in the solution of problems. We believe this can come only through conscientious practice in the use of the associated mathematical tools.

We wish to acknowledge the advice of Professor S. Treiman as to the most desirable content and organization of this book. The help of Mr. N. Vander Ven in editing the original notes on which this text is based is also acknowledged. This book has benefited from the detailed comments of Mr. Young Kim, who read the manuscript. We wish also to acknowledge the considerable help and encouragement given by our wives throughout the preparation of this book.

Finally, a word may be said about notation. Generally, symbols representing numbers are written in italics (a), and vector quantities are in boldface roman (**a**); operators are in lightface roman capitals (A), and matrices are in boldface sans serif (**a**). At times it is not obvious just how a given symbol should be considered; this is especially true in Chapter 13, on transformations of representations. In such ambiguous cases, we have tried to choose the type font that would make the significance of the expression at hand clearest to the reader. It is hoped that the choices help, rather than hinder, the reader in his study of this book.

March 1960

R.H.D.
J.P.W.

CONTENTS

CHAPTER 1

INTRODUCTION

1-1 Quantum mechanics, a system of dynamics. This study of quantum mechanics will begin with a brief discussion of the nature of physical theories and the scope of mechanics. A physicist is concerned with two worlds: a real external world, which is believed by physicists to have an objective reality, and an image of this world, an internal world, which he hopes is a reasonable model of the external world. The external world manifests itself through sense impressions; from birth, and indeed even before, the human brain is bombarded with data resulting from the stimulation of the sense organs by this external world. At first, these data represent a hopeless jumble, but gradually the brain correlates various data and begins remembering basic correlation patterns. Slowly a correlation structure evolves. For example, an object which on the basis of tactile sense data is round and smooth is associated with the visual sense pattern of a "ball." The recurrence of such correlation patterns in the sense data gradually becomes interpreted as evidence of a real external world.

By the time adulthood is reached, the picture of the external world obtained in this way has taken on such an apparently real and permanent form that it is difficult to believe that it is in fact just a picture. This internal picture, or model, of the external world may, of course, be as much conditioned by the nature of the human mind as by the nature of the external world. It is clearly affected by the limitations of the sense organs, and it may also be affected by the form of the brain, with its computer-type switching mechanisms. It seems reasonable to assume that a brain capable of an "on-off" type of digital reasoning will construct with ease a model such that a particle is either at a certain point in space or else not; it may have difficulty with a model for which the particle is neither there nor not there.

The difficulty with such a primitive concept as that of a particle which always possesses some definite position and velocity is that it is a generalization which has grown out of very crude, large-scale observations. A flying bird, or a thrown stone, can apparently be characterized by a trajectory. However, definite position and velocity at each instant of time are properties of the model only: the position and velocity are always determined observationally in only a rough manner.

Mechanics is the branch of physics dealing with the effects of forces on the motions of bodies. In what is known as the *classical* picture, the world is composed of distinct elements, each possessing a definite position and velocity. These elements, or particles, interact with one another via forces which, in principle at least, can be completely known and whose effects can be allowed for exactly in predicting the motions of the various interacting bodies. Classical mechanics is a computational scheme, based on Newton's famous laws of motion, for describing the motions of bodies in terms of given initial conditions by specifying the positions and velocities of all bodies as functions of time. Despite the many successful applications of classical mechanics to a wide range of physical phenomena, it was apparent at the beginning of the present century that not all of the then-known phenomena could find their explanation in classical mechanics and classical electromagnetic theory. To meet the challenge of these classically inexplicable observations, a completely new system of dynamics, quantum mechanics, was developed.

While there are many analogies and formal parallels between classical and quantum mechanics, the basic underlying assumptions of quantum theory are radically different from those of classical mechanics and may be considered to constitute a fundamentally different way of looking at nature. That is, the quantum model, or picture, of the world is radically different from the classical model. It should be emphasized at the start that one could no more "derive" quantum mechanics than one can derive Newton's laws of motion. Instead, quantum mechanics was developed on the basis of assumptions and postulates which were arrived at on the basis of intuition and analogy with classical concepts, and the predictions based on the *postulated* formalism were compared with observations of the external world. It is a tribute to the genius of the formulators of quantum theory that they were able to devise a scheme for predicting the behavior of physical systems that has stood the test, not only of experimental observations explicable within the scope of classical mechanics, but also of many others that clearly indicate the inadequacy of classical theory.

It is difficult in a few words to categorize the difference in underlying philosophies of classical and quantum mechanics. An example may suggest the scope of the difference, however. A basic concept of mechanics is that of an *observable,* that is, an aspect or parameter of a system that is at least in principle directly measurable. One of the fundamental differences between classical and quantum theory is that, in quantum mechanics, *not all observables can be measured with arbitrary accuracy at the same time,* whereas the contrary is true in classical mechanics. The act of measuring the value of any observable disturbs the system in such a way that some *other* observable is altered in value. The difference between the classical and quantum assumptions regarding this is that classically the effects of the disturbance due to the measurement can be exactly allowed for in predicting the future behavior of the system, whereas quantum-mechanically the exact effects of the disturbance accompanying any measurement are *inherently* unknown and unknowable. Thus, a measurement of the position of a particle introduces an unpredictable uncertainty regarding its momentum. If such a situation exists, the whole concept of trajectory clearly must be re-examined, as this classical concept can then lose much, if not all, of its significance.

1-2 Evidence of the inadequacy of classical mechanics. Before discussing in detail some of the observations that pointed up the necessity for a revision of classical mechanics, it is worth while to consider briefly the broad range of experience that classical mechanics *was* able to deal with successfully. From the motions of astronomical bodies (planets, satellites, and comets) to the motions of macroscopic objects freely falling under the influence of gravity, rolling down inclined surfaces, or oscillating elastically about equilibrium positions, classical mechanics provided an apparently accurate picture. The dynamics of charged bodies moving through electromagnetic fields, the vibrations of plucked strings, of membranes and deformed solids, and of sound waves in gases, the flow of fluids, heat, the kinetic theory of gases—all these are but a few examples of phenomena to which classical concepts had been successfully applied. One should realize that it was against the background of these many triumphs of classical mechanics that quantum theory arose.

One of the early observations that did not fit into the classical picture and whose *ad hoc* explanation on the basis of radical new assumptions by Planck pointed the way toward quantum theory dealt with the electromagnetic radiation from a "blackbody." A blackbody is defined as one that absorbs all electromagnetic radiation, of whatever frequency, that is incident upon it. By thermodynamic arguments, it can be shown that such a body is also a better radiator of energy at every frequency than any other body at the same temperature. It is possible to make a simple model of a blackbody consisting of a cavity radiator (a hollow enclosure with a small hole in the side). It is assumed that the cavity contains a small amount of some absorbing material and that the hole is small enough so that radiation falling on it and entering the cavity bounces around inside until it is completely absorbed by the internal absorber. In this case the hole acts as a blackbody in that it absorbs all radiation falling upon it. Such a model for a blackbody is valuable because it is possible to describe the electromagnetic field inside such a container in terms of waves bouncing back and forth between the walls. Any electromagnetic disturbances inside the box can be regarded as a superposition of various standing waves of this type. Electric energy becomes converted into magnetic energy and back into electric energy in a sinusoidally varying fashion for each of these standing electromagnetic waves. With respect to the energy, it can be shown that each of these waves behaves like an ordinary mechanical harmonic oscillator. It thus seems natural to apply the laws of classical statistical mechanics to these oscillators just as they can be applied to ordinary mechanical oscillators. Classical statistical mechanics states that the average kinetic energy in any collection of particles in thermal equilibrium is equal to $\frac{1}{2}kT$ times the total number of degrees of freedom of the collection of particles. Here k is Boltzmann's constant, $k = 1.38 \times 10^{-16}$ erg/°K, and T is the absolute temperature of the system. It is known that for any simple harmonic oscillator the time average of the potential energy is equal to the average of the kinetic energy. Thus, the total average energy per oscillator should be kT. It should therefore be necessary only to count the number of possible standing waves, and hence degrees of freedom, to compute what the average stored energy in the hollow enclosure will be at a given temperature of the box. It is found that the number of possible standing waves at a given frequency in a unit frequency range per unit volume of the box is equal to $2 \times 4\pi\nu^2/c^3$,* where ν is the frequency, and c is the velocity of light. The factor of two appears in this expression because any plane electromagnetic wave can have two orthogonal polarizations. If this expression is taken for the number of degrees of freedom per unit of volume and frequency range, an expression for the average energy per unit volume and unit frequency range in the box is obtained by multiplying by kT. This gives

$$u = 8\pi \frac{\nu^2}{c^3} kT \tag{1-1}$$

for the average electromagnetic energy in the box per unit volume and frequency. It is a simple matter to calculate the energy flux w through the hole in the side of the box if the energy density inside is known. Equation (1-1) leads to

$$w = 2\pi \frac{\nu^2}{c^2} kT \tag{1-2}$$

for the radiation flux through the hole in the side of the box, in units of energy per second per unit hole area and unit frequency range. Because all blackbodies are equivalent, as can be shown by thermodynamic argu-

* M. Born, *Atomic Physics,* Blackie and Son, Ltd., London, 5th ed., 1952, Chapter 8; F. K. Richtmyer and E. H. Kennard, *Introduction to Modern Physics,* McGraw-Hill Book Co., New York, 4th ed., 1947, Chapter 5. Both these books contain more detailed discussions of the various experiments that indicated the insufficiency of classical mechanics than will be given in this chapter.

ments, this is a predicted or theoretical value for the radiation flux from any blackbody. Unfortunately, it does not agree with experiment. It is in radical disagreement at high frequencies, and it leads to the completely absurd result that if one integrates over all frequencies, the rate of radiation from a blackbody is infinite (at all temperatures above absolute zero). On the other hand, this radiation law, derived in 1900 by Rayleigh and Jeans,* does give results in agreement with experiment in the limit of sufficiently small values of the frequency and sufficiently large values of the temperature (quantitatively, for $T/\nu \gg 10^{-10}$ °K-sec). That the theory is in agreement with experiment only in this limiting case and is otherwise in violent disagreement is very disturbing, inasmuch as the theory follows in a quite unambiguous way from the assumptions of classical statistical mechanics, the classical mechanics of Newton, and the field equations of Maxwell.

In 1901, Max Planck† was able to derive a valid expression for the spectral distribution of blackbody radiation by making assumptions which were very bold indeed. The following description of his work is not exactly the same as the one that he gave, but it is better suited for the modern interpretation of his results. The basic assumption is this: for a cavity radiator, the internal degrees of freedom (standing waves) are properly enumerated as above. However, each of these various standing waves in the box cannot take on all possible energies, as Maxwell's equations imply, but can take on only certain integrally related discrete energies, $0, h\nu, 2h\nu, 3h\nu, \ldots$ Here ν refers to the frequency of the standing wave, and h is a constant, now called *Planck's constant*, the value of which is to be determined in such a way as to make the prediction be in agreement with experiment. It is further assumed that the probability that a standing wave has one of these energies associated with it is given by the normal Boltzmann factor obtained from statistical mechanics, namely that the probability of excitation is given by a number proportional to $\exp(-E_n/kT)$, where $E_n = nh\nu$. With these assumptions, the mean energy of the oscillator can be written as

$$\overline{E} = \frac{\sum_n nh\nu \exp(-nh\nu/kT)}{\sum_n \exp(-nh\nu/kT)} = kT\left[\frac{h\nu/kT}{\exp(h\nu/kT) - 1}\right]. \tag{1–3}$$

This differs from the classical expression by the factor in the brackets.

* Lord Rayleigh, "Remarks upon the Law of Complete Radiation," *Phil. Mag.* **49,** 539 (1900); J. H. Jeans, "On the Partition of Energy between Matter and Aether," *Phil. Mag.* **10,** 91 (1905).

† M. Planck, "Ueber das Gesetz der Energieverteilung im Normalspectrum," *Ann. Physik* **4,** 553 (1901).

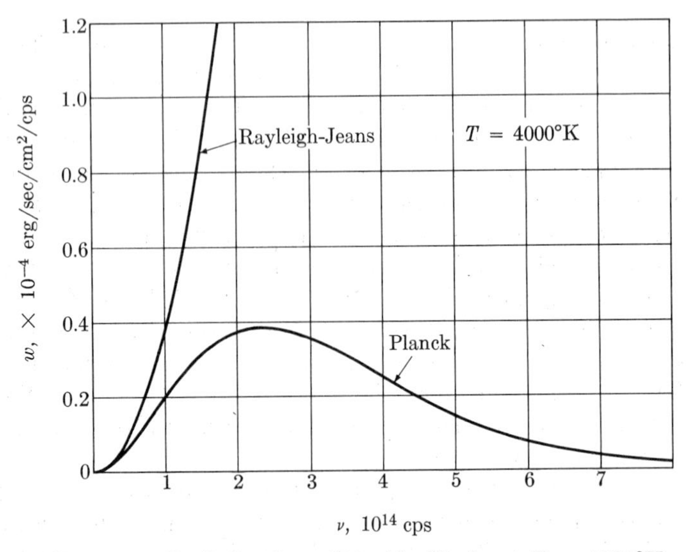

FIG. 1–1. Radiation laws for a blackbody at $T = 4000°K$.

Consequently, the classical expressions for radiation density u and flux w are modified by multiplying by this same factor to give

$$u = \frac{8\pi h\nu^3}{c^3} \frac{1}{\exp(h\nu/kT) - 1} \tag{1–4}$$

and

$$w = \frac{2\pi h\nu^3}{c^2} \frac{1}{\exp(h\nu/kT) - 1}. \tag{1–5}$$

This expression for the radiation rate, known as *Planck's law*, can be related to that of the classical Rayleigh-Jeans law by multiplying by the same factor:

$$w_{\text{Planck}} = w_{\text{R-J}} \times \frac{h\nu/kT}{\exp(h\nu/kT) - 1}. \tag{1–6}$$

Note that for a high temperature and/or low frequency, the two radiation rates become equal. These two laws are illustrated in Fig. 1–1.

Planck's law agrees very accurately with the observed spectral distribution of blackbody radiation provided the constant h is chosen to have the value $h = 6.624 \times 10^{-27}$ erg-second. If the spectral radiation density distribution, Eq. (1–4), predicted by Planck is integrated over all frequencies, an expression for the total radiation energy density in the cavity is obtained:

$$W = \frac{8}{15} \frac{\pi^5 k^4}{h^3 c^3} T^4. \tag{1–7}$$

Thus the energy density, and hence the radiation rate from a blackbody, is proportional to the fourth power of the temperature, a fact which was long known and was first discovered by Stefan.* The Stefan-Boltzmann constant σ relating radiation rate to blackbody temperature, which previously had to be obtained from radiation rate measurements, now could be derived from the constants of Planck's distribution law; it has the value

$$\sigma = \frac{2\pi^5}{15} \frac{k^4}{h^3c^2}. \tag{1–8}$$

Planck's success in obtaining the correct distribution law of blackbody radiation on the basis of the assumption that radiation oscillators can have only certain discrete energies suggested that the same approach be tried to see if a theoretical explanation of the experimentally observed temperature dependence of the specific heats of solids could be obtained. The form of the observed temperature variation was also inexplicable in terms of classical mechanics. A mole of a solid consists of N coupled molecules or mN atoms, where N is Avogadro's number and m is the number of atoms per molecule. Since each atom has three translational degrees of freedom when isolated, and since the total number of degrees of freedom will remain constant even when the interactions among atoms are considered, a mole of solid has $3mN$ degrees of freedom. Each of these classically should have an average energy kT associated with it, as seen above. Thus, the internal energy of a mole of a solid should be

$$U = 3mNkT \equiv 3mRT, \tag{1–9}$$

where R is the gas constant. From this, the molar specific heat should be a constant, $m(3R)$; this is the empirical law of Dulong and Petit.

While the molar heat of many monatomic substances is approximately $3R$ at room temperature, there are many solids for which the law of Dulong and Petit is not satisfied. Moreover, it is found that for all solids, the specific heat is a function of temperature, which at low temperatures varies as T^3. In 1907, Einstein† proposed that one should treat the solid as a set of harmonic oscillators, all having the frequency ν, and calculate the mean internal energy on the assumption that these oscillators have only the discrete energies proposed by Planck, namely, $nh\nu$. The average energy of the simple harmonic oscillator as calculated above for blackbody radiation then leads to a mean internal energy per mole equal to

$$U = 3RT \frac{h\nu/kT}{\exp(h\nu/kT) - 1}. \tag{1–10}$$

---

* J. Stefan, "Ueber die Beziehung zwischen der Wärmestrahlung und der Temperatur," *Fortsch. Physik,* 660 (1879).

† A. Einstein, "Die Plancksche Theorie der Strahlung und die Theorie der spezifischen Wärme," *Ann. Physik* **22,** 180 (1907).

This expression for the internal energy led to a theoretical value for the specific heat which for a proper choice of the frequency ν could be made to agree with the observed specific heat over a wide range of temperatures. However, at very low temperatures, this expression was also in disagreement with the observed T^3 variation of the specific heat. This variation of the specific heat with temperature was accounted for by Debye in 1912.* Debye assumed that the motions of the atoms in a solid could be treated in terms of various sound waves that bounce back and forth within the solid. This is similar to Planck's treatment of blackbody radiation. Just as one can express the blackbody radiation field inside a cavity in terms of the standing waves, thermal energy inside a solid can be expressed as the energy of internal sound waves. For example, in a solid of cubical shape, there are standing sound waves bouncing back and forth between the various boundaries of the cube which, when taken in superposition with one another, can be used to represent any real oscillatory motion of the atoms of the solid. Now in this case, as in the case of the blackbody radiation, these standing sound waves, or normal modes of vibration, have different frequencies. The number of these vibrational degrees of freedom of the solid per unit frequency can be computed as for blackbody radiation. Despite the similarities of this approach to that used for blackbody radiation, there is one distinguishing feature: in the case of vibrations in solids, there is a maximum frequency for the sound waves, corresponding to a wavelength roughly equal to twice the lattice spacing of the crystal. Except for this upper cutoff frequency, the theory of specific heats of solids according to Debye is substantially the same as Planck's theory of blackbody radiation.

In the case of low temperature, the high-frequency oscillations are not particularly excited, and effects coming from the imposition of an upper limit to the frequency are of no particular importance. In this case, it is possible to take over, essentially unchanged, the results of the blackbody radiation calculation. For example, if Eq. (1–4) is integrated over all frequencies, the internal energy per unit volume of the cavity radiator is seen to vary as the fourth power of the temperature. The corresponding relation in the case of solids is

$$U = \frac{4}{15} \frac{\pi^5 k^4}{h^3} T^4 \left(\frac{2}{v_T^3} + \frac{1}{v_L^3} \right). \tag{1–11}$$

Here the velocity of light, c, has been replaced by a term involving v_T, the transverse sound velocity in the solid, and an additional term involving v_L, the longitudinal velocity of the sound waves in the solid. In the case of light, only transverse waves occur, so only the first term appears. To

---

* P. Debye, "Zur Theorie der spezifischen Wärmen," *Ann. Physik* **39,** 789 (1912).

each direction of propagation of a plane wave in a solid there corresponds a single longitudinal mode as well as the two transverse modes, and this leads to the expression in parentheses in Eq. (1–11). It should be emphasized that this equation is valid only for temperatures which are small compared with Θ_D, the "Debye characteristic temperature" at which the higher modes in the vicinity of the cutoff frequency become excited. From Eq. (1–11), the T^3 variation of the specific heat at low temperatures is obvious. The excellent agreement between the Debye theory and the observed specific heat of solids as illustrated in Fig. 1–2 was another very strong piece of evidence that there was something profoundly wrong with newtonian mechanics when applied on an atomic scale to a solid, liquid, or gas.

The discovery of radioactivity by Becquerel in 1896 led to a revolution in ideas on the nature of the atom and to many observations that could not be reconciled with classical concepts. Certain radioactive materials provide a source of energetic alpha particles (helium nuclei) which can

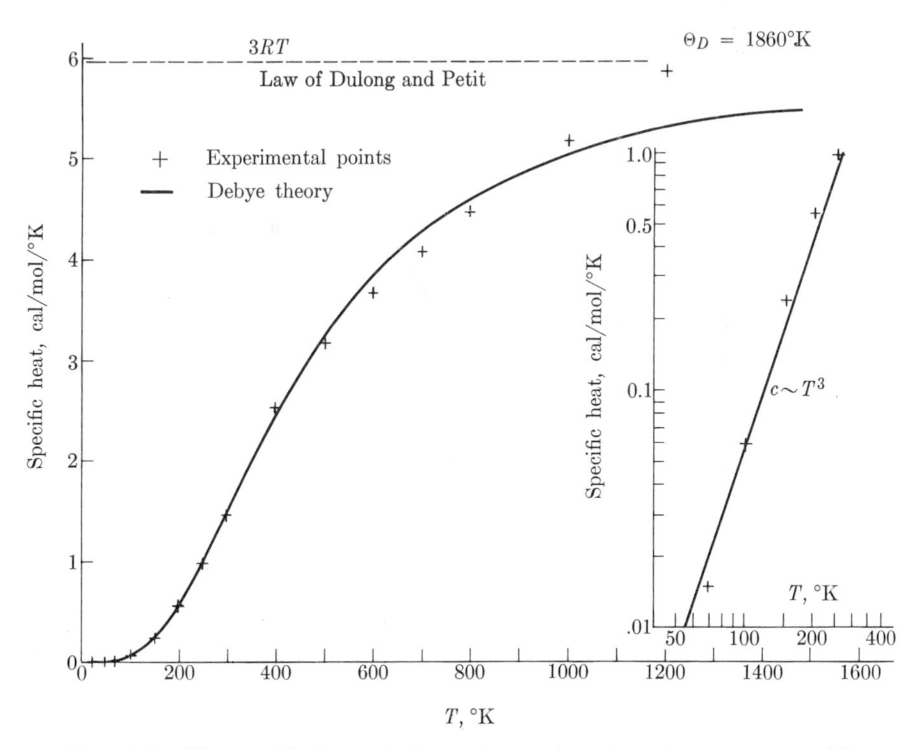

FIG. 1–2. The specific heat of diamond as a function of temperature. The crosses represent measured values, and the solid curve is the predicted relationship, according to the Debye theory, for a Debye temperature of $\theta_D = 1860°K$. The insert shows the T^3 dependence at low temperatures.

be used to probe the interior of the atom. Rutherford's celebrated experiments on alpha-particle scattering indicated that nearly the entire mass of an atom is located in a very small region, the atomic nucleus. Nuclei were found to have diameters very much smaller than those ascribed to the corresponding atoms from classical kinetic theory considerations. As a result of Rutherford's work, an atom was pictured as consisting of a heavy, small, positively charged particle, the nucleus, around which electrons move in such a way as to make the atom as a whole electrically neutral, as it was known to be. This picture of an atom classically leads to predictions in violent disagreement with experience. For example, in the application of statistics to specific heats discussed above, it should be necessary to ascribe to the solid many more degrees of freedom than simply three times the number of *atoms* making up the solid; this would lead to a predicted value for the specific heat very much larger than that which is actually observed.

These bits of evidence involving specific heats did not clearly indicate that Newton's laws of motion were necessarily at fault. The statistical mechanical ideas introduced by Gibbs were based on some fundamental assumptions concerning the nature of thermal equilibrium in a mechanical system, and because these fundamental statistical assumptions could not be proved, there was always the possibility that there might be something wrong with them. However, other difficulties, clearly not statistical in origin, arose from certain experimental results that were in contradiction to those which would be expected if the laws of Newton and Maxwell were applicable. For example, as the electrons move around the nucleus in the Rutherford model of the atom, they are continuously accelerated toward the nucleus and should radiate as a result of this acceleration in accordance with Maxwell's equations. However, it is observed that atoms normally do not radiate; it is necessary to excite them in some way (with an electric discharge or by heating) to make them radiate. Furthermore, a calculation of the magnitude of the radiation expected from atoms if electrons moved around in the classically predicted paths indicates that one would expect very strong radiation indeed, much stronger than anything observed in practice.

Because of these difficulties, Bohr* in 1913 extended Planck's very bold assumption, which had been so successful in the case of blackbody radiation and the treatment of the specific heats of solids. He assumed that an atom can exist only in certain possible states of definite energy. He assumed further that when an atom jumps from one state of energy E to a state of lower energy E', it emits light in the form of a single quantum

---

* N. Bohr, "On the Constitution of Atoms and Molecules," *Phil. Mag.* **26**, 1 (1913).

of energy, and that the frequency of the light emitted is given by the relation

$$E - E' = h\nu. \tag{1–12}$$

By introducing these ideas into a very simple model of a one-electron system, the hydrogen atom, Bohr was able to account for the long-known regularities in the line spectrum of light emitted by excited hydrogen atoms.

Bohr made the additional assumption that the energy quantization had its origin in a discreteness of the orbital angular momentum of the electron. To see this relation, consider the classical circular orbits of an electron of charge $-e$ and mass m about an essentially fixed nucleus of charge $+e$. Applying Newton's law of motion to the coulombic force and radial acceleration yields

$$\frac{e^2}{r^2} = \frac{mv^2}{r}. \tag{1–13}$$

Bohr assumed, as mentioned above, that the orbital angular momentum is quantized:

$$mvr = \frac{nh}{2\pi}, \tag{1–14}$$

where n is a positive integer greater than zero. The use of these equations to eliminate v and r from the expression for the energy gives for the possible energies of a hydrogen atom:

$$E_n = \tfrac{1}{2}mv^2 - \frac{e^2}{r} = -\tfrac{1}{2}mc^2\alpha^2\,\frac{1}{n^2}. \tag{1–15}$$

Here

$$\alpha \equiv \frac{2\pi e^2}{hc} \approx \frac{1}{137} \tag{1–16}$$

is a dimensionless number known as the *fine-structure constant.* Thus the binding energy of the hydrogen atom is at most roughly 1/40,000 of mc^2, the rest energy of the electron. The energy is negative, corresponding to the fact that the electron is bound to the atom and work must be done to free it. (The zero of energy corresponds to removal of the electron from the atom to infinity.)

In addition to accounting in a reasonably satisfactory manner for the optical spectrum of hydrogen, Bohr's theory was able to account for the quantization of a harmonic oscillator. For a three-dimensional oscillator, the central force acting on a particle of mass m moving in a circle of radius r is

$$F = kr. \tag{1–17}$$

Here k is the "spring constant" of the oscillator. If this expression for the force replaces e^2/r^2 in Eq. (1–13), again considering only circular orbits, and the angular momentum is again quantized as in Eq. (1–14), the allowed energies of the oscillator are found to be

$$E_n = \tfrac{1}{2}mv^2 + \tfrac{1}{2}kr^2 = nh\nu. \tag{1–18}$$

The existence of n in the denominator of Eq. (1–15) was a compelling reason for omitting $n = 0$. However, this reason does not exist for the harmonic oscillator, and it is assumed that n may be zero in this case.

Another group of experimental data that did not fit into the classical view of nature concerned the photoelectric effect. In 1887 Hertz, in connection with his experiments on the generation of electromagnetic waves, discovered that electrons could be ejected from solids by letting radiation fall onto the solid. Lenard and others found that the maximum energy of these photo-ejected electrons depended only upon the frequency of the light falling on the surface, and not upon its intensity. Furthermore, it was found that for shorter wavelengths the maximum energy of the electrons was greater than for longer wavelengths.

In 1905, Einstein* explained the photoelectric effect in a satisfactory way also by making use of the ideas of Planck. He assumed that radiation exists in the form of quanta of definite size, that is, that light consists of packets of energy of size $h\nu$. He also assumed that when light falls on a surface, individual electrons in the solid can absorb these energy quanta. Thus, the energy received by an electron depends only on the frequency of the light and is independent of its intensity; the intensity merely determines how many photoelectrons will leave the surface per second.

Assuming that some electrons might lose part of their energy before escaping from the surface of the solid, Einstein's assumption explained the observations that the *maximum* energy of the photoelectrons was dependent only on the frequency of the light. Furthermore, this dependence on frequency was in quantitative agreement with that observed.

It should be emphasized how far-reaching this result was. The wave theory of light had been thoroughly established on the basis of many interference and diffraction experiments. But this explanation of the photoelectric effect is essentially corpuscular! It says that light exists in the form of little particles (*quanta* or *photons*) that can interact with individual electrons, with the associated energy being transferred *as a unit* from the quantum to the electron. This is, of course, quite a paradoxical result: it is difficult to see how light can be both a wave and a particle. As will be seen, attempts to understand this paradox have resulted in a profound modification of fundamental physical concepts.

---

* A. Einstein, "Über einen die Erzeugung und Verwandlung des Lichtes betreffenden heuristischen Gesichtspunkt," *Ann. Physik* **17,** 132 (1905).

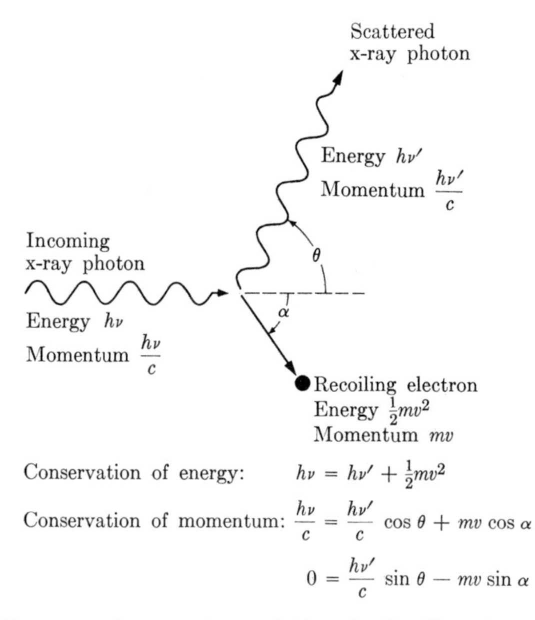

FIG. 1–3. Energy and momentum relations in the Compton scattering of an x-ray photon by an electron initially at rest.

Another experiment leading to the same paradoxical position was performed in 1923 by Compton.* While studying the scattering of x-rays by solids, Compton discovered that when monochromatic x-rays are scattered, not only does the original frequency appear in the scattered radiation, but also, for any given scattering direction, a new frequency appears which always corresponds to a longer wavelength. Compton was able to construct a very simple model to explain this effect: it is assumed that x-rays consist of a swarm of particlelike quanta, each having energy $h\nu$ and momentum $h\nu/c$. Further assuming that a solid contains lightly bound electrons, which can be considered as essentially free, the scattering of the x-ray quanta by these quasi-free electrons can be computed as a classical elastic collision between two billiard ball-like objects, as illustrated in Fig. 1–3.

With this model, one can compute for a given scattering angle the exact loss of energy an x-ray will experience and from this its frequency shift in scattering. The scattered x-rays of unshifted frequency that are observed are assumed to arise from strongly bound electrons near the atomic nucleus. The predictions of this model were found to agree quite closely with

* A. H. Compton, "Wave-length measurements of scattered x-rays," *Phys. Rev.* **21,** 715 (1923); "The Spectrum of Scattered X-Rays," *Phys. Rev.* **22,** 409 (1923).

observations. On the other hand, it was known from von Laue's earlier work that x-rays could be diffracted, and it was clear that they were simply very short-wavelength electromagnetic radiation and hence were similar to light. Thus, in the interaction between x-rays and free electrons, the x-rays acted very much like particles when they collided with the electrons, while in propagating through crystals they were refracted and diffracted like ordinary electromagnetic waves. Here again was an example of the dual character of electromagnetic radiation, which in some situations appeared as a wave phenomenon and in others appeared as particles. The new fact disclosed by the Compton effect was that not only is energy conserved in the interaction between photons and electrons, but momentum is conserved as well.

Another great experiment, which exhibited in even more spectacular fashion this paradoxical wave-particle duality, was the Davisson-Germer experiment of 1927. Although many seemingly conclusive experiments had shown that electrons were small charged particles, Davisson and Germer* showed that directing a stream of electrons at a crystal lattice led to scattering of the electrons, with typical diffraction effects. In other words, electrons striking a crystal are diffracted by the crystal lattice as waves would be, in contrast with the very obvious particlelike properties which they normally exhibit. The wave-particle duality therefore was not something limited to radiation, but appeared to be a more general phenomenon: any particle may under certain circumstances behave like a wave, and any wave, for example an electromagnetic wave, may have certain particle properties.

1–3 Some necessary characteristics of quantum theory. It has been seen above that the failures of classical mechanics were intimately associated with two general types of effects. One is that some physical quantities, such as the energies of electromagnetic waves and of lattice vibrations of given frequency, or the energies and angular momenta associated with electronic orbits in the hydrogen atom, which in classical theory can take on a continuous range of values, may be found to take on discrete values instead. The other type of effect is the so-called *wave-particle duality*, where both the wave nature of light, as shown by diffraction and interference effects, and the particle nature of light, as shown by the photoelectric and Compton effects, are exhibited; in the realm of matter, the parallel case is that of the particle and the wave aspects of electrons.

It is clear that quantum mechanics, to explain these paradoxes, must be of such a nature as to encompass these effects in its basic structure. The

---

* C. Davisson and L. H. Germer, "Diffraction of Electrons by a Crystal of Nickel," *Phys. Rev.* **30,** 705 (1927).

way in which this is done is the subject of the next chapter. However, the experiments discussed above strongly suggest that the classical concepts of "wave" or "particle" may not represent the nature of an electron or photon in an adequate way: the physical state of a "particle-wave" may not be adequately represented by a specification of such classical aspects as its position, momentum, amplitude, or phase. As will be seen, in quantum mechanics the formal description of the state of a mechanical system is contained in its *wave function*, ψ, a new mathematical entity which is not a wave in the classical sense of an undulation whose frequency, phase, and amplitude are measurable.

In addition to accounting for wave-particle duality, quantum mechanics must also explain quantization of energy and angular momentum. Wave-particle duality and angular momentum quantization are not independent of each other, but instead are closely related. This will be illustrated with the following example.

Consider the following *Gedanken* or "thought" experiment. Although this experiment may be impractical, it is nonetheless possible in principle, and if it were to be performed the outcome could be predicted with reasonable assurance. The experiment concerns the hollow squirrel cage, or drum, shown in Fig. 1–4(a). The squirrel cage consists of a large number of equally spaced pins which connect the two end discs around their peripheries. It is assumed that the number N of pins is large. The cage is mounted on suitable (frictionless) bearings so as to turn freely about the axis defined by the projecting shafts. Imagine that a monochromatic light source is mounted inside the cage on the axis and that it projects a beam of light radially outward. This is assumed to fall on a portion of the circumference that is small yet sufficiently large to include many pins.

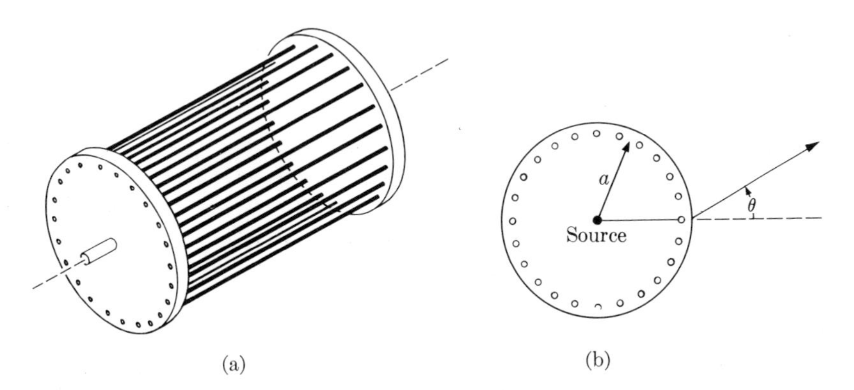

FIG. 1–4. (a) Drum for the "quantum squirrel cage" "thought" experiment, illustrating the relationship between wave-particle duality and angular momentum quantization. (b) Geometrical relations in the "quantum squirrel cage."

These pins constitute an approximately plane grating which diffracts the light, causing it to be scattered through various angles θ (see Fig. 1–4b). The sine of the angle of diffraction is given by the well-known expression

$$\sin\theta = \frac{nN\lambda}{2\pi a}. \tag{1–19}$$

Here n is any integer (giving the order of the diffraction spectrum), N is the number of pins distributed uniformly around the circumference of the drum, λ is the wavelength of the light, and a is the radius of the drum.

On the other hand, remembering the dual wave-particle nature of light, one may consider a single quantum of light leaving the light source at the center. As it moves radially outward, it can carry no angular momentum about the drum axis, but after being scattered through an angle θ by the pins on the circumference of the cage, it carries an angular momentum A equal to

$$A = pa\sin\theta, \tag{1–20}$$

where p, the momentum of the photon, is given by the relation

$$p = \frac{h\nu}{c}, \tag{1–21}$$

introduced earlier to explain Compton's results. Combining Eqs. (1–19), (1–20), and (1–21) gives

$$A = nN\hbar, \tag{1–22}$$

where $\hbar$, a constant that will arise frequently, is defined by

$$\hbar \equiv \frac{h}{2\pi} = 1.054 \times 10^{-27} \text{ erg-sec}. \tag{1–23}$$

Assuming (as in classical mechanics) conservation of angular momentum, it is seen from Eq. (1–22) that the angular momentum transferred to the drum by the photon is an integral multiple of $N\hbar$. If the drum is initially at rest, its only possible angular momentum states due to angular momentum transfers of this type are integral multiples of $N\hbar$. Thus the quantization of the angular momentum of the drum follows as a reasonable inference from the dual wave-particle aspects of the light, the wave behavior in the diffraction and the particle behavior in the Compton-type momentum transfer.

It is, of course, conceivable that the drum may have other angular momentum states in addition to those given by Eq. (1–22). However, it is difficult to see why such additional angular momentum states would not be excited by the light. It will be seen later that quantization of angular momentum results from the fundamental postulates of quantum theory.

That the angular momentum of the drum can take on only integral multiples of $N\hbar$, rather than $\hbar$, is a rather special quantum effect associated with the N-fold symmetry axis of the drum; a rotation of the drum through an angle of $2\pi/N$ will bring the drum from one configuration into an identical configuration so far as the location of the (indistinguishable) pins is concerned.

A consideration of the angular momentum associated with a photon gives further indication of the general nature of the quantization of angular momentum. It is a well-known result of classical electromagnetic theory that a circularly polarized plane light wave carries an angular momentum density of E/ω, where E is its energy density and ω is its circular frequency. Thus each circularly polarized photon of energy $\hbar\omega$ has an associated angular momentum of $\hbar$. This is in accordance with Bohr's theory of the hydrogen atom, where the photon emitted as the atom drops from one energy state to the next lower state must carry off $\hbar$ of angular momentum if the angular momentum of the entire system is to be conserved during a radiative transition.

With the assumption that the angular momentum of the squirrel cage is quantized in accordance with Eq. (1–22), it is possible to invert the above arguments and to show that this assumption leads to an expectation that all particles, whether electrons, helium atoms, or even baseballs, will be scattered by the pins lining the circumference of the drum as though they had the properties of a wave whose characteristic wavelength is a function of the momentum of the particle.

The argument is essentially identical to the one above, except that the assumptions and the conclusions are now inverted. Assume a source of particles at the center of the cage. As an example, consider an electron gun projecting a monoenergetic electron beam radially outward so as to strike a particular region of the circumference of the drum. If the momentum of an electron is designated by p, then since the total (drum plus electron) angular momentum must be conserved, the angular momentum of the electron after being scattered by the pins must have one of the values given by

$$A_e = pa \sin\theta = nN\hbar. \tag{1–24}$$

This is typical of equations describing a diffraction effect: $\sin\theta$ is equal to n times a constant, where n can assume integral values, both positive and negative.

Equation (1–24) is essentially identical to Eq. (1–19). As soon as this equation is recognized as a diffraction equation, it is easy, by comparing Eqs. (1–19) and (1–24), to calculate the characteristic wavelength of the diffracted wave. The result is

$$\lambda = \frac{h}{p} \tag{1–25}$$

One can conclude, therefore, that any particle, whether electron, atom, or even one of much greater size, is scattered from the cage grating as though it were a wave with a wavelength inversely proportional to the momentum of the particle. This particular equation relating particle wavelength to momentum was first obtained by de Broglie* from arguments involving the group velocities of waves and assumptions about the frequencies of oscillation. Electron diffraction experiments, such as those of Davisson and Germer, have confirmed Eq. (1–25) to a high degree of accuracy.

This "thought" experiment shows that the assumption of the dual wave-particle character of light is sufficient to lead, for a rotating cage, to angular momentum states which are integral multiples of $N\hbar$. Conversely, if momentum states of this type are assumed for the drum, we are led to conclude that any kind of a particle will be scattered by the drum through angles determined by a diffraction effect associated with a wavelength given by Eq. (1–25).

1–4 Summary. In this chapter, a brief discussion of the relationship of quantum to classical mechanics has been given and a basic difference in viewpoint mentioned. Several experiments that could not find a classical explanation were described. These experiments, dealing with blackbody radiation, the specific heat of solids, atomic line spectra, the photoelectric effect, electron diffraction, the Compton effect, and various other phenomena, were of great significance in indicating the way in which the basic ideas of classical mechanics had to be modified. Two aspects of nature, the wave-particle duality and quantization, were suggested by these experiments. These concepts were completely beyond the scope of classical theory, and it required quantum mechanics to resolve the many paradoxes that resulted. Finally, a "thought" experiment, the "quantum squirrel cage," illustrated the close connection between the wave-particle duality and the quantization of angular momentum and led to the de Broglie expression for the wavelength of material particles.

---

* L. de Broglie, "A Tentative Theory of Light Quanta," *Phil. Mag.* **47,** 446 (1926); "Recherches sur la Theorie des Quanta," *Ann. phys.* **3,** 22 (1925).

Problems

1–1. Assume that a hydrogen atom consists of a fixed nucleus around which an electron of charge $e = 4.8 \times 10^{-10}$ esu moves in a classical circular orbit of radius $a_0 = 5.29 \times 10^{-9}$ cm. Estimate the classical electromagnetic radiation from such an atom due to the acceleration of the electron charge, and compare this with the total classical energy of the atom. The radiation rate of an accelerated charge is $S = 2e^2a^2/3c^3$, where a is the acceleration and c is the velocity of light.

1–2. Rutherford's experiments on the scattering of alpha particles (from radioactive sources such as polonium and radium) by metal foils contributed greatly to our present picture of the "nuclear atom." (a) How did such experiments give evidence of the existence of the nucleus in an atom? (b) What energy must an alpha particle have to give noncoulombic scattering by a nucleus of charge $Z = 50$ and radius $R = 8 \times 10^{-13}$ cm? Assume that the potential is strictly coulombic outside the nucleus but departs from this form within the nucleus.

1–3. Discuss how the Franck-Hertz experiments on measuring the energy losses of electrons scattered from gas atoms require quantum concepts for their interpretation.

1–4. In 1913, Bohr proposed a procedure for quantizing certain systems. To what general kinds of physical systems could Bohr's procedure be applied? For what kinds of systems did it fail?

1–5. An x-ray beam is formed by bombarding a carbon target with energetic electrons. Monochromatic "soft" x-rays ($\lambda = 44.5$ A) are produced. What is the loss in energy of one of these x-rays when it is Compton-scattered by an electron? Assume that the electron recoils at an angle of 30° to the direction of the incident beam.

1–6. Compute in electron volts the maximum energy of photoelectrons emitted from a metal when yellow sodium resonance radiation is incident on it. Is this maximum energy dependent on the properties of the metal and, if so, what properties are of significance?

1–7. Show by the use of simple physical arguments that at low temperatures the ratio of the heat capacity per unit volume of a vacuum to that of a solid is $\frac{2}{3}(v/c)^3$, where c is the velocity of light, and v is the velocity of both longitudinal and transverse sound waves in the solid, assumed to be equal.

1–8. Atoms possessing a permanent magnetic dipole moment are projected as a beam through an inhomogeneous magnetic field and are collected on a suitable detector (Stern-Gerlach experiment). Explain what differences are to be expected if the atoms behave like classical particles or if the orientations of the atomic moments are quantized, as is actually the case.

1–9. Davisson and Germer scattered low-energy electrons from metal targets. For 45-ev electrons incident normally on a crystal face, compute the angle between the incident beam and the scattering maximum if the metal is assumed to be of simple cubic structure with a lattice constant of 3.52 A.

1–10. Compute the hydrogenlike quantum number n for the earth in its orbit around the sun.

1–11. Assuming that an electron moves about a proton with an inverse three-halves power law of force, use Bohr's rules for quantizing circular orbits to compute possible energy levels of the system.

1–12. Calculate the number of photons per second radiated by a radio station broadcasting 50 kw of power at a frequency of 570 kc/sec.

1–13. The shortest possible wavelength of sound in sodium chloride is twice the lattice spacing, about 5.6×10^{-8} cm. The sound velocity is approximately 1.5×10^{5} cm/sec. (a) Compute a rough value for the highest sound frequency in the solid. (b) Compute the energy of the corresponding phonons, or quanta of vibrational energy. (c) What temperature is required to excite these oscillators appreciably?

CHAPTER 2

WAVE MECHANICS

2–1 The wave-particle duality. As we have seen in the preceding chapter, particles seem to behave in certain situations as if they were waves, and vice versa. This paradox can be resolved only by making basic modifications in the conceptual pictures of waves and particles. The problem is thrown into particularly sharp focus by considering the idealized experiment illustrated in Fig. 2–1. A similar experiment is actually readily performed. The experiment is the famous Young's interference experiment with one important modification: the screen is now a photoelectric emitter. Monochromatic light from the point source S is focused by the lens L on the screen P. An opaque screen with slits A and B is placed between L and P. It is observed that photoelectrons tend to be emitted from the photoemissive screen P at the locations of the bright interference fringes, and never at the center of a black fringe. However, the locations of the bright and dark fringes on P are determined by the separation between A and B.

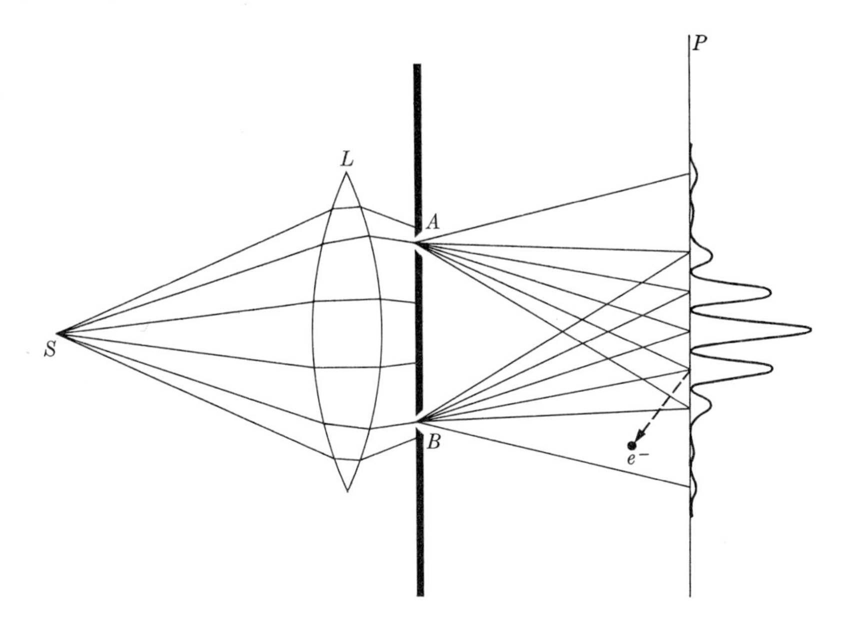

FIG. 2–1. Schematic representation of Young's interference experiment, illustrating the wave-particle duality paradox.

This result is paradoxical in several ways. As seen in Chapter 1, the photoelectric effect can be understood only on the basis of the photon picture of light. However, a photon sufficiently small to affect only one electron could presumably not go through both slits A and B. In fact, a photon detector placed at either A or B catches only whole photons or none, never a part of a photon. This raises the question of how a photon which passes through A can be influenced by the presence of B.

One obvious possibility is that some photons pass through A and some through B, and that the separate photons act on one another in such a way as to arrive only at the bright fringes on the screen P. This explanation must be incorrect, as can be seen by reducing the intensity of the light to the point where on the average only one photon per minute passes through the system. Even in this case the photons continue to arrive at only the bright fringes!

One striking thing about this experiment is that the behavior of any given photon is largely unpredictable. Although it will appear at a bright fringe on P, one cannot predict in advance which fringe. Furthermore, the intensity distribution over a fringe merely serves to give a probability distribution for the arrival of any given photon; it does not allow an exact prediction of where the photoelectron will appear.

This statistical aspect of the behavior of photons appears to differ in an essential way from the statistical considerations of classical mechanics. The difference can be illustrated with an example. It is found that with either slit A or B closed, the probability that a photon will pass through the system to the screen P is just one-half the probability with both slits open. This is what would be expected from classical considerations. However, if either slit A or B is closed, photons begin to arrive at locations where there were previously dark fringes: a decrease in the number of paths by which a photon can get from S to the position of a dark fringe has resulted in an increased probability that a photon will arrive there!

This interference experiment suggests several important new ideas. First, probability enters into quantum mechanics in a fundamental and nonclassical way. Considering light as a stream of photons reveals an associated wave the amplitude of which plays the role of a *probability amplitude.* The square of the amplitude (the wave intensity) gives a measure of the probability of finding a photon at a particular point. Inasmuch as the probability is measured by the *square* of an amplitude, there is a possibility of obtaining interference effects of the type discussed above.

Second, in the case of photons and presumably for other particles as well, the probability amplitude propagates as a typical wave. For photons, the propagation laws are known in detail: they are just the ones discovered by Maxwell. The major modification necessary is that of interpreting the wave intensity as a photon probability density. The implication is that the probability distributions of all particles propagate as some type of wave motion. One of the problems, then, is to discover the laws of propagation of the wave amplitudes for particles other than photons.

Third, it should be noted that, for photons, the wave amplitude contains all the information available about the photon probability distribution, even including the polarization state of the photon. Thus it is appropriate to consider knowledge of the wave distribution in space as equivalent to complete knowledge of the state of the photon. For this reason, the analogous wave function for a particle is sometimes called the *state function* of the particle.

The paradox of a particle which sometimes behaves like a wave or of a wave which sometimes behaves like a particle can thus be resolved by noting that the wave plays the role of a probability amplitude in the probabilistic description of particles. Alternatively, it is possible to formulate quantum mechanics by starting with the classical description of a wave and quantizing its equations of motion. The various quantized energy states of a plane wave then correspond to 0, 1, 2, . . . particles having the corresponding momentum. This approach to the quantum behavior of matter, known as quantum-mechanical *field theory*, will not be explored in this book.

2-2 The wave function. As a first step in formulating a wave mechanics for a material particle, consider a particle with a well-defined momentum. It was seen in the previous chapter that the wave associated with the particle should be propagated in the direction of motion of the particle and should have a wavelength given by

$$\lambda = \frac{h}{p}. \tag{2-1}$$

This implies that the wave should be a plane wave, such as

$$\psi = A \exp [i(kx - \omega t)], \tag{2-2}$$

where

$$k = \frac{2\pi}{\lambda}. \tag{2-3}$$

Here the wave is assumed to be traveling in the positive x-direction.

Equation (2-2) has been written with the tacit assumption that an angular frequency ω is to be associated with the particle wave ψ. It might be inferred by analogy with the case of photons that the frequency should be given by

$$\omega = \frac{E}{\hbar}, \tag{2-4}$$

where E is the energy of the particle. This identification of the frequency with the energy will be obtained in another way later.

It might be thought that the plane wave could be represented by the real function

$$\psi = A \sin (kx - \omega t + \alpha). \tag{2-5}$$

However, as will be discussed in detail later, there are reasons for believing that a particle with its momentum exactly known is in a state such that its position is completely uncertain. In such a case, the probability distribution measured by the wave intensity $|\psi|^2$ should be independent of position. This suggests that the wave function to be associated with a particle of definite momentum should be given by Eq. (2–2) rather than by Eq. (2–5).

For a plane wave traveling in an arbitrary direction, Eq. (2–2) can be written as

$$\psi = A \exp [i(\boldsymbol{k} \cdot \boldsymbol{r} - \omega t)], \tag{2-6}$$

where $\boldsymbol{k}$, the propagation vector of the wave, satisfies the equation

$$\boldsymbol{k} = \frac{1}{\hbar} \boldsymbol{p}. \tag{2-7}$$

The vector $\boldsymbol{p}$ represents the momentum of the particle.

In Young's interference experiment, the wave that falls upon the screen P is not a plane wave. However, such a complex wave can be decomposed into plane waves; i.e., it may be considered to be a linear superposition of many plane waves. It is therefore important to consider the state of a particle which has a wave function in the form of a superposition of two or more plane waves.

Let the wave function of a particle be

$$\psi = A_1 \exp [i(\boldsymbol{k}_1 \cdot \boldsymbol{r} - \omega t)] + A_2 \exp [i(\boldsymbol{k}_2 \cdot \boldsymbol{r} - \omega t)]. \tag{2-8}$$

In accordance with the fundamental probability interpretation of the wave function, $|\psi|^2$ is to be interpreted as a measure of the probability per unit volume of finding the particle at the point $\boldsymbol{r}$. This quantity is

$$|\psi|^2 = |A_1|^2 + |A_2|^2 + \{2A_1\overline{A_2} \exp [i(\boldsymbol{k}_1 - \boldsymbol{k}_2) \cdot \boldsymbol{r}]\}_{\text{real part}}. \tag{2-9}$$

It should be noted that this relative probability is not the simple sum of contributions from each of the two elementary plane waves, but in addition contains the *interference term* in braces. For this case, the position probability density is in a sense localized, not being uniform everywhere in space. However, if Eq. (2–9) is averaged over all space, the interference term (because of its oscillatory character) averages to zero. Averaged over all space, $|\psi|^2$ may be interpreted as a measure of the probability of finding the particle somewhere, without regard to location. This probability is unity. $|A_1|^2$ and $|A_2|^2$ may therefore be interpreted as measures of the probability of finding the particle *somewhere* (without regard to location) with the momenta p_1 and p_2 respectively. With this interpretation, the probability that the particle has a momentum p_1 is $|A_1|^2/(|A_1|^2 + |A_2|^2)$, and both the exact position and momentum of the particle are uncertain when it is characterized by the wave function of Eq. (2–8).

It must be emphasized that the probabilities associated with a particle in a state characterized by Eq. (2–8) refer to the situation prior to an observation. If the particle is later observed to be in a certain restricted region of space, it is surmised that the act of observation has disturbed the particle and its wave function. Alternatively, if the momentum of the particle is observed, it will be found to be either p_1 or p_2, never any other value. Again, it must be assumed that the act of observation has disturbed the system, changing its wave function. After the observation, the wave function is the plane wave appropriate to the observed momentum.

As an example of the consistency of the formalism outlined thus far, consider the motion of a stream of particles in space divided by a plane

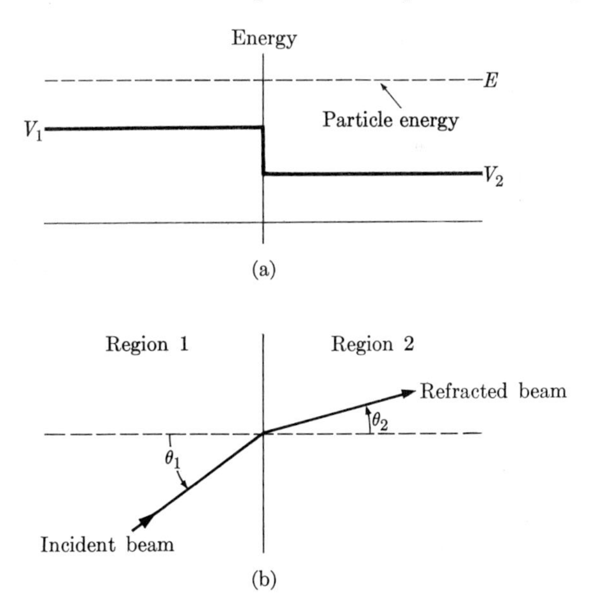

FIG. 2–2. (a) Potential-energy distribution, showing a potential discontinuity. (b) Geometrical relations for a beam of particles refracted at this potential discontinuity.

surface into two regions of (differing) constant potential energy (see Fig. 2–2). It is assumed that the particles, which may be thought of as a stream of electrons, are traveling from the left toward the interface between regions 1 and 2 in such a direction as to make an angle θ_1 with the normal to the plane surface dividing the two regions. By analogy with geometrical optics, the angle θ_1 will be called the *angle of incidence*, and the angle θ_2 the *angle of refraction* of the particles. If the incident particles are assumed to have exactly defined momenta, the wave function for an incoming particle is

$$\psi = A \exp\left[i\left(\frac{\mathbf{p}\cdot\mathbf{r}}{\hbar} - \frac{Et}{\hbar}\right)\right]. \tag{2–10}$$

Here the relation between wave frequency ω and particle energy E given by Eq. (2–4) has been used. The momentum $\mathbf{p}$ is related to the energy E through

$$p = [2m(E - V)]^{1/2}. \tag{2–11}$$

This shows that the momentum of the particle changes as it moves from region 1 into region 2. Consequently, the wavelength, which is related to the momentum by Eq. (2–1), will change in passing from region 1 to region 2. One can, in the usual way, define an index of refraction n of medium 2 relative to medium 1 by the ratio of the two wavelengths:

$$n = \frac{\lambda_1}{\lambda_2} = \frac{p_2}{p_1} = \left[\frac{E - V_2}{E - V_1}\right]^{1/2}. \tag{2–12}$$

Here use has been made of Eqs. (2–1) and (2–11). Having defined an index of refraction of region 2 relative to region 1, use can now be made of Snell's law, which is based on wave optics, to calculate the relation between the angles θ_1 and θ_2. This gives

$$\frac{\sin\theta_1}{\sin\theta_2} = n = \left[\frac{E - V_2}{E - V_1}\right]^{1/2}. \tag{2–13}$$

Inasmuch as this equation is based on the wave picture being developed, it is desirable to check this relation against the corresponding relation calculated on the basis of newtonian mechanics since the system in question can be considered as a large-scale system for which the laws of newtonian mechanics should hold.

To calculate the ratio between the angles in newtonian mechanics, use will be made of a very simple feature of the problem, namely, that the interface between regions 1 and 2 is such as to cause a force to act on the particle as it travels from one region to the other. This force acts in a direction perpendicular to the interface. Consequently, when a particle moves from region 1 to region 2, the component of the linear momentum which is parallel to the surface will not change. This constancy of the tangential component of the linear momentum of the particle will be used to calculate the relation between θ_1 and θ_2. That the tangential components of the linear momentum of the particle are the same for both regions 1 and 2 is given by

$$p_1 \sin \theta_1 = p_2 \sin \theta_2. \tag{2-14}$$

From this, one can obtain in a straightforward way the result previously obtained by the methods of wave optics. The equivalence of the wave optics formalism and classical newtonian mechanics has thus been established for this particular problem.

2-3 The uncertainty relation. The above discussion brings out a very important idea of quantum mechanics: if the characteristic wavelength to be associated with a particle, that is, the wavelength that determines its diffractive type of behavior, is related to the particle momentum by Eq. (2-1), a particle that is localized in a finite region of space must be considered to have a *spread of momenta.* Moreover, it can readily be shown that the sharper the localization in space, the greater is the spread of wavelengths, and hence momenta, required to describe the wave packet. This is a specific example of a very general idea in quantum mechanics concerning a variety of pairs of *complementary* observables in which an exact specification of the value of one observable can be achieved only at the expense of uncertainty regarding the value of the other complementary observable.

The idea that an aspect of a physical situation cannot be completely defined in the classical sense but can only be described in terms of an imprecise specification of a pair of complementary variables is known as the *complementarity principle.* It is closely related to the *uncertainty relation,* or principle, which defines quantitatively how accurately each of a pair of complementary variables can be measured. Several examples that illustrate this principle will now be discussed.

First consider a plane wave falling on an aperture in the form of a slit, as shown in Fig. 2-3. It is well known from physical optics that in this case the light wave spreads out after passing through the slit, due to the diffraction effect. Consequently, after passing through the slit, the light is not simply a plane wave, but must be represented by a superposition of plane waves traveling in various directions but all having the same frequency as the original wave. Each of the plane waves of this superposition represents photons of a particular momentum, as has been seen. In some strange manner, the slit interacts with the incident photons to change their momenta by an amount not completely predictable.

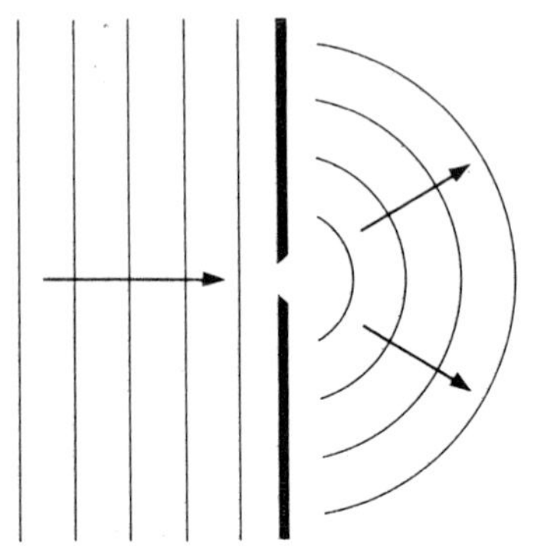

FIG. 2–3. Schematic representation of the diffraction of a plane wave by a slit.

A quantitative estimate of the disturbance to the momentum of the photon resulting from its passing through the slit can be obtained. Assume that the width of the slit is a and that the wavelength of the incident light is λ. The first zero of the Fraunhofer diffraction pattern of the slit occurs for a scattering angle of the photon given by

$$\sin\theta = \frac{\lambda}{a}\cdot \tag{2–15}$$

The width of the diffraction pattern, or the range of angles in which photons are scattered by the slit, is thus of the order of θ. Consequently, the momentum p_y in a direction perpendicular to the initial direction x of incidence of the light after it has passed through the slit has an uncertainty in value of the order

$$\Delta p_y \approx p\sin\theta = \frac{h}{\lambda}\cdot\frac{\lambda}{a} = \frac{h}{a}\cdot \tag{2–16}$$

Here the de Broglie relation

$$p = \frac{h}{\lambda} \tag{2–17}$$

has been used. The left side of Eq. (2–16) gives a rough estimate of the range of possible values of the y-component of momentum; a, the width of the slit, is the uncertainty in the photon position at the slit. Consequently, if the uncertainty in the y-component of the momentum is designated by Δp_y, and the position after passing through the slit by Δy, the product of these two uncertainties is given by

$$\Delta p_y\,\Delta y \approx h. \tag{2–18}$$

This is meant to represent only an approximate equality. For one thing, it has not been stated exactly what is meant by "uncertainty"; only rough

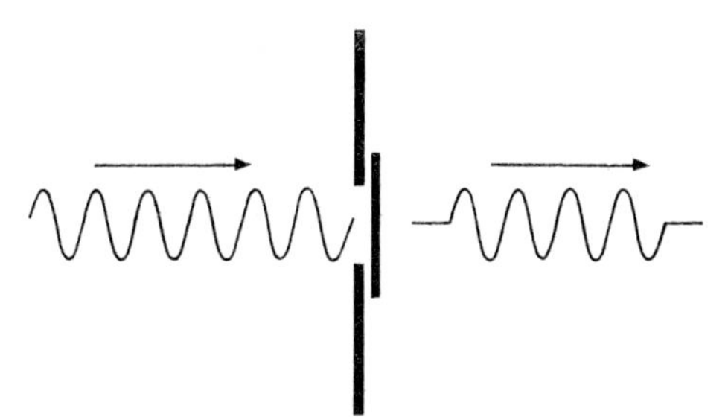

FIG. 2–4. A light shutter, illustrating the formation of a wave packet from a continuous wave.

indications of the measure of the uncertainty of the position of the photon and its momentum have been given. More exact definitions of the uncertainties will be given in Chapter 8.

For a second example, consider Fig. 2–4, which involves a shutter that opens and closes to allow a wave packet of light to pass through. This light pulse will be assumed to contain but one photon. The location of the photon inside the packet and the momentum of the photon are to be determined. If the direction of propagation of the wave is called the x-direction, and the length of the wave pulse is designated by Δx, it is clear that the position of the photon inside the wave packet must be uncertain to the order of Δx. At the same time, because a wave packet of this type requires for its representation a superposition of plane waves of different lengths, the momentum of the photon cannot be predicted with certainty. It would be necessary to make a measurement of momentum to determine its exact value. To obtain a wave packet having a length Δx, it is necessary to include a range of propagation constants Δk of the order

$$\Delta k \approx \frac{1}{\Delta x} \tag{2–19}$$

in the superposition of plane waves. Making use of the connection between the propagation constant k and the momentum of the particle, we see that this implies a range of momenta such that

$$\Delta k = \frac{\Delta p_x}{\hbar} \approx \frac{1}{\Delta x}, \tag{2–20}$$

which in turn can be written as

$$\Delta p_x \, \Delta x \approx \hbar. \tag{2–21}$$

This shows that the product of the uncertainty of the momentum in the

x-direction and the uncertainty in the position of the photon in this particular direction is of the order of $\hbar$.

Interestingly enough, the connection between the degree of knowledge of the position of the photon and its momentum as given by these two examples seems to be very general. Various experiments can be devised which would attempt to determine the momentum once the position is known, or to determine the position once the momentum is known, or to determine both of these to within certain prescribed limits of accuracy. However, it seems that it is not possible to devise an experiment which will determine the momentum *and* position of a photon simultaneously with arbitrary accuracy; the most accurate determination is one for which the uncertainties of Eqs. (2–18) and (2–21) hold.

It might be thought that this phenomenon is connected only with photons and would represent no limitation on other particles, but from an idealized experiment, again of the *Gedanken* variety, proposed by Heisenberg and known as the Heisenberg microscope, one can show, at least for this example, that the same limitations on momentum and position hold for electrons as for photons. Consider Fig. 2–5, in which an electron is viewed through a microscope. The electron is being bombarded by light from the left. Assume that its initial momentum is known; in fact, assume that it is initially stationary. With the momentum of the electron thus known, we can attempt to determine its position simultaneously. To observe where the electron is, one of the incident photons must strike the electron and be scattered into the microscope. However, when the photon bounces off the electron into the microscope, it transfers momentum to the electron and the amount of momentum transferred is not completely known because of the finite aperture of the microscope.

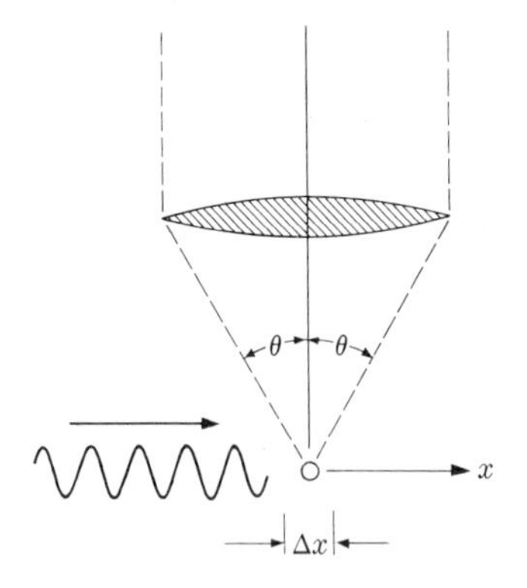

FIG. 2–5. Geometrical relations in the Heisenberg microscope. The position uncertainty is determined by the wavelength of the light and the angle θ. The uncertainty in momentum (after detection of the photon) is due to the uncertainty in the momentum transferred by the photon.

The photon can travel anywhere in the cone of illumination of the objective. Assume the half-angle of this cone to be designated by θ. In this case, the resolving power of the microscope, from wave optics, is equal to

$$\Delta x \approx \frac{\lambda}{\sin\theta}, \tag{2–22}$$

where λ represents the wavelength of the light employed. Δx, then, represents the accuracy with which the position of the electron can be determined by using light of this wavelength. On the other hand, the momentum transfer to the electron has an uncertainty given by

$$\Delta p_x \approx p \sin\theta. \tag{2–23}$$

If these two equations are taken together, the connection between the uncertainty in the momentum and the uncertainty in the position of the electron after the experiment is expressed by the relation

$$\Delta p_x \, \Delta x \approx p\lambda = h. \tag{2–24}$$

Once again, this should be regarded only as an order-of-magnitude equation. It states that the product of the uncertainty of the momentum of the electron in the x-direction and the uncertainty of its position in the x-direction is of the order of Planck's constant.

2–4 Wave packets. It has been seen that in quantum mechanics a particle with exactly defined momentum is not localized in space. The wave-mechanical analogue that perhaps most closely resembles a classical particle is a wave packet, a superposition of a group of plane waves of nearly the same wavelength that interfere destructively everywhere except at the (localized) wave packet. For a wave packet to be a close analogue of a classical particle, the classical connection between the velocity and momentum of the particle should hold for the wave packet. This assumption can then be used to obtain Eq. (2–4).

Assume as before that a linear superposition principle holds for ψ waves. This assumption means that quantum mechanics is a linear theory. In such a case, a wave packet can be represented by the superposition of a number of plane waves. Such a superposition for a wave packet along the x-axis can be written as the integral

$$G(x, t) = \int_{-\infty}^{\infty} A(k) \exp\left[i(kx - \omega t)\right] dk, \tag{2–25}$$

where $\omega = \omega(k)$. For this to represent a wave group traveling with a characteristic group velocity, it is necessary that the range of propagation vectors k included in the superposition be fairly small. In other words, it is assumed that the function $A(k)$ is nonzero only for a small range of values about a particular k_0 of k. This condition is

$$A(k) \neq 0, \qquad k_0 - \epsilon < k < k_0 + \epsilon, \qquad \epsilon \ll k_0. \tag{2-26}$$

It is assumed that for a small range of values in the vicinity of k_0, $\omega(k)$ can be expanded in a power series about k_0:

$$\omega = \omega_0 + (k - k_0)\left(\frac{d\omega}{dk}\right)_{k_0} + \cdots \tag{2-27}$$

If this expansion is used, Eq. (2-25) can be written as

$$G(x, t) \approx \exp\left[i(k_0 x - \omega_0 t)\right] \int_{-\infty}^{\infty} A(k) \exp\left[i(k - k_0)\left(x - \frac{d\omega}{dk}\,t\right)\right] dk. \tag{2-28}$$

The integral considered as a function of x and t has the form

$$\int_{-\infty}^{\infty} A(k) \exp\left[i(k - k_0)\left(x - \frac{d\omega}{dk}\,t\right)\right] dk = B\left(x - \frac{d\omega}{dk}\,t\right)\cdot \tag{2-29}$$

Then Eq. (2-28) becomes

$$G(x, t) = B\left(x - \frac{d\omega}{dk}\,t\right) \exp\left[i(k_0 x - \omega_0 t)\right]. \tag{2-30}$$

This is in the form of a product of an envelope function (B) and a plane wave. It represents the propagation of a group of waves for which the envelope or group velocity is given by

$$v_g = \frac{d\omega}{dk}\cdot \tag{2-31}$$

The situation is illustrated schematically in Fig. 2-6. The velocity at which the wave packet moves is to be identified as the velocity of the

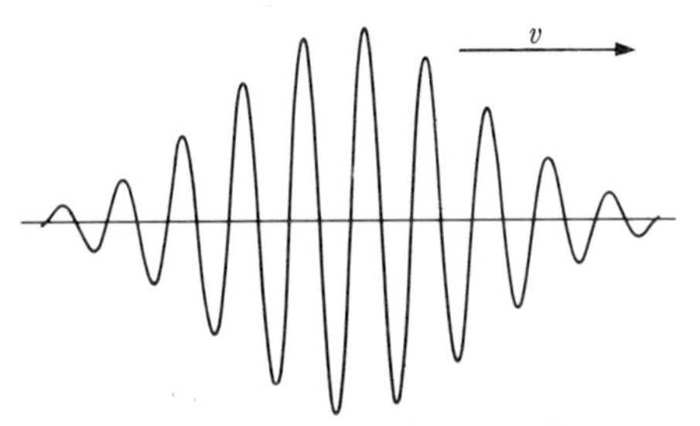

FIG. 2-6. A schematic representation of a complex wave packet. The real part of the ψ wave is plotted *vs.* distance for a one-dimensional situation.

associated particle. On the other hand, the phase velocity is given by the velocity of the plane wave, namely

$$v_p = \frac{\omega_0}{k_0}. \tag{2–32}$$

If the wave packet is to be associated with a classical particle, the group (packet) velocity v must be given by the classical relation

$$v = \frac{p}{m}, \tag{2–33}$$

where p is the particle momentum and m is its mass, or

$$\frac{d\omega}{dk} = \frac{p}{m}. \tag{2–34}$$

With the use of Eq. (2–7), this becomes

$$\frac{d\omega}{dk} = \frac{\hbar}{m}\, k, \tag{2–35}$$

which can be integrated directly to give

$$\hbar\omega = \frac{\hbar^2 k^2}{2m} + \text{constant} = \frac{p^2}{2m} + \text{constant}. \tag{2–36}$$

The first term on the right of this equation is the kinetic energy of the particle. The second term is a constant of integration which also has the dimensions of an energy. It appears reasonable to interpret this constant as the potential energy of the freely moving particle. This is a possible interpretation, since a particle moving without forces acting upon it moves in a region where its potential energy is in fact constant. It can be shown that this interpretation is indeed valid by considering the case of a particle (described by a plane wave) moving from one region where the potential energy is constant to another region where the potential energy is again constant but of a different value. In this particular case, although the wavelength would be expected to change as the wave moves from one region to the other, we would not expect the frequency to change; a sinusoidal wave of a given frequency will, as it propagates through space, preserve this frequency from one point to another. Consequently, if the frequency of the wave is to remain constant as it propagates from a region of constant potential energy into a region where the potential energy has a different constant value, the assumption that the constant of integration represents the potential energy is the only assumption permissible. With this example in mind, Eq. (2–36) can be rewritten as

$$\hbar\omega = \frac{p^2}{2m} + V(x) = E, \tag{2–37}$$

where $V(x)$ is the potential energy of the particle at the point x, and E is the total energy of the particle. This is, of course, the relation between wave frequency and energy obtained before. It should be noted that although the above arguments make the momentum dependence of ω completely definite, there is still ambiguity arising from the arbitrariness of the zero-level of potential energy. In other words, the actual frequency of this wave is determined by the choice of the zero of potential energy and is arbitrary. Therefore the frequency cannot be of direct physical significance. This is a clue to the proper physical interpretation of the nature of the wave: as suggested earlier, it is a wave which does not have the direct physical meaning that one associates, for example, with a sound wave.

It is now possible to draw another important conclusion from the example of the motion of a wave packet. The classical description of a particle as an entity localized in space and moving on a definite space-time trajectory is really an idealization of the motion of a wave packet. Because of the inadequacy of the sense organs, the extended character of such wave packets is not usually observed and the physical concepts based on these observations are an idealization of the observations. Thus a wave packet moves like a classical particle under conditions where newtonian mechanics gives an adequate description of the motion.

2–5 Summary. The double-slit interference experiment of Young was considered with regard to the photon (particle) picture of light, and the resulting paradoxes were resolved by introducing a statistical aspect into the nature of light. Quantum mechanics postulates this probabilistic aspect of nature to extend to the behavior of material particles as well. The concept of wave function was introduced. This provides the complete quantum-mechanical description of a system. A brief argument made it plausible that the wave function be complex rather than real. The idea of a superposition wave function was considered and illustrated by the case of two plane waves. The consistency of the formalism was shown by a consideration of the refraction of a stream of particles that occurs when they move from one region of constant potential energy into another region where they have a different constant potential energy. The uncertainty principle, relating the limits on the accuracy of the simultaneous measurement of each of a pair of complementary variables, was discussed in a semiquantitative way by means of several illustrative examples. Finally, the formation of localized wave functions by the superposition of plane waves into wave packets was treated, and the correspondence between the motion of such a wave packet and a classical particle was discussed.

Problems

2–1. (a) Compute energy levels for a hydrogen atom by assuming that the electron moves in circular orbits around the nucleus such that the circumference of an orbit is an integral number of de Broglie wavelengths. (b) From the expression for E_n thus obtained, compute the frequency of radiation emitted when an atom goes from the $(n + 1)$st to the nth state from

$$f = \frac{E_{n+1} - E_n}{h}.$$

(c) Show that in the limit of large quantum numbers, this is identical with the classical frequency of an electron of energy E_n traveling around the nucleus.

2–2. Estimate from the uncertainty principle how long an ordinary lead pencil can be balanced upright on its point.

CHAPTER 3

SCHRÖDINGER'S EQUATION

3–1 The equation of motion of a wave function. In the preceding chapter, the concept of the quantum-mechanical wave function was introduced, and a brief discussion was given of its relation to the wave-particle duality problem of classical mechanics. A quantum-mechanical view of matter was thus suggested. However, no consideration has yet been given to the quantum-mechanical "laws of motion" that determine the time dependence of the wave function. It is the purpose of this chapter to show how classical analogy and arguments of the type used previously *suggest* a form for a quantum-mechanical law of motion.

Since the laws of motion for particles and waves in classical mechanics can generally be expressed as second-order differential equations, it is natural to look for a suitable second-order differential (wave) equation such that

$$\psi = A \exp\left(i \frac{\mathbf{p} \cdot \mathbf{r}}{\hbar} - i \frac{Et}{\hbar}\right) \tag{3-1}$$

is a solution for the case of a particle moving in a region of constant potential energy. One might expect to find the potential energy and the mass as externally given parameters in the desired quantum equation of motion. However, as in the classical case, one would not expect the wave equation to contain the momentum or the energy of the particle explicitly, since these quantities differ in general for each solution and the desired wave equation should be valid for an entire class of solutions. The general connection between the total energy of the particle, its kinetic energy, and its potential energy enables us to write an equation that satisfies these requirements.

First consider the application of the Laplacian operator to the plane-wave function given by Eq. (3–1):

$$\nabla^2\psi \equiv \left(\frac{\partial^2}{\partial x^2} + \frac{\partial^2}{\partial y^2} + \frac{\partial^2}{\partial z^2}\right)\psi = -\frac{p^2}{\hbar^2}\psi. \tag{3-2}$$

In a similar fashion, differentiation of Eq. (3–1) with respect to time yields

$$\frac{\partial\psi}{\partial t} = -\frac{iE}{\hbar}\psi. \tag{3-3}$$

However, the total energy can be expressed as the sum of the kinetic and (a constant) potential energy:

$$E = \frac{p^2}{2m} + V. \tag{3-4}$$

These equations can then be combined to give the differential equation

$$\left[-\frac{\hbar^2}{2m}\nabla^2 + V\right]\psi = i\hbar\frac{\partial}{\partial t}\psi. \tag{3-5}$$

Strangely enough, this equation is only first-order in time rather than second-order.

Although this equation has been shown to be satisfied by solutions of the form of Eq. (3-1), it is obvious from the linearity of Eq. (3-5) that any linear combination of functions of the form of Eq. (3-1) is also a solution. It is reasonable, as will be seen in the discussion to follow, to assume that Eq. (3-5) is valid, not only for free particles, but also for particles acted upon by a conservative force field. In such a case, Eq. (3-5) is assumed to hold when V is a function of position.

The differential equation (3-5) can have, in general, a large number of solutions. However, since the solutions are to have the physical interpretation as *probability amplitudes*, as discussed earlier, only a certain type of mathematically possible solution is physically acceptable. For the wave function to be physically suitable, it must be a single-valued function of position and must be everywhere finite. Moreover, given the spatial (and temporal) behavior of the (finite) potential V and the value of the wave function and its derivative over a surface, the above equation can be integrated to give ψ and its gradient at every point in space; both ψ and its first derivative are *continuous* functions.

If it furthermore is required that the quantity $|\psi|^2$ be interpretable as a probability density rather than a *relative* probability density, the wave function ψ should be square-integrable, i.e., the integral $\int|\psi|^2\,d\tau$ must exist. If this integral has the value unity, the wave function is said to be *normalized.* In this case, the quantity $|\psi|^2$ may be interpreted directly as the spatial probability density of the particle.

It has been noted that Eq. (3-5) is linear. Hence for any solution, another can be obtained by multiplying by a constant. If the function is square-integrable the constant can be chosen to normalize the wave function. It is clear that the question of normalization cannot be profound; indeed, the physical significance of a wave function is not modified if it is multiplied by any arbitrary complex number.

Although there are good reasons for believing that a physically significant wave function is continuous in value and first derivative, bounded, and square-integrable, there will frequently occur cases in which, for purposes of mathematical convenience, one or more of these conditions may be relaxed. An example of this has already been encountered: a plane wave representing a particle of definite momentum is not square-integrable. This is an idealization, for exactly known values do not occur; further, a particle found with equal probability everywhere is obviously an idealization of a situation in which the location of the particle is indefinite on a macroscopic scale.

Equation (3–5) contains no terms involving the momentum or energy of the particle, but it does contain the particle mass and the potential energy. The plane wave of Eq. (3–1) is clearly a solution. Furthermore, reference to the problem discussed in the preceding chapter, where the potential function took on different values in two different regions of space, shows that the results previously obtained can also be obtained from Eq. (3–5) by assuming that ψ and its derivatives are continuous across the boundary separating the regions of different (constant) potential. Because any continuously varying potential function can be approximated by a series of step functions in each step of which the potential is a constant, the validity of the solution for this particular example suggests that Eq. (3–5) may also be valid when the potential energy is a continuous function of position. In this case, the V appearing in Eq. (3–5) is to be taken as a function of the position of the particle. Equation (3–5), known as *Schrödinger's equation*, was discovered by him in 1926.* As remarked before, this equation is only of first order in time. The wave equations encountered in classical physics, such as the equations for electromagnetic waves or for sound waves, are of second order in time.

The expression in brackets on the left side of Eq. (3–5) can be considered to be an *operator* which operates on the wave function ψ. If this operator is designated by the symbol H (its physical significance will appear later), the equation can be written as

$$\mathrm{H}\psi = i\hbar \frac{\partial}{\partial t} \psi. \tag{3–6}$$

This equation is a partial differential equation in four variables, the three position coordinates of the particle and the time, and is separable whenever the potential energy V is not a function of time. In such a case, to separate the time-dependent part of the differential equation, ψ is expressed in the form

$$\psi = u(x, y, z)v(t). \tag{3–7}$$

* The Schrödinger equation in the form of Eq. (3–5) appeared in the fourth of a series of papers by E. Schrödinger entitled "Quantisierung als Eigenwertproblem." The earlier papers in the series dealt with conservative systems and concerned the time-independent form of the Schrödinger equation, which will be considered later (Eq. 3–10). These four important papers of Schrödinger are found in *Ann. Physik* **79,** 361 (1926); **79,** 489 (1926); **80,** 437 (1926); and **81,** 109 (1926).

Substituting this into Eq. (3–5) and dividing through by $u(x, y, z)v(t)$ yields

$$\frac{1}{u(x, y, z)}\left[-\frac{\hbar^2}{2m}\nabla^2 + V(x, y, z)\right]u(x, y, z) = i\hbar\,\frac{1}{v(t)}\,\frac{\partial}{\partial t}\,v(t) = E. \tag{3–8}$$

The left side of this equation is a function only of the coordinates x, y, and z, and the right side is a function only of the time t. Consequently, since these four variables are independent, each side of Eq. (3–8) must be equal to a constant, which we shall designate by E.

The solution of the time-dependent part of Eq. (3–8) leads to

$$v(t) = \exp\left(-\frac{i}{\hbar}\,Et\right). \tag{3–9}$$

It is clear why it is appropriate to designate the constant, which has the dimensions of energy, by E if one compares this equation with that for a plane wave, Eq. (3–1): E designates the energy of the particle which is described by this solution to the Schrödinger equation. The position-dependent part of Eq. (3–8) becomes

$$\mathrm{H}u(x, y, z) = Eu(x, y, z). \tag{3–10}$$

This differential equation is in the form known as an *eigenvalue* equation, with the constant E the eigenvalue. It will be seen later that, in general, for bound particles, i.e., particles localized in or confined to a finite region of space by some sort of a potential well or a box of some type, Eq. (3–10) has allowable solutions only for certain definite values of E and that these values for E are the possible energies of the particular system in question. Thus quantization, as well as the wave-particle duality, has been incorporated into the very framework of quantum mechanics.

In the theory of linear partial differential equations, it is shown that the most general solution of Eq. (3–6) that is physically acceptable can be written as a linear superposition of solutions of the form of Eq. (3–7). Consequently, the most general solution of Schrödinger's equation for a time-independent potential energy V can be put into the form

$$\psi = \sum_E c_E \exp\left(-i\,\frac{E}{\hbar}\,t\right)u_E(x, y, z), \tag{3–11}$$

where the c_E are constants determined by the conditions imposed on the system.

This equation presents another example of the idea of superposition, encountered earlier in connection with the momentum of a free particle. There it was seen that if the wave function was the sum of two plane waves, it represented a state of the particle for which the result of a momentum measurement was uncertain. Such a measurement could yield one of the two corresponding values of the momentum, but which one was defined only in a probabilistic way. In a certain sense, such a wave function can be said to represent a state of the particle for which it *simultaneously* has two different momenta.

Equation (3–11) introduces the same idea with respect to energy. Each of the terms in the sum represents a wave function for which the energy of the particle is well-defined. The sum, however, is a wave function which is a superposition of various energy states: if the energy is measured, some definite one of the energies given by terms present in the sum would be measured, but which one can be predicted only in a probabilistic way. By analogy with the previous arguments involving momentum, one would expect that $|c_E|^2$ would be a measure of the probability of obtaining the result E if the energy is measured. Additional credibility is given to this expectation by considering the absolute square of Eq. (3–11) integrated over all space. It is assumed that the functions ψ and u_E are normalized to unity. The resulting integral can be written as

$$1 = \int |\psi|^2 \, dv = \sum_{E,E'} \overline{c_E} c_{E'} \exp\left[\frac{i(E' - E)t}{\hbar}\right] \int \overline{u_E} u_{E'} \, dv$$

$$= \sum_E |c_E|^2, \tag{3–12}$$

inasmuch as it will be shown in Chapter 6 that these integrals are all zero when $E \neq E'$. For simplicity, the energies E in Eq. (3–12) are all assumed to be different. The square integral of ψ is unity, the probability of finding the particle somewhere in space. This is equal to a sum which may be interpreted as the sums of the probabilities of finding the particle in the various energy states.

3–2 One-dimensional motion past a potential hill. The simplest solutions of the Schrödinger equation are those corresponding to problems involving motion of a particle in only one dimension. By this it is meant that the potential energy V in Eq. (3–5) is a function of only one coordinate, for example x; the motion of the particle in the y- and z-directions is then that of a free particle, which for simplicity may be ignored. If the y- and z-motions of the particle are thus ignored, H, which is called the *Hamiltonian operator*, has the form

$$\mathrm{H} = -\frac{\hbar^2}{2m}\frac{\partial^2}{\partial x^2} + V(x). \tag{3–13}$$

Particle motions in one dimension can be divided naturally into three classes characterized by the form of the potential energy function $V(x)$.

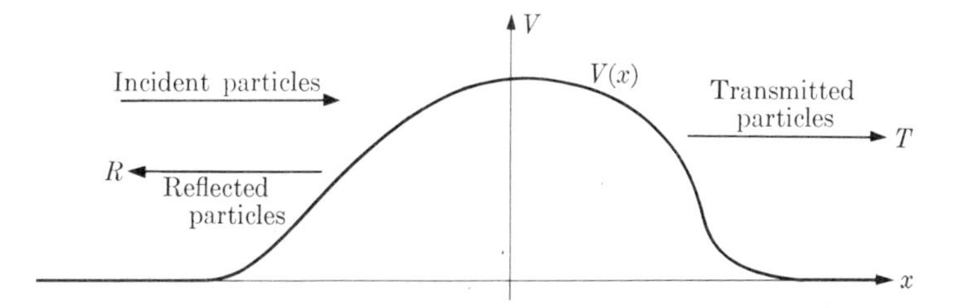

FIG. 3-1. General one-dimensional potential hill.

In the first class, which can be designated as motion past a potential hill, the potential energy of the particle is a function of position of the general form plotted in Fig. 3-1. The potential energy function in this case is in the form of a potential hill such that the forces are equal to zero everywhere except in a finite region of space corresponding to the hill. In this class of problems, one normally considers a wave incident upon the potential hill from either the left or the right, with some particles being transmitted past the hill and the others being reflected. The flux of incident particles may be measured in some sort of convenient unit; for example, unit flux may represent one particle per second incident on the potential hill with a particular momentum. The intensity R of the reflected wave and the intensity T of the transmitted wave in Fig. 3-1 designate respectively the number of reflected particles and transmitted particles per second with unit incident particle flux. There are several mathematical and physical points to be noted about this class of problems. First of all, any solution is characterized by four parameters, of which only two are physically significant. These may be in the form of two complex numbers representing the amplitude and phase of waves incident upon the potential hill both from the left and from the right. However, since we are dealing with a linear theory, it is possible to treat each of these incident waves separately. Thus, without loss of generality, the problem can be reduced to a two-parameter problem with only one wave incident on the scattering potential. Solutions to this simpler problem can be superposed if necessary to satisfy the conditions of the more general case.

A point of interest is that it is possible to obtain physically significant solutions for any positive energy of the particle. A further matter of great physical interest and importance is that even for a total energy of the particle less than the maximum height of the potential hill, there is a transmitted wave T. This is a situation without any classical analogue, corresponding to particles "tunneling" their way through the hill without "going over the top"; from a classical point of view, one would never expect the particle to be found in a region where its potential energy was greater than its total energy, since this would correspond to a negative kinetic energy, a concept without physical significance. The physical resolution of this paradox will be discussed in Chapter 8.

Barrier penetrations of this type are important in connection with nuclear physics, for example, in the alpha-particle decay of a radioactive nucleus. Here the alpha particle must travel through the potential barrier of the coulomb energy between the charged alpha particle and the charged nucleus, a barrier that is higher at the edge of the nucleus than the total energy of the alpha particle. (This particular problem is treated in detail in Chapter 14.)

Consider, as an example, the simple potential barrier illustrated in Fig. 3–2. The potential energy is a (positive) constant V in the region $-a \leq x \leq a$ and is zero outside this region. It is assumed that particles are incident upon the potential barrier from the left only and that there is a reflected wave and a transmitted wave. It is further assumed that the energy of the particle is less than V, so that any transmitted particle must be characterized as resulting from a penetration of the barrier.

The potential of Fig. 3–2 has been chosen so as to be symmetric about $x = 0$:

$$V(x) = V(-x). \tag{3–14}$$

Because of the corresponding even character of the second derivative with respect to x, the total Hamiltonian operator H of Eq. (3–13) is left unchanged under a transformation in which x is replaced by $-x$. Conse-

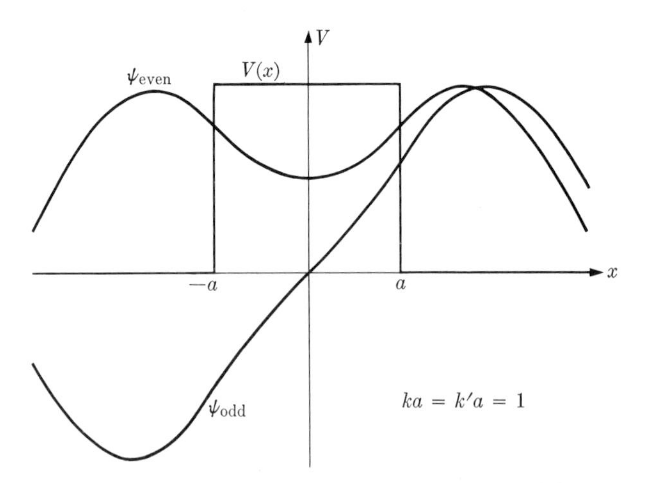

Fig. 3–2. One-dimensional rectangular potential barrier, with representative odd and even wave functions associated with the rectangular potential barrier.

quently, if $u(x)$ is a solution to Eq. (3–10), this simple transformation leads to

$$\mathrm{H}u(-x) = Eu(-x). \tag{3–15}$$

Thus both $u(x)$ and $u(-x)$ are solutions to the eigenvalue equation (3–10), with the same eigenvalue E. Consequently, any linear combination is also a solution; in particular, the even and odd combinations

$$\mathrm{H}[u(x) \pm u(-x)] = E[u(x) \pm u(-x)] \tag{3–16}$$

are solutions. Solutions to Eq. (3–10), which from Eq. (3–13) can be written as

$$\frac{d^2u}{dx^2} = \frac{2m}{\hbar^2}[V(x) - E]u, \tag{3–17}$$

can therefore be chosen to be either even or odd in x without loss of generality. The function in the brackets in Eq. (3–16) may be trivially zero. For example, if $u(x)$ is an even function of x, the odd combination in Eq. (3–16) is identically zero. The symmetric choice of potential of Fig. 3–2 was made to simplify the discussion of the quantitative nature of the solutions; the problems encountered in practice will not necessarily have this particular symmetry.

Since the potential energy is an even function of x, one can, as indicated, choose the solutions of the energy eigenvalue equation to be always even or odd. The problem is somewhat simplified by thus considering either even or odd solutions to the differential equation. First consider even solutions. The wave function u that is a solution to Eq. (3–17) can be written for the three regions of x as

$$\begin{aligned} u &= A_1 \cosh k'x, && -a < x < a, \\ &= B_1 \cos(kx - \delta_1), && x > a, \\ &= B_1 \cos(kx + \delta_1), && x < -a. \end{aligned} \tag{3–18}$$

Here k and k' are given by

$$\begin{aligned} k' &= \frac{1}{\hbar}[2m(V - E)]^{1/2}, \qquad E < V, \\ k &= \frac{1}{\hbar}[2mE]^{1/2}. \end{aligned} \tag{3–19}$$

Note that in the region lying between $-a$ and a, the even function u is a hyperbolic cosine. The functions in the region $x > a$ and $x < -a$ are also even.

The constants A_1 and B_1 must be so chosen as to join these expressions properly at the boundaries a and $-a$; as mentioned earlier, it is necessary that u and its derivative be continuous functions. If u and its first derivative are to be continuous at the points $x = \pm a$, the logarithmic derivative

$$\frac{d}{dx}(\log u) = \frac{1}{u}\frac{du}{dx} \tag{3-20}$$

will also be continuous. The continuity of the logarithmic derivative of u with respect to x at $x = a$ gives

$$\frac{1}{u}\frac{du}{dx} = k' \tanh(k'a) = -k \tan(ka - \delta_1). \tag{3-21}$$

If we make the assumptions that

$$ka \ll k'a \ll 1, \tag{3-22}$$

Eq. (3-21) can be simplified to

$$\delta_1 = \frac{k^2 + k'^2}{k} a = \frac{V}{E} ka. \tag{3-23}$$

In a similar manner, the odd solution to the differential equation can be written as

$$\begin{aligned} u &= A_2 \sinh k'x, & -a < x < a, \\ &= B_2 \sin(kx - \delta_2), & x > a, \\ &= B_2 \sin(kx + \delta_2), & x < -a. \end{aligned} \tag{3-24}$$

Here the continuity in the logarithmic derivative gives

$$\frac{1}{u}\frac{du}{dx} = k' \coth(k'a) = k \cot(ka - \delta_2), \tag{3-25}$$

which can be written as

$$k \tanh(k'a) = k' \tan(ka - \delta_2). \tag{3-26}$$

If we again make the assumptions of Eq. (3-22), the result is

$$\delta_2 = 0. \tag{3-27}$$

The wave functions of Eqs. (3-18) and (3-24) are shown for representative values of particle energy and potential-barrier height in Fig. 3-2.

By a suitable choice of the constants B_1 and B_2 in Eqs. (3-18) and (3-24), the even and odd solutions which have been considered can be made such that the amplitudes of the incident waves from each side are equal. These two solutions can then be superposed in such a way that the amplitude of the incident wave from the right becomes zero, so that waves are incident only from the left. In this case, the solutions give directly the amplitudes of the transmitted and reflected waves. Superposing the even and odd solutions yields, for $x > a$,

$$u = B_1 \cos (kx - \delta_1) + B_2 \sin kx. \tag{3-28}$$

Remembering that in this region there is only a transmitted wave to the right, we see that this must have the form of the space part of a plane wave:

$$u = C \exp (ikx). \tag{3-29}$$

Combining these equations, we obtain

$$B_1 \exp (i\delta_1) + iB_2 = 0 \tag{3-30}$$

and

$$C = \tfrac{1}{2}[B_1 \exp (-i\delta_1) - iB_2]. \tag{3-31}$$

Combining these gives

$$C = B_1 \cos \delta_1. \tag{3-32}$$

In the region $x < -a$, the wave function has the form

$$u = \left[\tfrac{1}{2}B_1 \exp (i\delta_1) - \frac{i}{2} B_2\right] \exp (ikx) + \left[\tfrac{1}{2}B_1 \exp (-i\delta_1) + \frac{i}{2} B_2\right] \exp (-ikx), \tag{3-33}$$

where the first term represents the incident wave and the second the reflected wave. When Eq. (3-30) is substituted into this equation, it becomes

$$u = -iB_2 \exp (ikx) + \tfrac{1}{2}B_1 [\exp (-i\delta_1) - \exp (i\delta_1)] \exp (-ikx), \quad x < -a. \tag{3-34}$$

If the amplitude of the wave incident from the left is assumed to be unity, B_2 may be chosen $B_2 = i$, giving $B_1 = \exp (-i\delta_1)$ and

$$\begin{aligned} u &= \exp (ikx) - i \exp (-i\delta_1) \sin \delta_1 \exp (-ikx), && x < -a, \\ &= \exp (-i\delta_1) \cos \delta_1 \exp (ikx), && x > a. \end{aligned} \tag{3-35}$$

From these expressions the amplitudes of the transmitted and reflected waves are given directly in terms of the "phase shift" δ_1. The probability that a particle will be transmitted through the barrier is given by the square of the absolute value of the amplitude of the transmitted wave:

$$T = \cos^2 \delta_1 = \frac{1}{1 + \tan^2 \delta_1} = \frac{1}{1 + V^2/E \cdot 2ma^2/\hbar^2}. \tag{3-36}$$

By approximating the r^{-1} potential by an equivalent square barrier and applying the above results, this equation can be used to obtain a rough estimate of the probability that an alpha particle will escape from a nucleus by penetrating the potential barrier of the nuclear electrostatic coulomb field. More exact calculations will be made later. (See Chapter 14.)

Only the case of low-energy particles has been treated above. However, an interesting effect also occurs when the energy of the particles is greater than the maximum energy V_m of the scattering potential. In this case, the solution of Schrödinger's equation shows that, contrary to classical expectations, there is a finite probability that an incident particle will be reflected. This will be discussed further after we have considered another class of problems.

3–3 One-dimensional motion: reflection by an infinitely wide barrier. The second class of one-dimensional motions concerns the reflection of particles by a potential barrier, as illustrated in Fig. 3–3. In this case, for particles incident upon the potential hill from the left with an energy less than the potential energy of the top of the hill, the particles are totally reflected, as in the classical case. With energies greater than the potential energy, there will in general be both a transmitted and a reflected wave. In this class of problems, as in that discussed above, physically meaningful solutions can be found for any positive energy of the particle, but for low-energy particles where reflection is total, these solutions are characterized by only a two-parameter system. The solution is then completely specified when the amplitude and phase of a wave incident upon the barrier from the left are specified.

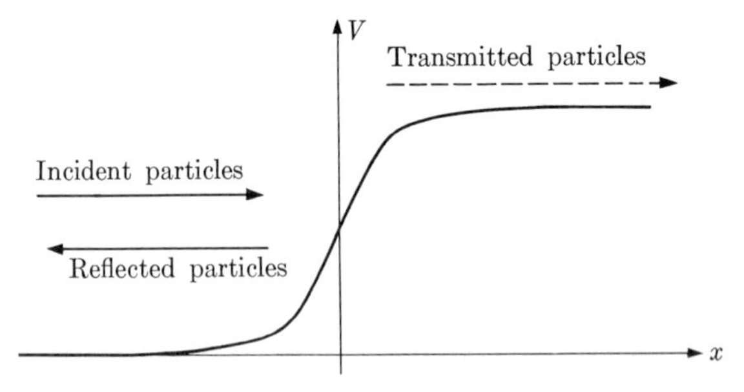

FIG. 3–3. General infinitely wide one-dimensional potential barrier.

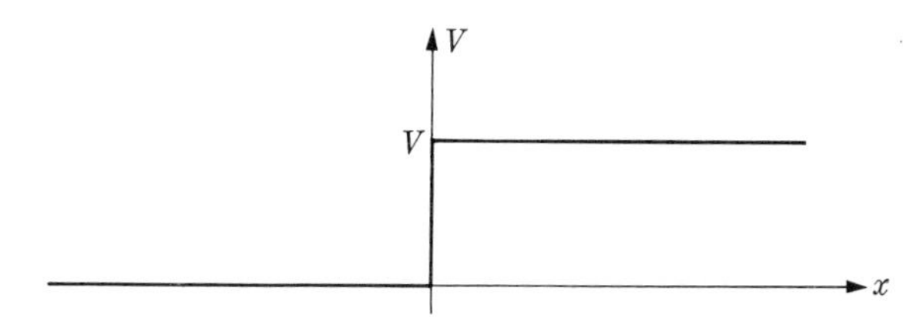

FIG. 3–4. Potential step.

As an example of this second type of potential, consider the barrier shown in Fig. 3–4. This is a potential energy function which has the form of a simple step occurring at $x = 0$:

$$V(x) = 0, \qquad x < 0,$$
$$= V > 0, \qquad x > 0. \tag{3–37}$$

Consider first the case where the energy is greater than the potential energy V for positive x. Classically, in this case all the incident particles are able to move continuously to the right. If the total energy of the particle is everywhere greater than the potential energy, the most general solution of Eq. (3–17) for negative x is of the form

$$u = \exp[i(kx - \omega t)] + A \exp[-i(kx + \omega t)], \qquad x < 0,$$
$$k = \left[\frac{2mE}{\hbar^2}\right]^{1/2}, \qquad \omega = \frac{E}{\hbar}. \tag{3–38}$$

This corresponds to a unit incident flux. For positive x, the solution is of the form

$$u = B \exp[i(k'x - \omega t)], \qquad x > 0,$$
$$k' = \left[\frac{2m(E - V)}{\hbar^2}\right]^{1/2}. \tag{3–39}$$

As before, it is assumed that the function and its first derivative, and hence the logarithmic derivative, are everywhere continuous. The logarithmic derivative has, on the negative side of the boundary, the value

$$\frac{1}{u}\frac{du}{dx} = \frac{ik(1 - A)}{1 + A}, \qquad x = -0. \tag{3–40}$$

On the positive side of the boundary it has the value

$$\frac{1}{u}\frac{du}{dx} = ik', \qquad x = +0. \tag{3–41}$$

Continuity in the logarithmic derivative across the boundary then requires that

$$\frac{1 - A}{1 + A} = \frac{k'}{k} = \left[\frac{E - V}{E}\right]^{1/2}. \tag{3-42}$$

Solving for A, we find

$$A = \frac{\sqrt{E} - \sqrt{E - V}}{\sqrt{E} + \sqrt{E - V}}. \tag{3-43}$$

The square of A represents the intensity of the reflected wave or the probability that a particle is reflected at the interface between the regions of different potential energy. To compare this with the classical result, it is only necessary to remember that from classical mechanics there should be no reflections of particles, and A should be zero. In the limit of E much greater than V, this is also the case quantum-mechanically.

Consider next the case of the energy of the particle less than the height of the potential barrier. Classically, in this case all particles are reflected. Now k' in Eq. (3–39) is purely imaginary, corresponding to solutions decaying exponentially toward the right for positive x. Only the positive imaginary root is admissible for k', since the negative root would correspond to a solution exponentially increasing to the right. This is physically inadmissible: it corresponds to an infinite outgoing particle flux for unit incident intensity. Except that k' becomes imaginary, the formalism is as outlined above and the reflection probability is again given by the square of the magnitude of A in Eq. (3–43). However, in this equation the radical $\sqrt{E - V}$ now is purely imaginary and the numerator is just the complex conjugate of the denominator. Consequently, the absolute value of A is unity, corresponding to a reflection of all particles. This agrees with the classical result for these conditions. The reflection coefficient $|A|^2$ is plotted in Fig. 3–5.

An interesting case to consider is the limiting case obtained as the height of the potential barrier V goes to infinity. Examination of Eq. (3–43) shows that the limit of A as V goes to infinity is

$$\lim_{V \to \infty} A = -1. \tag{3-44}$$

The substitution of $A = -1$ in Eq. (3–38) leads to the condition

$$u(0) = 0. \tag{3-45}$$

This is equivalent to the statement that the condition to be satisfied at any boundary for which the potential energy is infinite is the vanishing of the wave function. Actually, this is proved here only for the one-dimensional problem, but it can be shown to be valid generally.

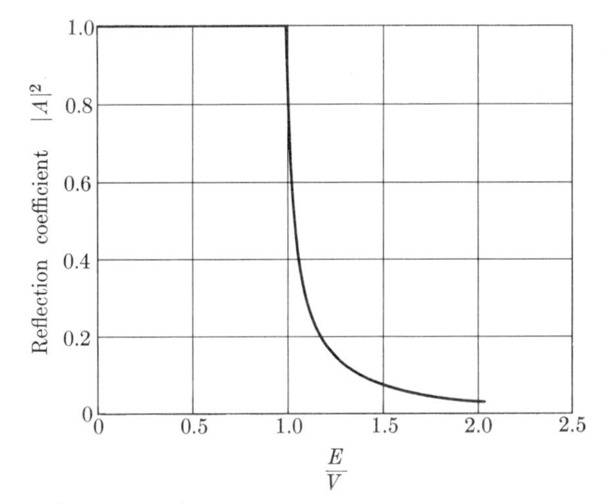

FIG. 3–5. Reflection coefficient for particles incident on the step-potential barrier. Note that some particles whose energy is sufficient to ensure transmission classically are quantum-mechanically reflected.

In both the classes of potentials discussed, it has been seen that potential barriers can reflect particles that have sufficient energy to ensure transmission classically. This rather unexpected behavior does, nonetheless, have a classical analogue that becomes apparent when one remembers that the quantum-mechanical formalism encompasses wavelike as well as particlelike behavior. One may, for example, treat the problem by analogy with classical wave optics, as was done earlier in this chapter, where the classical Snell's law of wave optics was seen to give results equivalent to those obtained by quantum-mechanical considerations. The reflection of particles of energy E by a potential barrier of height $V < E$ can be compared with the reflection of light by a transparent medium whose index of refraction differs from its surroundings. Writing Eq. (3–43) as

$$A = \frac{\sqrt{E/(E - V)} - 1}{\sqrt{E/(E - V)} + 1} \tag{3–46}$$

and using the "index of refraction" defined by Eq. (2–12), we have

$$A = \frac{n - 1}{n + 1}, \tag{3–47}$$

which is the classical optical reflection coefficient for a boundary where the index of refraction changes abruptly. Analysis shows that if the potential (or index of refraction) varies gradually enough, instead of abruptly, reflections can be neglected in both the classical and quantum cases.

3–4 One-dimensional motion in a potential well. The third class of motions to be discussed is that of a particle bound in a potential well. In this case, the potential energy function is of the general form shown in Fig. 3–6, and the particle can exist in states (Schrödinger's equation can have solutions) for which the total energy of the particle is negative as well as positive. Classically, for negative energies the particle oscillates back and forth between the two sides of the potential well. An analogous situation can exist quantum-mechanically; there are then *bound solutions* to Schrödinger's equation. As will be made clear below, such bound solutions are obtainable only for certain discrete negative-energy eigenvalues of the Schrödinger equation. Consequently, there is a quantized energy-level structure for the possible energies of the particle within the well. On the other hand, there are also solutions for positive energies of the particle, which are just like the solutions of the first class of problems described above, namely, the scattering of particles incident from one side. In this case, the incident particles will be partially reflected and partially transmitted through the potential-well region. There is, of course, a characteristic difference between this type of behavior and the classical behavior. In the case of the classical system, the particle would certainly traverse the potential well and emerge on the other side. In other words, there would be only transmitted particles and no reflected particles. Quantum-mechanically, because of the wavelike behavior of particles, there are reflected as well as transmitted particles.

The bound states of the particle in a potential well will now be discussed from a qualitative point of view to see why this class of solutions is characterized by a definite discrete set of energy eigenvalues E. Referring to Eq. (3–17), consider first the region where the potential energy is less than the total energy, so that the coefficient of u on the right side of the equation is negative. For a positive u, the second derivative of u is negative. In other words, the solution is such that in a plot of u as a function of x, for positive u the curve is concave downward, or toward the axis. On the other hand, for negative u the second derivative is positive and the solution is again curving upward toward the axis. Thus the solution is characterized by having an oscillatory character in which the curvature is always toward the $u = 0$ axis. (See Fig. 3–7, Region 1.) Whenever V

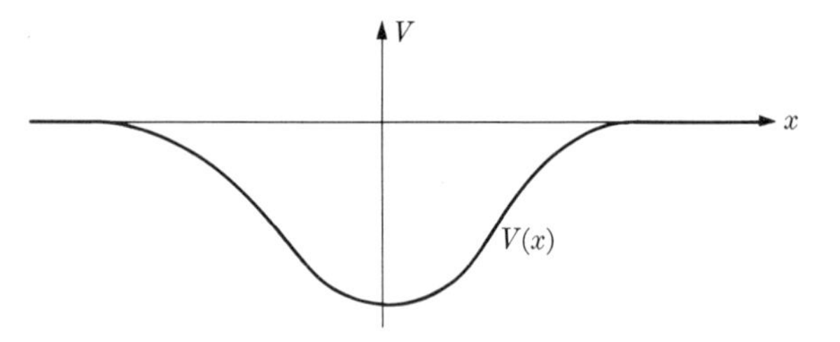

FIG. 3–6. General potential well.

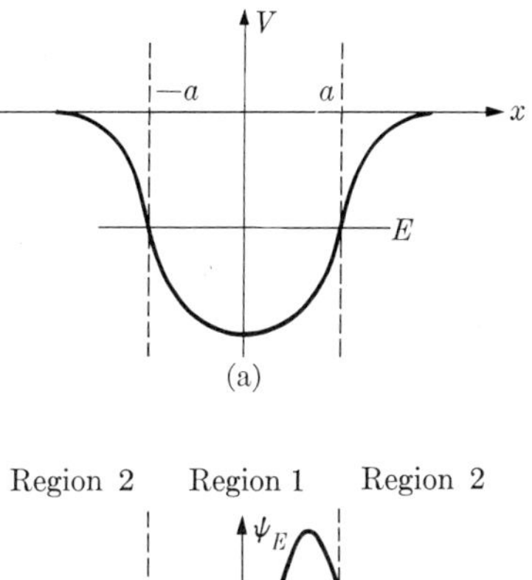

(a)

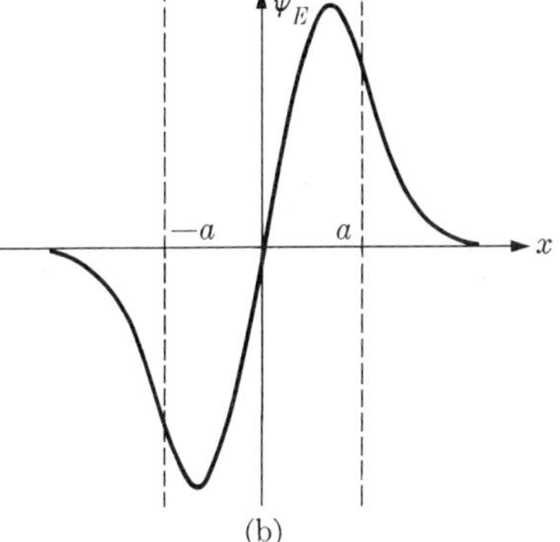

(b)

FIG. 3–7. (a) A potential well. (b) The wave function for a bound state of the well. Note the oscillatory nature of ψ in the classically allowed region 1 and the exponential behavior in the classically forbidden region 2. The wave function shown is a computed eigenfunction of the potential well of (a) for the energy E.

is larger than E (Region 2, Fig. 3–7), the coefficient of u is positive: for positive u the function curves upward, or away from the axis, and for negative u it curves downward, also away from the axis. Thus the solutions are such that the behavior about $u = 0$ is oscillatory in regions where the particle is allowed classically (i.e., where the total energy of the particle is greater than its potential energy) and divergent or exponential whenever the total energy is less than the potential energy.

To see how this type of behavior leads to discrete allowed eigenenergies E, consider the potential energy function plotted in Fig. 3–8. For simplicity, it is assumed that the potential energy function is symmetrical about $x = 0$. Consider a solution to the differential equation for a particular value of the energy E. The points at $x = a$ and $x = -a$, corresponding to where the energy E equals the potential energy V, have been marked. In the region $-a < x < a$, the function u is, as seen above, such that it is oscillatory, always curving toward the axis. For x greater than a, and for x less than $-a$, the particle is in a classically forbidden

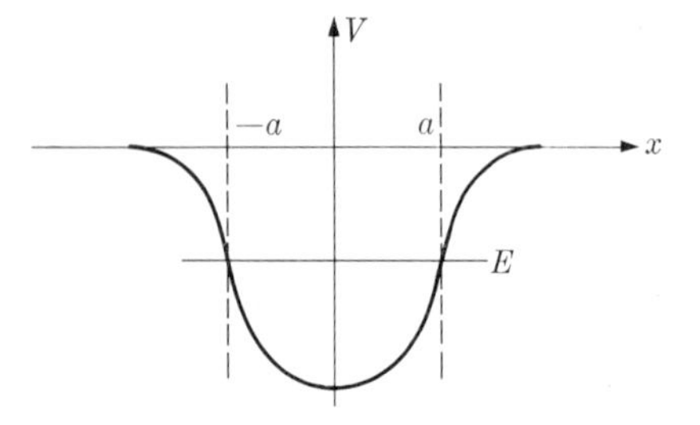

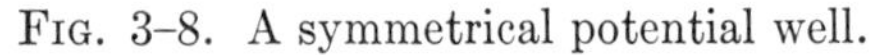
FIG. 3–8. A symmetrical potential well.

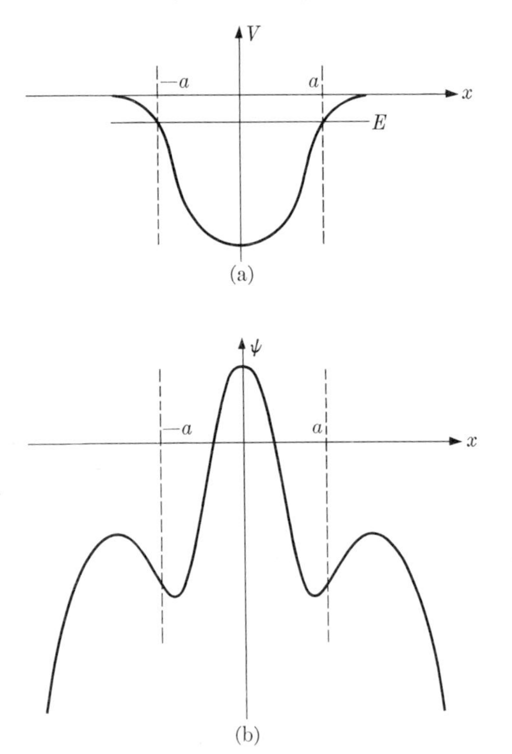

FIG. 3–9. (a) The potential well of Fig. 3–8. (b) An inadmissible solution to Schrödinger's equation corresponding to an energy E somewhat lower than that of an allowed state.

region and the wave function has a form in which it curves away from the axis.

As before, because of the assumed symmetry of the function $V(x)$, only even or odd solutions can be considered, without loss of generality. Consider the solution plotted in Fig. 3–9 for a particular choice of the parameter E, where it has been assumed that the solution is an even function of x. Such a solution has a finite intercept on the u-axis and zero slope at $x = 0$.

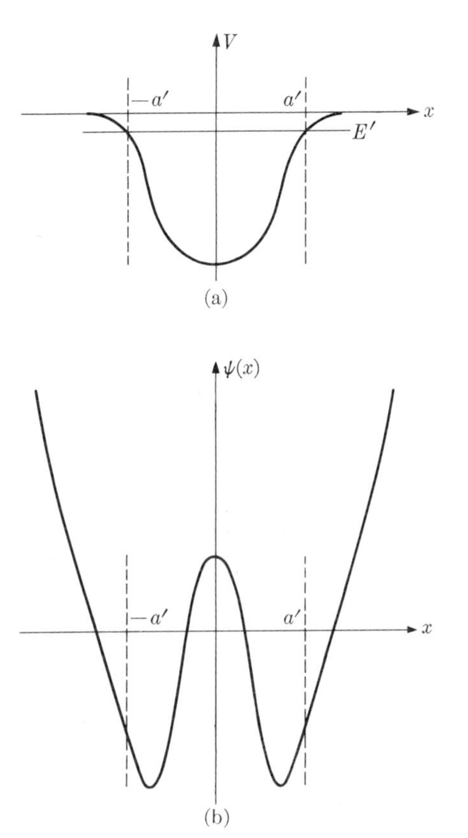

Fig. 3–10. (a) The potential well of Fig. 3–8. (b) An inadmissible solution to Schrödinger's equation corresponding to an energy E' somewhat higher than that of an allowed state.

The function is oscillatory in character in the region $0 < x < a$, but it begins curving away from the axis for $x > a$. It should be noted that the solution of Fig. 3–9 is of a form that diverges as x goes to infinity and is therefore not a suitable solution to a physical problem. On the other hand, for a somewhat more positive value of the parameter E', the function oscillates with a shorter wavelength in the region $0 < x < a'$ and the solution is of the type shown in Fig. 3–10. Here the function again diverges as x becomes infinite, this time crossing the axis outside $x = a'$. For some particular value of the parameter E lying between these two, a solution will be obtained for which the function u approaches the x-axis asymptotically, as in Fig. 3–11. It is clear from the qualitative nature of the solution for this particular value of E that the solution is mathematically "well-behaved" and can have physical significance. Therefore, this E has the physical significance of being a possible energy of the particle.

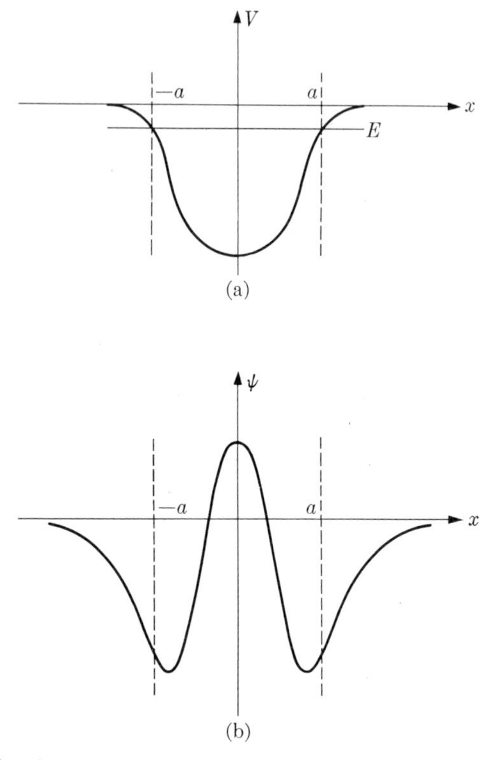

FIG. 3–11. (a) The potential well of Fig. 3–8. (b) An allowed solution to Schrödinger's equation corresponding to an allowed energy E.

As a simple example of this class of problem, consider a "square" potential well with infinitely high sides, as indicated in Fig. 3–12(a). This corresponds to a particle bound by impenetrable walls to a region of width $2a$. As indicated earlier, the proper boundary condition to be imposed for this type of potential is that the wave function vanish at the walls. The proper form for the wave function is then an oscillatory function which vanishes at the walls. This suggests a sine or a cosine, and again because of the symmetry of the potential well, the functions can be either even or odd. The even functions are given by

$$u = \cos kx, \qquad -a < x < a,$$
$$ka = \frac{\pi}{2}, \frac{3\pi}{2}, \frac{5\pi}{2}, \ldots, \tag{3–48}$$

and the odd functions are given by

$$u = \sin kx, \qquad -a < x < a, \qquad ka = \pi, 2\pi, \ldots \tag{3–49}$$

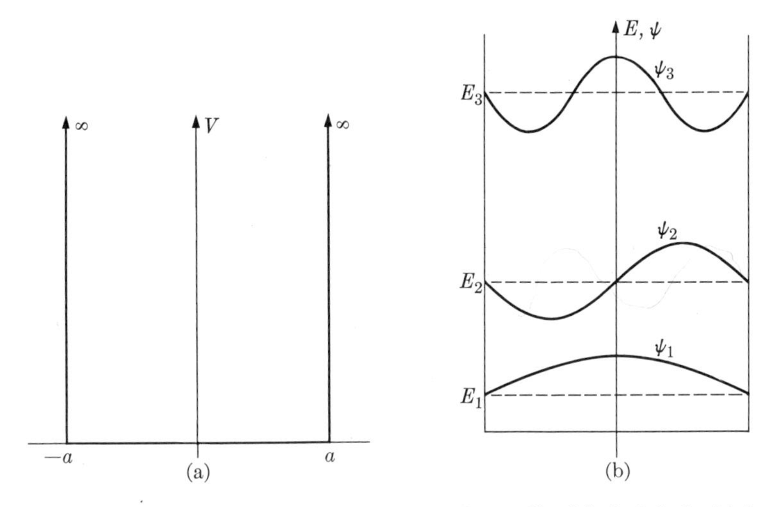

FIG. 3–12. (a) One-dimensional rectangular well with infinitely high walls. (b) Allowed energies and wave functions for the three lowest states of this well. The broken lines represent both energies and abscissas for the corresponding wave functions.

The possible values of k are determined above from the boundary condition. They are, from Eqs. (3–48) and (3–49),

$$ka = \frac{\pi}{2}, \pi, \frac{3\pi}{2}, 2\pi, \ldots = \frac{n\pi}{2}, \tag{3–50}$$

where n is any positive integer. Using the relation given by Eq. (2–7) between the parameter k and the momentum, we obtain an expression for the possible energies of a particle in a one-dimensional box:

$$ka = \frac{pa}{\hbar} = \frac{\sqrt{2mE_n}}{\hbar}\, a = \frac{n\pi}{2}, \tag{3–51}$$

or

$$E_n = \frac{\pi^2\hbar^2}{8ma^2}\, n^2. \tag{3–52}$$

The wave functions for $n = 1, 2, 3$ are shown in Fig. 3–12(b). The general solution to the Schrödinger equation for this problem can be written, as in Eq. (3–11), as

$$\begin{gathered} \psi = \sum_{n=1}^{\infty} c_n \sin\left(k_n x - n\,\frac{\pi}{2}\right) \exp\left(-i\omega_n t\right), \\ k_n = \frac{n\pi}{2a}, \qquad \omega_n = \frac{1}{8m\hbar}\left(\frac{\pi\hbar}{a}\, n\right)^2. \end{gathered} \tag{3–53}$$

To match the classical situation, the constants c_n can be so chosen as to represent a wave packet, and hence a particle, initially ($t = 0$) at $x = 0$ and moving to the right with a certain velocity. Equation (3–53) then shows that the wave packet oscillates back and forth between the two walls at the velocity assumed initially. However, it gradually spreads out, becoming broader in time until the motion becomes irregular, with the initial oscillatory behavior lost. This initial motion of the wave packet is the quantum-mechanical analogue of the classical description of the particle.

As a further example of this extremely important class of bound-state problems, consider the one-dimensional simple harmonic oscillator. This particular system has the same great importance in quantum mechanics that it has in classical mechanics. The Hamiltonian operator is given by

$$\mathrm{H} = -\frac{\hbar^2}{2m}\frac{\partial^2}{\partial x^2} + \tfrac{1}{2}kx^2, \tag{3–54}$$

where k now refers, not to the propagation vector of a plane wave as heretofore, but to the spring constant of the oscillator. The eigenvalue equation which gives the possible energies of the oscillator is

$$-\frac{\hbar^2}{2m}\frac{d^2u_n}{dx^2} + \tfrac{1}{2}kx^2u_n = E_nu_n. \tag{3–55}$$

This differential equation can be simplified by choosing a new measure of length and a new measure of energy, each of which is dimensionless:

$$y \equiv \left(\frac{mk}{\hbar^2}\right)^{1/4} x \qquad \text{and} \qquad \lambda \equiv \frac{2E}{\hbar\omega}, \tag{3–56}$$

where

$$\omega = \sqrt{\frac{k}{m}}\cdot \tag{3–57}$$

With these substitutions, Eq. (3–55) becomes

$$\frac{d^2u_n}{dy^2} + (\lambda - y^2)u_n = 0. \tag{3–58}$$

In looking for physically permissible bounded solutions to this equation, consider first the asymptotic dependence of the solutions. As y becomes infinite, it is clear that λ becomes negligible compared with y^2. The resulting differential equation is easily solved to yield

$$u \sim \exp\left(\pm\tfrac{1}{2}y^2\right). \tag{3–59}$$

This expression for the asymptotic dependence is suitable only for the negative sign in the exponent. Also, it is clear that because of the very rapid decay of the resulting gaussian function as y goes to infinity, the function will still have the same asymptotic dependence if it is multiplied by any *finite* polynomial in y:

$$u = H(y) \exp\left(-\tfrac{1}{2}y^2\right). \tag{3–60}$$

Here $H(y)$ is a finite polynomial in y. Inasmuch as this has the correct asymptotic dependence, it suggests that a solution of the differential equation (3–58) of this form be considered. By substituting Eq. (3–60) into Eq. (3–58), we obtain

$$\frac{d^2H(y)}{dy^2} - 2y\,\frac{dH(y)}{dy} + (\lambda - 1)H(y) = 0. \tag{3–61}$$

Assume a solution to this in the form of a finite polynomial:

$$H(y) = a_0 + a_1 y + a_2 y^2 + \cdots + a_N y^N. \tag{3–62}$$

If this is substituted into Eq. (3–61), a recursion formula connecting the coefficients is obtained:

$$a_{s+2} = \frac{2s + 1 - \lambda}{(s + 2)(s + 1)}\, a_s, \qquad s \geq 0. \tag{3–63}$$

For there to be an upper cutoff to the coefficients so that the polynomial equation (3–62) is not an infinite series, the condition

$$\lambda = 2n + 1, \qquad n \text{ an integer}, \tag{3–64}$$

must be satisfied. Inasmuch as the recursion formula connects even subscripts with even subscripts and odd with odd, Eq. (3–64) will form a cutoff for either even or odd terms but will leave the opposite members unaffected. Consequently, it is necessary to make the auxiliary assumption that the terms are either all even or all odd:

$$a_1 = 0, \qquad n \text{ even},$$

or

$$a_0 = 0, \qquad n \text{ odd}. \tag{3–65}$$

This is as expected, since $V = \frac{1}{2}kx^2$ is an even function.

Expressing Eq. (3–64) in terms of the original energy through Eq. (3–56), we obtain

$$E_n = (n + \tfrac{1}{2})\hbar\omega \tag{3–66}$$

for the allowed energies of a simple harmonic oscillator. This should be compared with Planck's original assumption discussed in the first chapter.

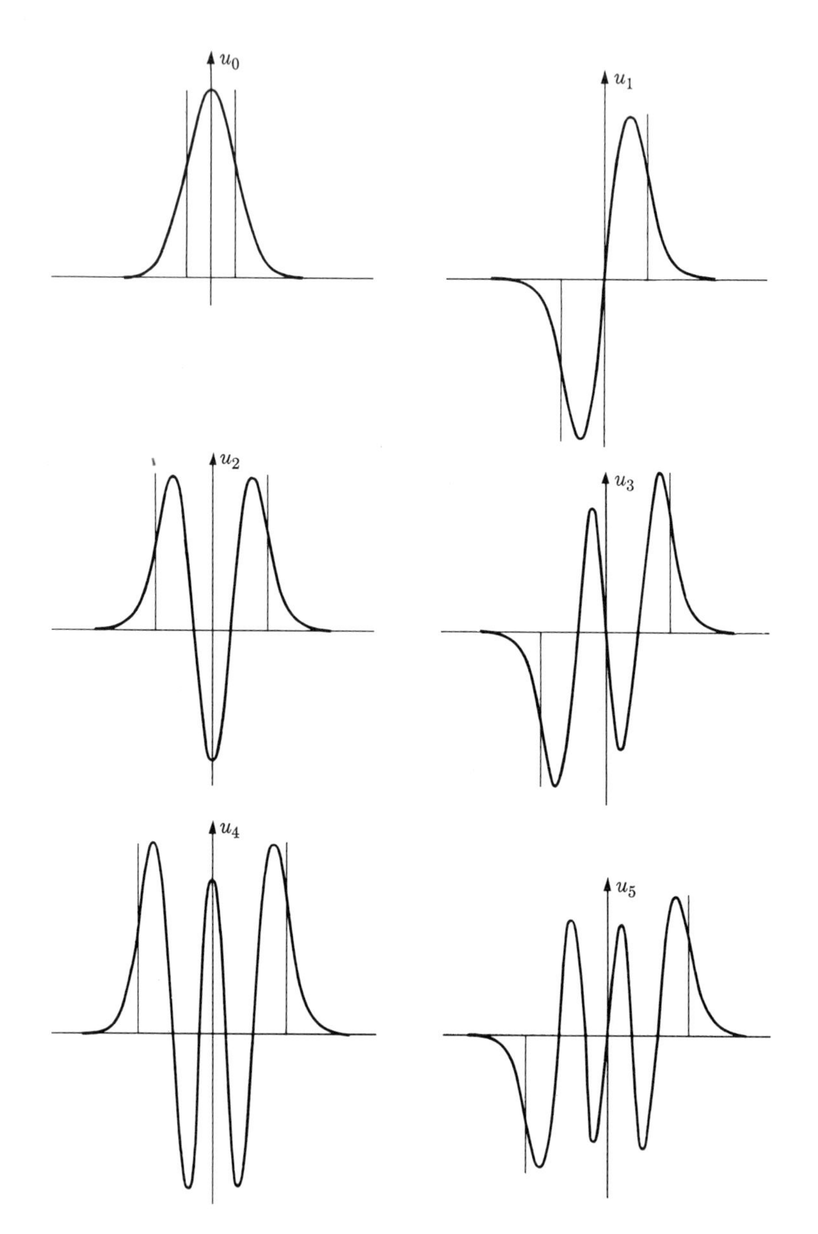

FIG. 3–13. The first six simple harmonic oscillator wave functions. The vertical lines indicate the classical limits of motion for the oscillator with the corresponding energy.

The first six polynomials obtained from the recursion formula, Eqs. (3–64) and (3–65), are given below. These polynomials have been normalized in a particular way of no present importance; normalized in this way they are called *Hermite polynomials.*

$$
\begin{aligned}
H_0 &= 1, \\
H_1 &= 2y, \\
H_2 &= 4y^2 - 2, \\
H_3 &= 8y^3 - 12y, \\
H_4 &= 16y^4 - 48y^2 + 12, \\
H_5 &= 32y^5 - 160y^3 + 120y.
\end{aligned}
\tag{3–67}
$$

The corresponding wave functions u_n are plotted in Fig. 3–13 for the same values of n. It should be noted that these functions curve toward the axis for the inner region $|x| < \sqrt{2E/k}$ and curve away from the axis for values of $|x| > \sqrt{2E/k}$, and that for large values of n the wave function looks very much like a standing wave with nodes and loops. Thus one may think of the wave function as being reflected back and forth between the retaining walls of the harmonic oscillator potential well.

It should also be noted that for large values of n the probability density rises to its largest value in the vicinity of $|x| = \sqrt{2E/k}$. This corresponds to the classical result that a simple harmonic oscillator is most likely to be found near the end of its swing, where its speed is zero. In fact, for classical mechanics the probability density is given by the reciprocal of the speed. This function is shown as the broken curve in Fig. 3–14 in comparison with the function $|u_n|^2$ for $n = 10$.

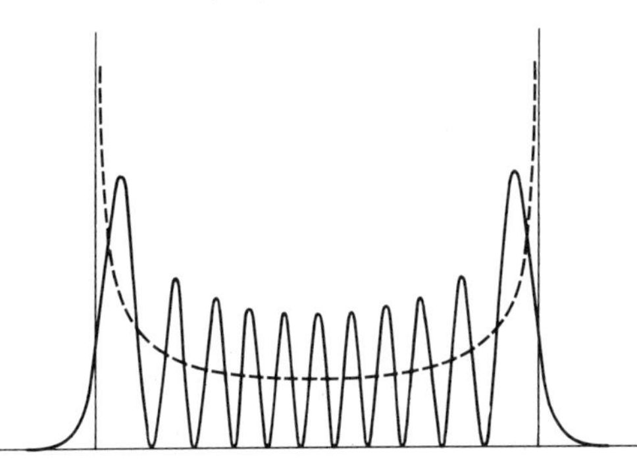

FIG. 3–14. $|u_{10}|^2$ for the simple harmonic oscillator. The classical probability-distribution function is shown by the broken curve. Note that the internodal distance (half wavelength) is least nearest $x = 0$, where classically the particle moves fastest.

The existence of nodes in the probability distribution $|u_n|^2$ is paradoxical. If classical concepts were valid, the particle could move through a node only with infinite speed or its probability of being found there would be nonzero. Once again the picture of a particle as always being exactly localized in space is inadequate.

Both of the bound-state problems treated above (the infinite square well and the simple harmonic oscillator) have infinite potentials associated with them (at least as x becomes infinite) and an infinite spectrum of bound states. An infinite potential is by no means a necessary condition for bound states: the potential shown in Fig. 3–6 will in general also have bound states associated with it. Now, however, there will be only a finite number of (negative) energies for which bound states exist, the exact number depending on the depth and width of the potential well.

3–5 Particle flux. In dealing with scattering problems, a simple example of which was treated in a preceding section, the concept of particle flux arises. Since it has been seen that the wave function is to be interpreted as a particle probability amplitude, the motion of the particle is clearly to be associated with the motion of the wave function. This general idea can be made quantitative by the introduction of a *probability density current.*

Since the square of the amplitude of the wave function of a particle gives the probability of finding the particle at a particular point in space, the probability P of finding the particle in a region of space bounded by a surface A (see Fig. 3–15) is given by

$$P = \int \bar{\psi}\psi \, d\tau. \qquad (3\text{–}68)$$

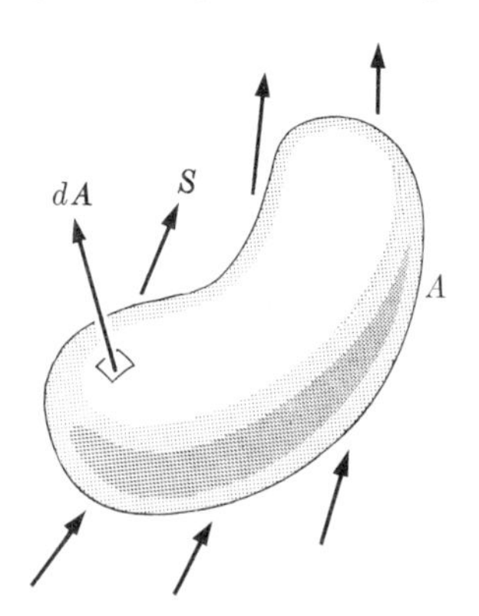

FIG. 3–15. Region of space bounded by the surface A, showing the particle flux density vector $\boldsymbol{S}$ and an infinitesimal element of surface $d\boldsymbol{A}$. The direction of the vector $d\boldsymbol{A}$ is normal to the surface A.

Here $d\tau$ represents a volume element:

$$d\tau \equiv dx\, dy\, dz. \qquad (3\text{–}69)$$

To be able to discuss the flow of probability, we must know how the probability that the particle will be found within the surface A changes with time. Differentiating Eq. (3–68) with respect to time gives

$$\frac{dP}{dt} = \frac{d}{dt}\int \bar{\psi}\psi \, d\tau$$

$$= \int \left(\frac{\partial \bar{\psi}}{\partial t}\,\psi + \bar{\psi}\,\frac{\partial \psi}{\partial t}\right) d\tau. \qquad (3\text{–}70)$$

Using Schrödinger's equation, Eq. (3–5), and its complex conjugate, we can write this as

$$\frac{dP}{dt} = \frac{i\hbar}{2m} \int (\bar{\psi}\nabla^2\psi - \psi\nabla^2\bar{\psi})\, d\tau. \tag{3–71}$$

The right side of this equation can be converted into an integral over the surface A by use of Green's theorem:

$$\frac{dP}{dt} = \frac{i\hbar}{2m} \int_A (\bar{\psi}\boldsymbol{\nabla}\psi - \psi\boldsymbol{\nabla}\bar{\psi}) \cdot d\boldsymbol{A}. \tag{3–72}$$

The form of this equation suggests that a *probability density current* $\boldsymbol{S}$ be defined:

$$\boldsymbol{S} \equiv -\frac{i\hbar}{2m} (\bar{\psi}\boldsymbol{\nabla}\psi - \boldsymbol{\nabla}\bar{\psi}\,\psi). \tag{3–73}$$

If this definition is substituted into Eq. (3–72), the result is

$$\frac{dP}{dt} = -\int_A \boldsymbol{S} \cdot d\boldsymbol{A}. \tag{3–74}$$

This has a simple physical interpretation: the rate of change of the probability that the particle will be inside the surface is equal to the negative of the probability density current through the surface A. Taking the divergence of $\boldsymbol{S}$ and again making use of the Schrödinger equation, we obtain

$$\boldsymbol{\nabla} \cdot \boldsymbol{S} = -\frac{\partial}{\partial t} (\bar{\psi}\psi), \tag{3–75}$$

which is the familiar differential form of the equation of continuity.

As an example, consider a plane wave at a fixed time,

$$\psi = \exp\left(i\,\frac{\boldsymbol{p} \cdot \boldsymbol{r}}{\hbar}\right) \cdot \tag{3–76}$$

A wave function of this type cannot be normalized, so the absolute square of ψ can represent only the relative probability of finding a particle at a particular point in space. This probability density is clearly independent of position. One may think of this wave as representing a swarm of particles with an average density of one particle per cubic centimeter. In this case, the particles are moving with momentum $m\boldsymbol{v}$, or have a velocity

$$\boldsymbol{v} = \frac{\boldsymbol{p}}{m} \cdot \tag{3–77}$$

With this velocity and with an average density of one particle per cubic centimeter, v particles per second pass through a surface area of one square centimeter perpendicular to the direction of motion of the particles. This constitutes the probability flux of the wave. As a check on this, we compute the probability density current given by Eq. (3–73) for the plane wave of Eq. (3–76). Applying the gradient operator to Eq. (3–76) gives

$$\nabla\psi = \frac{i\boldsymbol{p}}{\hbar}\,\psi. \tag{3–78}$$

If this and its complex conjugate are substituted into Eq. (3–73), we have

$$\boldsymbol{S} = \frac{\boldsymbol{p}}{m}. \tag{3–79}$$

This is in agreement with the classical calculation for the rate at which particles would cross one square centimeter of surface area under these conditions.

As a second example, it is easily verified that for a wave function of the form of two plane waves oppositely directed,

$$\psi = A_1 \exp\left(i\,\frac{\boldsymbol{p}\cdot\boldsymbol{r}}{\hbar}\right) + A_2 \exp\left(-i\,\frac{\boldsymbol{p}\cdot\boldsymbol{r}}{\hbar}\right), \tag{3–80}$$

the probability density flux $\boldsymbol{S}$ is given by

$$\boldsymbol{S} = (|A_1|^2 - |A_2|^2)\,\frac{\boldsymbol{p}}{m}. \tag{3–81}$$

This is in agreement with the result from classical considerations: the net flux of particles across a surface at right angles to the vector $\boldsymbol{p}$ is equal to the difference between the two fluxes of the waves taken separately. On the other hand, for more general cases, such as two plane waves *not* directed oppositely, there are interference effects, as seen earlier, and the net probability flux is not a simple sum of the individual fluxes.

3–6 Summary. Arguments based on plane-wave functions suggested the plausibility of Schrödinger's equation as an equation determining the behavior of the wave function of a particle in time. This equation was discussed with regard to superposition states and their physical interpretation. Three types of one-dimensional motion, motion past a potential hill, reflection by an infinite barrier, and motion in a potential well, were discussed with illustrative examples. These included the important case of the simple harmonic oscillator, which was treated in some detail. Finally, particle flux was considered and the concept of probability density current was introduced and applied to examples involving plane waves.

Problems

3–1. In classical mechanics, the reference level for potential energy is arbitrary. What are the effects on the wave function and energy of adding a constant potential V in Schrödinger's equation?

3–2. In the text, the rectangular barrier penetration problem was treated under the assumptions $ka \ll k'a \ll 1$. Compute the transmission for the case $E < V$ when these assumptions are relaxed.

3–3. Calculate the reflection coefficient of sodium metal for low-energy electrons as a function of electron energy and angle of incidence. For sufficiently long-wavelength electrons, the potential barrier at the metal surface can be treated as discontinuous. Assume that the potential energy of an electron in the metal is −5 electron volts. Calculate the index of refraction of the metal for electrons.

3–4. Compute the probability density current $\mathbf{S}$ for the region $x > 0$ for the case of the step potential at $x = 0$ treated in the text. What is the physical interpretation to be given $\mathbf{S}$ when $E < V$?

3–5. Compute the transmission probability of the barrier of Fig. 3–2 for particles of mass m and energy $E > V$. Assume that the barrier is thin enough so that the condition $\hbar/(2mE)^{1/2} \gg a$ is valid. (This is equivalent to assuming that the de Broglie wavelength for the particle is much longer than the thickness of the barrier. Show this equivalence.)

3–6. Calculate an explicit expression representing the envelope of a free-particle wave packet given by

$$\psi(x, t) = \int_{-\infty}^{\infty} \exp\left[\frac{-(k - k_0)^2}{a}\right] \exp\left[i(kx - \omega t)\right] dk.$$

Find the group velocity of this (gaussian) packet. Show that the packet expands as it travels.

3–7. The transmission of a thin rectangular potential barrier of height V and width $2a$, with $a \ll \hbar/(2mE)^{1/2}$, was treated in the text. Compute the transmission of two such barriers separated a distance b. Discuss the *resonance effects* that can occur for certain energies of the particles and barrier separations b.

3–8. A perfectly elastic ball is bouncing between two plane parallel walls. Using classical mechanics, compute the change in the energy of the ball as the walls are slowly and uniformly moved closer together. Show that the change in energy is just what one has quantum-mechanically if the ball's quantum number n does not change.

3–9. In an ideal point-contact crystal rectifier operated in the "back" direction, the electric current fails to flow because of a potential barrier met by the electrons. Compute a rough value for the corresponding barrier-penetration probability for an electron that has kinetic energy of 2.5 volts incident on a rectangular barrier 3 volts high and 10^{-7} cm wide.

CHAPTER 4

FOURIER TECHNIQUES AND EXPECTATION VALUES

4–1 The Fourier integral. Before discussing eigenvalue equations and expectation values, certain formal mathematical techniques will be considered briefly. It is assumed that the student is familiar with much of the following, so that this chapter will, in part at least, constitute a review. If this is not true, it would be well to consult other texts where the material is developed more fully.

Consider first the Fourier series expansion. Any function of x, real or complex, defined within the limits $-\pi \leq x \leq \pi$, that has only a finite number of discontinuities can be expanded in the Fourier series

$$f(x) = \sum_{n=0}^{\infty} a_n \cos(nx) + \sum_{n=0}^{\infty} b_n \sin(nx). \tag{4–1}$$

By making use of

$$\exp(ix) \equiv \cos x + i \sin x, \tag{4–2}$$

Eq. (4–1) can be put into the equivalent form

$$f(x) = \frac{1}{\sqrt{2\pi}} \sum_{n=-\infty}^{+\infty} A_n \exp(inx). \tag{4–3}$$

The square root of 2π is inserted for convenience in the later development. Multiplying both sides of this equation by the exponential $\exp(-imx)$ and integrating from $-\pi$ to $+\pi$, where the function is defined, gives

$$A_m = \frac{1}{\sqrt{2\pi}} \int_{-\pi}^{+\pi} f(x) \exp(-imx)\, dx \tag{4–4}$$

as an equation for the coefficients in the expansion of the function.

Changing the domain over which the function $f(x)$ is defined to run from $-\pi a$ to $+\pi a$ yields simple generalizations of Eqs. (4–3) and (4–4):

$$f(x) = \frac{1}{\sqrt{2\pi}} \sum_{n=-\infty}^{\infty} A_n \exp\left(i \frac{n}{a} x\right), \tag{4–5}$$

$$aA_n = \frac{1}{\sqrt{2\pi}} \int_{-\pi a}^{+\pi a} f(x) \exp\left(-i \frac{n}{a} x\right) dx. \tag{4–6}$$

When we introduce a new variable k defined by

$$k \equiv \frac{n}{a} \tag{4-7}$$

and define a new function of k by

$$F(k) \equiv aA_n, \tag{4-8}$$

for a suitable class of functions $f(x)$, the limit as a approaches infinity exists. In this case, Eq. (4-5) becomes an integral over k:

$$f(x) = \frac{1}{\sqrt{2\pi}} \int_{-\infty}^{\infty} F(k) \exp(ikx)\, dk, \tag{4-9}$$

where

$$F(k) = \frac{1}{\sqrt{2\pi}} \int_{-\infty}^{\infty} f(x) \exp(-ikx)\, dx. \tag{4-10}$$

The function $F(k)$ is known as the *Fourier transform of the function* $f(x)$, and the function $f(x)$ is the *Fourier transform of* $F(k)$. The Fourier transform as defined by Eq. (4-10) exists only when the function $f(x)$ is square-integrable, that is, when

$$\int_{-\infty}^{\infty} |f(x)|^2\, dx < \infty. \tag{4-11}$$

The Fourier integral definitions, Eqs. (4-9) and (4-10), are easily extended to a three-dimensional space. A function of the three variables x, y, and z can be related to a Fourier integral over the variables as follows:

$$f(x, y, z) = \left(\frac{1}{2\pi}\right)^{3/2} \int_{-\infty}^{\infty}\int_{-\infty}^{\infty}\int_{-\infty}^{\infty} F(k_x, k_y, k_z) \exp[i(k_x x + k_y y + k_z z)]\, dk_x\, dk_y\, dk_z. \tag{4-12}$$

This notation can be greatly simplified if the integral is considered as a volume integral over a three-dimensional k-space in which the coordinates are given by a vector $\boldsymbol{k}$:

$$f(\boldsymbol{r}) = \left(\frac{1}{2\pi}\right)^{3/2} \int_{-\infty}^{\infty} F(\boldsymbol{k}) \exp(i\boldsymbol{k}\cdot\boldsymbol{r})\, d\boldsymbol{k}. \tag{4-13}$$

Here $d\boldsymbol{k}$ refers, of course, not to the differential of a vector but rather to an element of volume in k-space. In a similar fashion, the inverse equation can be written as

$$F(\boldsymbol{k}) = \left(\frac{1}{2\pi}\right)^{3/2} \int_{-\infty}^{\infty} f(\boldsymbol{r}) \exp(-i\boldsymbol{k}\cdot\boldsymbol{r})\, d\boldsymbol{r}. \tag{4-14}$$

4–2 The Kronecker delta and the Dirac delta function. As will be seen in later sections, in quantum mechanics one frequently encounters mathematical expressions containing summations over one or more indices. In many cases, the expressions for these summations can be greatly simplified by the use of a symbol known as the Kronecker delta, δ_{nm}. This symbol has two indices and is defined by the properties

$$\begin{aligned} \delta_{nm} &= 1, \qquad n = m, \\ \delta_{nm} &= 0, \qquad n \neq m. \end{aligned} \tag{4–15}$$

The Kronecker delta will find its most frequent application in later sections (Chapter 11 *et seq.*) where matrix representations are used.

Another mathematical concept that will also prove to be of great usefulness is the Dirac delta function.* While this is, strictly speaking, an exceedingly "improper" function, it can be given a satisfactory meaning by the use of suitable limiting procedures. Consider Eq. (4–14). This can be thought of as an expansion of an arbitrary function $f(\mathbf{r})$ in terms of exponential periodic functions (plane waves) of $\mathbf{k} \cdot \mathbf{r}$. Unfortunately, it is not possible to obtain a Fourier transform of the exponential function itself, since for such a function the condition of (square) integrability is not satisfied. Although a plane wave thus does not have a true Fourier transform, one can define the improper Dirac delta function so as to perform the role of such a transform. To do this, we write the exponential periodic function as

$$f(x) = \exp(ik_0 x) = \lim_{\alpha \to 0} \exp(-\alpha x^2 + ik_0 x). \tag{4–16}$$

For any finite, real, positive value of α, the Fourier integral of Eq. (4–16) exists. This allows the calculation of the Fourier transform of Eq. (4–16):

$$F(k) = \lim_{\alpha \to 0} \frac{1}{\sqrt{2\pi}} \int_{-\infty}^{\infty} \exp(-\alpha x^2 + ik_0 x) \exp(-ikx)\, dx. \tag{4–17}$$

The resulting limit vanishes for $k \neq k_0$ and diverges for $k = k_0$, giving as the form of the improper function $F(k)$:

$$\begin{aligned} F(k) &= 0, \qquad k \neq k_0, \\ &= \infty, \qquad k = k_0. \end{aligned} \tag{4–18}$$

Singular as this function is, it is still possible to define its integral over all k by performing the integration before taking the limit:

---

* P. A. M. Dirac, *Principles of Quantum Mechanics*, Oxford University Press, Oxford, 3rd ed., 1947, Section 15.

$$\int_{-\infty}^{\infty} F(k)\, dk = \lim_{\alpha \to 0} \frac{1}{\sqrt{2\pi}} \int_{-\infty}^{\infty} dk \int_{-\infty}^{\infty} \exp\left[-\alpha x^2 + i(k_0 - k)x\right] dx. \tag{4–19}$$

This suggests the definition of a new singular function which is called the *Dirac delta function:*

$$\delta(k) \equiv \frac{1}{2\pi} \int_{-\infty}^{\infty} \exp(ikx)\, dx. \tag{4–20}$$

The integral here means, of course, the integral defined in accordance with the limiting procedure outlined in Eq. (4–16). Defined in this way, the function $\delta(k)$ has the properties

$$\begin{aligned} \delta(k) &= 0, \qquad k \neq 0, \\ &= \infty, \qquad k = 0, \\ \int_{-\infty}^{\infty} \delta(k)\, dk &= 1. \end{aligned} \tag{4–21}$$

In any computations involving the delta function, it is assumed that the computations are made prior to taking the limit. When dealing with regular well-behaved functions, the limiting process must be taken after the computations are made. The Dirac delta function is meaningful only under integral signs, where this limiting technique can be used. A few of the properties of the delta function are outlined below:

$$\begin{aligned} \delta(x) &= \delta(-x), \\ \int f(x)\, \delta(x - a)\, dx &= f(a), \\ \delta(ax) &= \frac{1}{a}\, \delta(x), \qquad a > 0, \\ \int \delta(x - x_1)\, \delta(x_1 - x_2)\, dx_1 &= \delta(x - x_2), \\ f(x)\, \delta(x - a) &= f(a)\, \delta(x - a). \end{aligned} \tag{4–22}$$

In a fashion similar to that used to define the delta function, it is possible to define the derivative of the delta function:

$$\delta'(k) = \frac{1}{2\pi} \int_{-\infty}^{\infty} ik \exp(ikx)\, dx. \tag{4–23}$$

This function, defined by a formal differentiation under the integral sign of Eq. (4–20) is, of course, meaningful only in the sense of a limit, as discussed in connection with Eq. (4–20). Some of the formal properties of the derivative of the delta function are

$$
\begin{aligned}
-\delta'(x) &= \delta'(-x), \\
\int f(x)\,\delta'(x-a)\,dx &= -f'(a).
\end{aligned}
\tag{4-24}
$$

The definition of the delta function can be easily extended to three dimensions to give the delta function of the vector variable $\boldsymbol{k}$:

$$
\begin{aligned}
\delta(\boldsymbol{k}) &\equiv \delta(k_x)\,\delta(k_y)\,\delta(k_z) \\
&= \frac{1}{(2\pi)^3}\int_{-\infty}^{\infty}\int_{-\infty}^{\infty}\int_{-\infty}^{\infty} \exp\,[i(k_x x + k_y y + k_z z)]\,dx\,dy\,dz \\
&= \frac{1}{(2\pi)^3}\int_{-\infty}^{\infty} \exp\,(i\boldsymbol{k}\cdot\boldsymbol{r})\,d\boldsymbol{r}.
\end{aligned}
\tag{4-25}
$$

Strictly speaking, it is always necessary to bear in mind the sense in which these functions are defined as the limit of a sequence of properly behaved functions. However, in practice it is usually possible to calculate in a perfectly straightforward manner with these functions, as though they were well-behaved functions. For example, consider the use of the above functional relations to "derive" the connection between a function of x and its Fourier transform. Assume that a function of x is given and that its Fourier transform is defined by use of Eq. (4–10). If Eq. (4–10) is multiplied on both sides by $1/\sqrt{2\pi}\exp(ikx')$ and integrated over all k, the result is

$$
\frac{1}{\sqrt{2\pi}}\int_{-\infty}^{\infty} F(k)\exp\,(ikx')\,dk = \frac{1}{2\pi}\int_{-\infty}^{\infty}\int_{-\infty}^{\infty} f(x)\exp\,[ik(x'-x)]\,dk\,dx.
\tag{4-26}
$$

Interchanging the order of integration and making use of the definition of the delta function given in Eq. (4–20) yields

$$
\frac{1}{\sqrt{2\pi}}\int_{-\infty}^{\infty} F(k)\exp\,(ikx')\,dk = \int_{-\infty}^{\infty} f(x)\,\delta(x-x')\,dx,
\tag{4-27}
$$

from which, making use of the second of the relations given in Eq. (4–22), we obtain

$$
f(x') = \frac{1}{\sqrt{2\pi}}\int_{-\infty}^{\infty} F(k)\exp\,(ikx')\,dk.
\tag{4-28}
$$

In a similar fashion, the relation

$$
\int |f|^2\,dx = \int |F|^2\,dk
\tag{4-29}
$$

is easily obtained.

4-3 Eigenvalue equations. In Chapter 3 it was pointed out that the time-independent Schrödinger equation,

$$\mathrm{H}u(\boldsymbol{r}) = Eu(\boldsymbol{r}), \tag{4-30}$$

is of the form known as an *eigenvalue equation.* The component parts of this equation are the operator (in this case symbolized by H), which operates on a (wave) function $u(\boldsymbol{r})$ and, on the other side of the equality, a number E, called the *eigenvalue,* which multiplies the same function. An eigenvalue equation thus states that an operator, acting on a function, reproduces the same function multiplied by a constant factor. The function which satisfies the equation is called the *eigenfunction* of the equation corresponding to the particular corresponding eigenvalue. Note that in Eq. (4-30), the eigenvalue is the energy of the particle.

In discussing the Schrödinger equation, it was seen that the Laplacian operator acting on the plane wave function

$$\psi = A \exp\left[\frac{i}{\hbar}(\boldsymbol{p}\cdot\boldsymbol{r} - Et)\right] \tag{4-31}$$

reproduced the function times the factor $-p^2/\hbar^2$, or that

$$-\hbar^2\nabla^2\psi = -\hbar^2\boldsymbol{\nabla}\cdot\boldsymbol{\nabla}\psi = +p^2\psi. \tag{4-32}$$

Thus the operator $-\hbar^2\nabla^2$ has the square of the momentum of a particle as eigenvalue and Eq. (4-31) as eigenfunction. This suggests that one should associate with the momentum component in the x-direction the operator

$$\mathrm{P}_x \equiv -i\hbar\frac{\partial}{\partial x}, \tag{4-33}$$

or, in general, that one should associate with the (vector) momentum the operator

$$\mathbf{P} \equiv -i\hbar\boldsymbol{\nabla} \equiv -i\hbar\,\mathrm{grad}. \tag{4-34}$$

The eigenvalue equation for momentum is then

$$\mathbf{P}\psi = -i\hbar\boldsymbol{\nabla}\psi = \boldsymbol{p}\psi, \tag{4-35}$$

with the solutions

$$\psi = \exp\left(\frac{i\boldsymbol{p}\cdot\boldsymbol{r}}{\hbar}\right). \tag{4-36}$$

Equation (4-36) may be multiplied by a constant or a function of the time, and Eq. (4-35) is still satisfied. Thus the plane waves met before are the eigenfunctions of the momentum operator.

In discussing the application of the Schrödinger equation to the one-dimensional simple harmonic oscillator, Eq. (3–55), it was implicitly assumed that the proper operator to associate with the square of the displacement x was merely x^2. This would be consistent with the identification of the position operator x with x as a factor. In three dimensions, this leads to the eigenvalue equation

$$\mathbf{r}\psi = \mathbf{r}_0\psi. \tag{4–37}$$

Here $\mathbf{r}_0$ represents the eigenvalue, a constant vector, whereas the operator on the left side is a variable taking on all values corresponding to the argument of the function ψ. The only solution to this equation is the improper function

$$\psi = \delta(\mathbf{r} - \mathbf{r}_0), \tag{4–38}$$

namely, a delta function which vanishes everywhere except for $\mathbf{r} = \mathbf{r}_0$. This eigenfunction is exactly what one needs for a wave function where the square of the amplitude of the function represents the probability that the particle will be found at a particular point. If the particle is known with certainty to be at the point $\mathbf{r}_0$, the function has to vanish everywhere except at this particular point.

The functions given by Eqs. (4–36) and (4–38) are unnormalizable. A further significant point about these two functions which should be noted is that each has the form of the Fourier transform of the other.

As has been seen, if these operators are formally inserted into the classical Hamiltonian of a particle moving in a potential $V(\mathbf{r})$,

$$H = \frac{1}{2m} p^2 + V(\mathbf{r}), \tag{4–39}$$

an operator for the energy of the particle is obtained whose eigenvalue equation, Eq. (4–30), determines the position dependence of the wave function for a state of definite energy E. To obtain the time dependence, one must use the energy-eigenvalue equation obtainable from Eqs. (3–7) and (3–8):

$$i\hbar \frac{\partial}{\partial t} \psi = E\psi. \tag{4–40}$$

This shows that the energy operator is

$$\mathrm{E} \equiv i\hbar \frac{\partial}{\partial t} \cdot \tag{4–41}$$

Equation (4–40) taken in combination with Eq. (4–30) becomes the time-dependent Schrödinger equation

$$\mathrm{H}\psi = i\hbar \frac{\partial}{\partial t} \psi. \tag{4–42}$$

This equation determines the time dependence of any (arbitrary) wave function describing the state of the system whether or not it corresponds to a state of definite energy.

4-4 Expectation values. It has been seen that the absolute square of the wave function is to be taken as a measure of the probability of finding a particle at a particular point in space. A word of explanation is necessary as to what is meant by "probability" in this context. When thus speaking of probability, one has in mind the following situation: imagine an ensemble of similarly prepared systems. By "similarly prepared" is meant that the systems, insofar as any physical measurement is concerned, are identical, that is, they are described by identical wave functions. Now, if a measurement is made on one of these systems to determine whether the particle is in a particular volume element, the result will be definite: either the particle is there or it is not. When the same measurement is made on a large number of similarly prepared systems, the relative number of times that the particle is found in any particular volume is taken as a measure of the probability that the particle will be in that volume element.

It is assumed in the following that the wave function is normalizable and is normalized to unity:

$$\int |\psi|^2 \, d\tau = 1. \tag{4-43}$$

This represents no real limitation, inasmuch as for any realizable physical system it is always possible to imagine that the system is enclosed in a very large box for which it is always possible to define normalizable wave functions. It may at times be convenient to use unnormalized wave functions, but this is not essential. With normalized wave functions, the absolute square of the wave function represents the actual probability per unit volume of finding a particle at a particular point in space. As such, the average value of a particular coordinate of the particle is given by

$$\begin{aligned} \langle x \rangle &= \int x \cdot (\text{probability that particle is in volume element } d\tau \text{ at } x) \\ &= \int x |\psi|^2 \, d\tau. \end{aligned} \tag{4-44}$$

Here the product of the absolute square of the wave function and the volume element is the element of probability that a particle will be found at this point; the integral of this element of probability multiplied by the coordinate of the point x gives the mean, or expectation, value for the coordinate x. Again it must be noted that by this is meant the average of a number of measurements of the coordinate x carried out over an ensemble of identically prepared systems. This average value of x, or the *expectation value* of x, is designated by $\langle x \rangle$. For reasons that will appear shortly, Eq. (4–44) is often written in the form

$$\langle x \rangle = \int \bar{\psi} x \psi \, d\tau. \tag{4–45}$$

A similar expression for the average value of a component of the momentum of the particle will now be calculated. This is done by expanding the wave function in plane waves. As discussed in connection with Eq. (2–9), the square of the amplitude of a particular plane wave is assumed to be a measure of the probability that a particle will have the corresponding momentum. First we write the wave function as a Fourier integral:

$$\psi = \left(\frac{1}{2\pi}\right)^{3/2} \int \Psi(\boldsymbol{k}) \exp (i\boldsymbol{k} \cdot \boldsymbol{r}) \, d\boldsymbol{k}. \tag{4–46}$$

This equation is assumed to hold for one particular time, the time variable having been suppressed. (If the wave function is regarded as a function of position and time, the time variable would appear under the integral, with Ψ being a function of $\boldsymbol{k}$ and t.) Consequently, the momentum measurements under consideration are assumed to be made at a particular time for which the wave functions have the particular value given in Eq. (4–46). The propagation vector $\boldsymbol{k}$ is related to the momentum through

$$\boldsymbol{k} = \frac{\boldsymbol{p}}{\hbar}. \tag{4–47}$$

As a result of Eq. (4–29), since ψ is normalized,

$$\int |\Psi(\boldsymbol{k})|^2 \, d\boldsymbol{k} = 1. \tag{4–48}$$

Thus $|\Psi(\boldsymbol{k})|^2$ can be interpreted as the probability per unit volume in k-space that a particle has a given momentum. Consequently, the proper expression for the average value of a particular component of the momentum of the particle is given by

$$\langle p_x \rangle = \int |\Psi(\boldsymbol{k})|^2 p_x \, d\boldsymbol{k}. \tag{4–49}$$

This can be transformed into an integral over ordinary space by starting with the momentum eigenvalue equation, Eq. (4–35), and using Eq. (4–46):

$$-i\hbar \frac{\partial}{\partial x} \psi = \left(\frac{1}{2\pi}\right)^{3/2} \int \Psi(\boldsymbol{k}) p_x \exp (i\boldsymbol{k} \cdot \boldsymbol{r}) \, d\boldsymbol{k}. \tag{4–50}$$

Multiplying by the complex conjugate of the wave function and integrating over all position space yields

$$\int \bar{\psi}\left(-i\hbar\,\frac{\partial}{\partial x}\right)\psi\,dr = \left(\frac{1}{2\pi}\right)^3 \int \bar{\Psi}(\boldsymbol{k}')\Psi(\boldsymbol{k})p_x \exp\left[i(\boldsymbol{k}-\boldsymbol{k}')\cdot \boldsymbol{r}\right] d\boldsymbol{k}'\,d\boldsymbol{k}\,d\boldsymbol{r}. \tag{4-51}$$

Combined with Eq. (4–25), this becomes

$$\int \bar{\psi}\left(-i\hbar\,\frac{\partial}{\partial x}\right)\psi\,dr = \int \bar{\Psi}(\boldsymbol{k}')\Psi(\boldsymbol{k})p_x\,\delta(\boldsymbol{k}-\boldsymbol{k}')\,d\boldsymbol{k}'\,d\boldsymbol{k}. \tag{4-52}$$

If we make use of the properties of the δ-function given in Eq. (4–22), Eqs. (4–49) and (4–52) give

$$\langle p_x\rangle = \int |\Psi(\boldsymbol{k})|^2 p_x\,d\boldsymbol{k} = \int \bar{\psi}\left(-i\hbar\,\frac{\partial}{\partial x}\right)\psi\,dr. \tag{4-53}$$

Here the expectation value for the x-component of momentum is given as an integral over position space. Note the similarity in form between this and Eq. (4–45). In Eq. (4–45), the integrand is the complex conjugate of the wave function times an operator (x) operating on the wave function, integrated over all space; in this case the operation is simply multiplication by the coordinate x. In Eq. (4–53) the integral is of the same form except that the operator here involves a differentiation with respect to x. This formal relationship can be made a little clearer by use of the notation P_x for the momentum operator:

$$\mathrm{P}_x \equiv -i\hbar\,\frac{\partial}{\partial x}\cdot \tag{4-54}$$

Using this notation, the expression for the expectation value of the x-component of the momentum becomes

$$\langle p_x\rangle = \int \bar{\psi}\mathrm{P}_x\psi\,dr. \tag{4-55}$$

This is a further hint of the general importance of operators in the quantum-mechanical formalism being developed; many more important applications of the operator concept will be seen later. The procedure used above to calculate these average values is easily generalized to enable the calculation of the average values of various powers of the coordinates and momenta of the particles. The resulting expressions for these expectation values are

$$\langle p_x^n\rangle = \int \bar{\psi}\mathrm{P}_x^n\psi\,dr. \tag{4-56}$$

$$\langle x^n\rangle = \int \bar{\psi}x^n\psi\,dr. \tag{4-57}$$

There is one physical point which should be emphasized in connection with these equations. The wave function is, of course, a solution to the Schrödinger equation, Eq. (4–42), and hence is a function of both position and time coordinates. Consequently, the expectation values appearing in Eqs. (4–45) and (4–55) are functions of time. This is to be interpreted in the following way. If, at a given time, a measurement, either of position or of momentum, is made upon an ensemble of particles described by a common wave function, the averages of the several measurements will be given by these equations. Once this measurement has been made, however, the ensemble has been disturbed as a result of the measurement and the wave function is no longer of the form that it had previous to the measurement. The exact form of the new wave function will, in general, depend upon the result of the measurement. Thus the average values given by Eqs. (4–56) and (4–57) no longer apply unless one inserts the new wave functions describing the ensembles which result from the disturbance of the measurement. Consequently, these expressions will in general predict only the result of the first measurement made on a system. After such a measurement has been made, a new wave function must be used to describe the expectation values for any future measurements.

It has been seen thus far that the expectation values of the operators x^n and P_x^n are related to the wave function by an expression of the form

$$\langle\text{operator}\rangle = \int \bar{\psi}\,(\text{operator})\,\psi\,d\tau. \tag{4–58}$$

Reasoning by analogy, one might expect the expression for the average value of the energy of a particle in a state for which the energy is not well-defined or sharp to be given by

$$\langle E\rangle = \langle \mathrm{H}\rangle = \int \bar{\psi}\mathrm{H}\psi\,d\tau. \tag{4–59}$$

This will be discussed in greater detail in Chapter 6.

As an example, consider expectation values for the one-dimensional simple harmonic oscillator treated earlier. Assume that the particle is in the state of lowest energy. The wave function is given by

$$\psi_0(x) = \left(\frac{k}{\pi\hbar\omega}\right)^{1/4} \exp\left(-\frac{kx^2}{2\hbar\omega}\right). \tag{4–60}$$

This equation is identical to that obtained previously, Eq. (3–60), except for the constant factor which normalizes the function to unity. With this normalized wave function, the following expectation values for the ground state of the simple harmonic oscillator are easily obtained:

$$
\begin{aligned}
\langle x \rangle &= \int \bar{\psi}_0 x \psi_0 \, d\tau = 0, \\
\langle x^2 \rangle &= \int \bar{\psi}_0 x^2 \psi_0 \, d\tau = \frac{\hbar\omega}{2k}, \\
\langle p_x \rangle &= \int \bar{\psi}_0 \mathrm{P}_x \psi_0 \, d\tau = 0, \\
\langle p_x^2 \rangle &= \int \bar{\psi}_0 \mathrm{P}_x^2 \psi_0 \, d\tau = \frac{m\hbar\omega}{2}, \\
\langle \mathrm{H} \rangle &= \left\langle \frac{1}{2m} p_x^2 + \frac{k}{2} x^2 \right\rangle = \frac{\hbar\omega}{2}.
\end{aligned}
\tag{4-61}
$$

Note that the expectation value of the Hamiltonian in the last equation of this set is obtainable from the expectation values of the square of x and the square of p_x. Also note that the wave function of Eq. (4-60) is an eigenfunction of the Hamiltonian and consequently every measurement of the energy made on a member of an ensemble of such systems will give this particular value. This is true only for the energy measurement. In the case of the other four quantities, one would obtain a variety of different results for the measurements and the expectation values are, in these cases, just the average values.

4-5 Summary. In this chapter, a brief review was given of the Fourier integral, and the Kronecker and Dirac deltas were introduced and their computational properties summarized. Next, eigenvalue equations were considered and their place in the quantum formalism sketched. Finally, the calculation of average, or expectation, values of system parameters was considered.

Problems

4–1. Compute the Fourier transform of the wave function given by

$$\psi = 0, \qquad |x| > a,$$

$$\psi = \frac{1}{\sqrt{2a}}, \qquad -a \leq x \leq +a.$$

(Although this is not strictly a physical wave function, it can be considered as the limit of a class of allowable functions.)

4–2. Compute the expectation values $\langle x \rangle$, $\langle x^2 \rangle$, $\langle p_x \rangle$, $\langle p_x^2 \rangle$, and $\langle \mathrm{H} \rangle = \langle p_x^2/2m \rangle$ for a particle in the square potential well of width $2a$ with infinitely high sides treated in Chapter 3, when it is in an energy eigenstate.

4–3. Solve the eigenvalue equation and find the eigenfunctions and allowed energies for a particle confined to the inside of the two-dimensional region bounded by the circle $R = a$. Assume that the potential is zero inside this circle and becomes infinite at $R = a$.

4–4. A one-dimensional simple harmonic oscillator is constructed in such a way that the spring constant may be adjusted. The oscillator is in its lowest energy state when suddenly the spring constant is reduced to zero, without changing the wave function. What is the subsequent behavior of the wave function?

4–5. A free particle of momentum p is represented by a plane wave. A measuring apparatus determines that the particle lies inside a region of length l. The resulting interaction with the particle is assumed to leave the wave function unchanged for a length l but to reduce it to zero outside this region. What are the average momentum and the average kinetic energy of the particle after the measurement has been made?

4–6. Show that the average momentum of any wave packet representing a free particle does not change with time.

4–7. Show that the average position of a wave packet representing a free particle moves with a constant velocity even though the wave packet may distort so badly as to lose its original shape.

CHAPTER 5

REVIEW OF CLASSICAL MECHANICS

5–1 Introduction. Although, as the preceding chapters have indicated, quantum mechanics differs radically from classical mechanics both in the physical picture it presents and in the way its ideas are mathematically formulated, nevertheless the many areas in which classical theory has proven successful suggest that, in a sense, quantum theory must be an *extension* of classical theory, rather than a complete replacement. Indeed, quantum mechanics was developed by close analogy with classical formulations, especially the classical Hamilton-Jacobi formulation of mechanics. As will become apparent as quantum theory is further developed in the following chapters, there is a very close formal relationship between the classical and quantum theories. For this reason, the various more general classical formulations of mechanics will be reviewed briefly in this chapter. It is assumed that the reader is familiar with the material covered; if this is not the case, reference should be made to texts in which this material is treated in more detail.*

5–2 Generalized coordinates and Lagrange's equations. The basis of classical, nonrelativistic mechanics is Newton's law of motion for a single particle,

$$\boldsymbol{F} = m\ddot{\boldsymbol{r}}, \tag{5–1}$$

relating the forces acting on the particle to the acceleration experienced. For conservative forces, the force is derivable from a potential, and

$$\boldsymbol{F} = -\nabla V, \tag{5–2}$$

where V is a function of coordinates and possibly of time. Equation (5–1) is a second-order differential equation (actually, because it is a vector equation, it is equivalent to three equations obtained by resolving the vectors along three orthogonal axes) whose solution in terms of the initial particle position and velocity specifies the motion of the particle for all future, and past, time. The resolution of the vector equation in terms of three cartesian coordinates is straightforward. However, in

---

* H. Goldstein, *Classical Mechanics,* Addison-Wesley Publishing Co., Inc., Reading, Mass., 1950; H. C. Corben and P. Stehle, *Classical Mechanics,* John Wiley and Sons, Inc., New York, 1950; E. T. Whittaker, *Analytical Dynamics,* Dover Publications, New York, 4th ed., 1944.

many cases the symmetries of the problem or the constraints imposed indicate that it would be convenient to use some other set of orthogonal coordinates. For example, in the case of a particle moving about a fixed center with the forces acting on the particle being directed toward the center and dependent only on the distance between it and the center, it is clear that spherical coordinates are natural to the problem: the solution will reflect the symmetry of the situation and this can be most simply expressed in spherical coordinates. For this reason, it is desirable to formulate the laws of mechanics in a form which can be readily applied to an arbitrary coordinate system.

Consider a system consisting of N particles; it thus has $3N$ degrees of freedom. One may choose any convenient set of "generalized coordinates" q_i $(i = 1, 2, 3, \ldots, 3N)$ to describe the system. These will be related to the $3N$ cartesian coordinates describing the particles by the equations

$$\begin{aligned} x_j &= x_j(q_1, q_2, \ldots, q_{3N}, t), \\ y_j &= y_j(q_1, q_2, \ldots, q_{3N}, t), \\ z_j &= z_j(q_1, q_2, \ldots, q_{3N}, t), \end{aligned} \tag{5–3}$$

or, more simply,

$$\mathbf{r}_j = \mathbf{r}_j(q_i, t). \tag{5–4}$$

As written, the connecting equations contain the time explicitly. In the case where one fixed set of cartesian coordinates is to be replaced by another fixed coordinate set (e.g., spherical coordinates), this explicit time dependence will not appear.

While the coordinate transformation of Eq. (5–3) can be substituted directly into Eq. (5–1), and for conservative forces into Eq. (5–2), the resulting equations are, in general, complex and difficult to solve. For this reason, it has been proven useful to make use of a more general mathematical technique which can, with appropriate assumptions, yield Eq. (5–1) as a "derivable" result. Moreover, this general method, the *variational technique*, yields results valid for all coordinate systems.

Consider the function L, any function of generalized coordinates q_i, generalized velocities $\dot{q}_i$, and time t. It is assumed that the functions $q_i(t)$ are so chosen as to make the integral W, defined by

$$W \equiv \int_{t_1}^{t_2} L\, dt, \tag{5–5}$$

an *extremum*, i.e., a maximum or a minimum. Here t_1 and t_2 are to be considered as fixed times. This condition on the functions $q_i(t)$ can be expressed by saying that an arbitrary small variation δq_i in the function $q_i(t)$ does not alter the value of the integral W. The variations δq_i are assumed to be such as to vanish at t_1 and t_2, the end points of the path of integration. In the language of the calculus of variation,

$$\delta W = \delta \int_{t_1}^{t_2} L\,dt = \int_{t_1}^{t_2} \sum_i \left(\frac{\partial L}{\partial q_i}\,\delta q_i + \frac{\partial L}{\partial \dot{q}_i}\,\delta \dot{q}_i\right) dt = 0. \tag{5-6}$$

The functions $\dot{q}_i$ are clearly not independent of q_i, and hence

$$\delta \dot{q}_i = \frac{d}{dt}\,(\delta q_i). \tag{5-7}$$

The second term in the parentheses of Eq. (5-6) can be integrated by parts:

$$\int_{t_1}^{t_2} \frac{\partial L}{\partial \dot{q}_i}\,\delta \dot{q}_i\,dt = \int_{t_1}^{t_2} \frac{\partial L}{\partial \dot{q}_i}\,\frac{d}{dt}\,\delta q_i\,dt = \frac{\partial L}{\partial \dot{q}_i}\,\delta q_i \bigg|_{t_1}^{t_2} - \int_{t_1}^{t_2} \frac{d}{dt}\left(\frac{\partial L}{\partial \dot{q}_i}\right)\delta q_i\,dt. \tag{5-8}$$

Since the variations δq_i vanish at t_1 and t_2,

$$\int_{t_1}^{t_2} \frac{\partial L}{\partial \dot{q}_i}\,\delta \dot{q}_i\,dt = -\int_{t_1}^{t_2} \frac{d}{dt}\left(\frac{\partial L}{\partial \dot{q}_i}\right)\delta q_i\,dt. \tag{5-9}$$

With the use of this expression, Eq. (5-6) can be written as

$$\sum_i \int_{t_1}^{t_2} \left[\frac{\partial L}{\partial q_i} - \frac{d}{dt}\left(\frac{\partial L}{\partial \dot{q}_i}\right)\right]\delta q_i\,dt = 0. \tag{5-10}$$

Since the variations δq_i were assumed to be arbitrary, this equation can be valid only if the bracketed expression vanishes:

$$\frac{\partial L}{\partial q_i} - \frac{d}{dt}\left(\frac{\partial L}{\partial \dot{q}_i}\right) = 0. \tag{5-11}$$

This equation is known as the *Euler equation* of the calculus of variation. It represents a set of differential equations determining the functions $q_i(t)$ in such a way as to minimize (or maximize) the integral W of Eq. (5-5). It should be noted that the derivatives in Eq. (5-11) are to be formed as though the q_i and $\dot{q}_i$ are independent variables.

To obtain the equations of motion for conservative forces,

$$m\ddot{x}_i = -\frac{\partial V}{\partial x_i}, \qquad \text{etc.}, \tag{5-12}$$

one need only assume that

$$L = T - V = \sum_i \tfrac{1}{2} m(\dot{x}_i)^2 - V(x_i, t), \tag{5-13}$$

where T is the kinetic energy and V is the potential energy of the particle. For this choice of the function L, Euler's equations become *Lagrange's equations* and the function L is known as the *Lagrangian.*

Inasmuch as the integral W is minimized by trajectories $q_i(t)$ corresponding to the actual motion of the particle (Lagrange's equations correspond to Newton's law of motion), it will be minimized regardless of the system of coordinates used. Lagrange's equations are thus the desired equations of motion in an *arbitrary* coordinate system.

As an example, consider the equations of motion in cylindrical coordinates when the potential energy is a function of only r and z. The Lagrangian is

$$L = \tfrac{1}{2}m(\dot{r}^2 + r^2\dot{\theta}^2 + \dot{z}^2) - V(r, z), \tag{5-14}$$

and Lagrange's equations are

$$\begin{aligned} m\ddot{z} + \frac{\partial V}{\partial z} &= 0, \\ m\,\frac{d}{dt}\,(r^2\dot{\theta}) &= 0, \\ m\ddot{r} - mr\dot{\theta}^2 + \frac{\partial V}{\partial r} &= 0. \end{aligned} \tag{5-15}$$

The second of these equations expresses the conservation of the component of angular momentum about the z-axis. The $mr\dot{\theta}^2$ term in the third equation is the familiar "centrifugal force" term.

The above results can be generalized to the case of nonconservative systems if the velocity-dependent forces can be related to a generalized potential function U by

$$F_j = -\frac{\partial U}{\partial q_j} + \frac{d}{dt}\left(\frac{\partial U}{\partial \dot{q}_j}\right), \tag{5-16}$$

where F_j is a generalized force in the direction of the generalized coordinate q_j. The Lagrangian function then takes the form

$$L = T - U. \tag{5-17}$$

An extremely important example of a velocity-dependent force that fits this specification is that of the (*Lorentz*) force acting on a charged particle in an electromagnetic field. In this case, the force can be written (in gaussian units) as

$$\boldsymbol{F} = q\left[\boldsymbol{\mathcal{E}} + \frac{1}{c}\,(\boldsymbol{v} \times \boldsymbol{\mathcal{B}})\right]. \tag{5-18}$$

The fields will be expressed in terms of the scalar potential ϕ and the vector potential $\boldsymbol{A}$:

$$\begin{aligned} \mathcal{E} &= -\nabla\phi - \frac{1}{c}\frac{\partial \boldsymbol{A}}{\partial t}, \\ \mathcal{B} &= \nabla \times \boldsymbol{A}. \end{aligned} \tag{5–19}$$

These equations do not uniquely specify ϕ and $\boldsymbol{A}$. Maxwell's equations, expressed in terms of ϕ and $\boldsymbol{A}$, take their simplest form when the scalar and vector potentials are related to each other through the Lorentz condition

$$\nabla \cdot \boldsymbol{A} + \frac{1}{c}\frac{\partial \phi}{\partial t} = 0. \tag{5–20}$$

From Eqs. (5–18) and (5–19),

$$\boldsymbol{F} = q\left\{-\nabla\phi - \frac{1}{c}\left[\frac{\partial \boldsymbol{A}}{\partial t} - \boldsymbol{v} \times (\nabla \times \boldsymbol{A})\right]\right\}. \tag{5–21}$$

Since

$$\frac{d\boldsymbol{A}}{dt} = \frac{\partial \boldsymbol{A}}{\partial t} + (\boldsymbol{v} \cdot \nabla)\boldsymbol{A} \tag{5–22}$$

and

$$\boldsymbol{v} \times (\nabla \times \boldsymbol{A}) = \nabla(\boldsymbol{v} \cdot \boldsymbol{A}) - (\boldsymbol{v} \cdot \nabla)\boldsymbol{A}, \tag{5–23}$$

Eq. (5–21) can be written as

$$\boldsymbol{F} = q\left[-\nabla\left(\phi - \frac{1}{c}\,\boldsymbol{v} \cdot \boldsymbol{A}\right) - \frac{1}{c}\frac{d\boldsymbol{A}}{dt}\right]. \tag{5–24}$$

From this it can be seen that by choosing the generalized potential U as

$$U \equiv q\left(\phi - \frac{1}{c}\,\boldsymbol{v} \cdot \boldsymbol{A}\right) \tag{5–25}$$

(since ϕ and $\boldsymbol{A}$ do not depend on the velocity), the proper Lagrangian is

$$L = T - q\phi + \frac{q}{c}\,\boldsymbol{v} \cdot \boldsymbol{A}. \tag{5–26}$$

The Lagrangian formalism sketched above is advantageous because the dynamical problem is formulated in terms of a single scalar function L, rather than in terms of the set of vector relations in Eq. (5–1). In addition, by a suitable choice of generalized coordinates, simplifying features may become more apparent. For example, consider the case in which the Lagrangian is independent of one (or more) of the generalized coordinates. Such coordinates are then said to be *cyclic*. Lagrange's equation for this coordinate reduces to the form

$$\frac{d}{dt}\left(\frac{\partial L}{\partial \dot{q}_k}\right) = 0, \tag{5-27}$$

which shows that $\partial L/\partial \dot{q}_k$ is a constant of the motion. The discovery of constants of the motion greatly simplifies the solution of a dynamical problem; in fact, the alternative formulation of mechanics to be discussed next seeks to exploit this situation further.

5-3 Hamilton's equations. Lagrange's equations are a system of $3N$ second-order differential equations for the $3N$ generalized equations. In the Hamiltonian formulation of mechanics, an additional set of $3N$ independent variables is introduced. This leads to $6N$ first-order differential equations describing the motion of the system. Since for conservative systems, the Lagrangian is given in cartesian coordinates by

$$L = \sum_{i=1}^{N} \tfrac{1}{2} m_i \dot{r}_i^2 - V(r_1, r_2, \ldots, r_N, t), \tag{5-28}$$

the cartesian momenta are given by

$$m_i \dot{x}_i = \frac{\partial L}{\partial \dot{x}_i}. \tag{5-29}$$

This suggests that we define a generalized momentum p_i by

$$p_i \equiv \frac{\partial L}{\partial \dot{q}_i}. \tag{5-30}$$

In the Hamiltonian formulation of dynamics, these momenta are considered as independent variables on an equal footing with the coordinates q_i; the set of $6N$ variables q_i and p_i are called *canonical variables.* A Hamiltonian function is defined by

$$H \equiv \sum_i (p_i \dot{q}_i) - L. \tag{5-31}$$

From Eq. (5-30), since $L = L(q_i, \dot{q}_i, t)$, the momenta p_i are seen also to be functions of q_i, $\dot{q}_i$, and t. The defining equation (5-30) for the momenta can then be solved for the $\dot{q}_i$ in terms of the p_i and q_i, and the resulting expressions can be used in Eq. (5-31) to eliminate the $\dot{q}_i$. The Hamiltonian H can thus be expressed as a function of the canonical variables:

$$H = H(p_i, q_i, t). \tag{5-32}$$

Therefore, upon differentiation, we obtain

$$dH = \sum_i \left(\frac{\partial H}{\partial q_i}\, dq_i + \frac{\partial H}{\partial p_i}\, dp_i\right) + \frac{\partial H}{\partial t}\, dt. \tag{5-33}$$

From Eq. (5–31), however,

$$dH = \sum_i \left(p_i\, d\dot{q}_i + \dot{q}_i\, dp_i - \frac{\partial L}{\partial q_i}\, dq_i - \frac{\partial L}{\partial \dot{q}_i}\, d\dot{q}_i\right) - \frac{\partial L}{\partial t}\, dt. \tag{5-34}$$

The first and fourth terms in the sum cancel because of Eq. (5–30), leaving

$$dH = \sum_i \left(\dot{q}_i\, dp_i - \frac{\partial L}{\partial q_i}\, dq_i\right) - \frac{\partial L}{\partial t}\, dt. \tag{5-35}$$

Equating coefficients of the independent differentials dp_i, dq_i, and dt in Eqs. (5–33) and (5–35) gives the *canonical* equations of motion:

$$\dot{q}_i = \frac{\partial H}{\partial p_i}, \qquad \dot{p}_i = -\frac{\partial H}{\partial q_i}, \qquad \frac{\partial H}{\partial t} = -\frac{\partial L}{\partial t}\cdot \tag{5-36}$$

If one eliminates the momentum variables p_i that have been introduced into the Hamiltonian formalism, the result is, not unexpectedly, Lagrange's equations. The Hamiltonian formalism has other aspects, however, of great importance. Some of these will now be considered. From Eq. (5–33),

$$\frac{dH}{dt} = \sum_i \left(\frac{\partial H}{\partial q_i}\, \dot{q}_i + \frac{\partial H}{\partial p_i}\, \dot{p}_i\right) + \frac{\partial H}{\partial t}\cdot \tag{5-37}$$

From the canonical equations (5–36), this reduces to

$$\frac{dH}{dt} = \frac{\partial H}{\partial t}\cdot \tag{5-38}$$

Therefore, if the Hamiltonian function is not an explicit function of the time, it is a constant of the motion.

In the case of a dynamical system and a coordinate system such that the time does not appear in the equations defining the generalized coordinates, the kinetic energy T is a homogeneous quadratic function of the $\dot{q}_i$:

$$T = \sum_{i,j} \alpha_{ij}\dot{q}_i\dot{q}_j, \qquad \alpha_{ij} = \alpha_{ji}. \tag{5-39}$$

From this, it is seen that

$$\sum_i \dot{q}_i\, \frac{\partial T}{\partial \dot{q}_i} = 2T. \tag{5-40}$$

Assuming further that the system is conservative ($L = T - V$),

$$p_i \equiv \frac{\partial L}{\partial \dot{q}_i} = \frac{\partial T}{\partial \dot{q}_i}. \tag{5-41}$$

The use of these latter two relations in Eq. (5–31) yields

$$\begin{aligned} H &= \sum_i \frac{\partial T}{\partial \dot{q}_i} \dot{q}_i - (T - V) = 2T - (T - V) \\ &= T + V. \end{aligned} \tag{5-42}$$

In this case, therefore, the Hamiltonian function can be physically interpreted as the sum of the kinetic and potential energies of the system expressed as a function of the canonical variables.

Cyclic variables have the same significance in the Hamiltonian formalism that they have in the Lagrangian: if H is independent of a generalized coordinate, the corresponding canonical momentum is a constant of the motion. This follows directly from Eq. (5–36).

An important special case is that of a charged particle moving in an electromagnetic field. From Eq. (5–26), the Lagrangian is

$$L = T - q\phi + \frac{q}{c}\, \boldsymbol{v} \cdot \boldsymbol{A}. \tag{5-43}$$

The generalized momenta, from Eq. (5–30), are given by

$$p_i = \frac{\partial L}{\partial \dot{q}_i} = \frac{\partial T}{\partial \dot{q}_i} + \frac{q}{c} \frac{\partial}{\partial \dot{q}_i} (\boldsymbol{v} \cdot \boldsymbol{A}). \tag{5-44}$$

If the generalized coordinates do not depend explicitly on the time,

$$\boldsymbol{v} \cdot \boldsymbol{A} = \sum_j \dot{q}_j A_j, \tag{5-45}$$

where A_j is not necessarily a cartesian component of $\boldsymbol{A}$. Hence

$$\frac{\partial}{\partial \dot{q}_i} (\boldsymbol{v} \cdot \boldsymbol{A}) = \sum_j A_j\, \delta_{ij} = A_i \tag{5-46}$$

and

$$p_i = \frac{\partial T}{\partial \dot{q}_i} + \frac{q}{c} A_i, \tag{5-47}$$

where

$$\sum_i \dot{q}_i \frac{\partial T}{\partial \dot{q}_i} = 2T \tag{5-48}$$

as before.

The Hamiltonian is given by

$$H = \sum_i \left(\frac{\partial T}{\partial \dot{q}_i} + \frac{q}{c}\,A_i\right)\dot{q}_i - \left[T - q\phi + \frac{q}{c}\,\boldsymbol{v}\cdot\boldsymbol{A}\right]$$

$$= 2T + \frac{q}{c}\,\boldsymbol{v}\cdot\boldsymbol{A} - T + q\phi - \frac{q}{c}\,\boldsymbol{v}\cdot\boldsymbol{A}$$

$$= T + q\phi, \qquad (5\text{–}49)$$

and it is seen that in this case the Hamiltonian is just the total energy, since $q\phi$ is the potential energy of the particle.

For cartesian coordinates, the canonical momenta of Eq. (5–47) are given by

$$p_x = mv_x + \frac{q}{c}\,A_x, \qquad \text{etc.}, \qquad (5\text{–}50)$$

or, vectorially,

$$\boldsymbol{p} = m\boldsymbol{v} + \frac{q}{c}\,\boldsymbol{A}. \qquad (5\text{–}51)$$

Note that the canonical momentum no longer is the ordinary linear momentum $m\boldsymbol{v}$. From this, the Hamiltonian, Eq. (5–49), is

$$H = \frac{[\boldsymbol{p} - (q/c)\boldsymbol{A}]^2}{2m} + q\phi. \qquad (5\text{–}52)$$

5–4 Poisson brackets. It is frequently convenient to introduce another mathematical expression, known as the *Poisson bracket*. If F and G are two functions of the canonical variables, the Poisson bracket of F and G, $\{F, G\}$, is defined by

$$\{F, G\} \equiv \sum_i \left(\frac{\partial F}{\partial q_i}\frac{\partial G}{\partial p_i} - \frac{\partial F}{\partial p_i}\frac{\partial G}{\partial q_i}\right). \qquad (5\text{–}53)$$

To illustrate where this expression can arise, consider an arbitrary function F, a function of the coordinates, canonical momenta, and the time. Its time derivative can be written as

$$\frac{dF}{dt} = \frac{\partial F}{\partial t} + \sum_i \left(\frac{\partial F}{\partial q_i}\,\dot{q}_i + \frac{\partial F}{\partial p_i}\,\dot{p}_i\right). \qquad (5\text{–}54)$$

When Hamilton's equations, Eq. (5–36), are introduced, this becomes

$$\frac{dF}{dt} = \frac{\partial F}{\partial t} + \{F, H\}. \qquad (5\text{–}55)$$

This clearly is a very concise way of writing the dynamical equations of motion for a system. Choosing F in Eq. (5–55) to be in turn q_i, p_i, and H yields the Hamiltonian equations (5–36) and (5–38). Another feature of

Poisson brackets is that they provide a test for recognizing constants of the motion: if

$$\frac{\partial F}{\partial t} = -\{F, H\}, \tag{5-56}$$

F is a constant of the motion. In particular, if F does not depend explicitly on the time, it is a constant of the motion if its Poisson bracket with the Hamiltonian vanishes.

As will be seen later, the Poisson bracket provides a powerful tool in formulating quantum theory. For this reason, several simple but important properties of Poisson brackets will be developed. From the definition of the Poisson bracket, Eq. (5–53), the following identities can readily be obtained:

$$\{F, F\} = 0, \qquad \{F, c\} = 0, \tag{5-57}$$

where c is independent of q_i and p_i, but may depend explicitly on the time. Further,

$$\begin{aligned} \{F, G\} &= -\{G, F\}, \\ \{E + F, G\} &= \{E, G\} + \{F, G\}, \\ \{E, FG\} &= \{E, F\}G + F\{E, G\}. \end{aligned} \tag{5-58}$$

Also important are the special cases in which F and G are q_i and p_i:

$$\{q_i, q_j\} = 0, \qquad \{p_i, p_j\} = 0, \qquad \{q_i, p_j\} = \delta_{ij}. \tag{5-59}$$

5–5 Canonical transformations. In solving problems, the symmetries of the physical situation often indicate that one set of generalized coordinates is preferable to another. For example, in the case of motion under the influence of a central force $F(r)$, spherical coordinates, rather than cartesian, are the obvious choice. Although transformation from one set of generalized coordinates q_i to another, Q_i, is straightforward, the situation becomes somewhat more complex when the Hamiltonian formalism, in which momenta are on a par with coordinates as independent variables, is considered. What is then wanted are transformations which are *canonical*, that is, which leave the form of the equations of motion, Eq. (5–36), unchanged. Another term for such a transformation is *contact* transformation.

In setting up new canonical variables (coordinates Q_i and momenta P_i) to replace the original variables q_i and p_i, $2N$ additional variables are introduced. It is clear that of the $4N$ variables q_i, p_i, Q_i, and P_i, only $2N$ can be independent; $2N$ must be expressible in terms of the other $2N$. If the desired new variables Q_i and P_i are expressed in terms of the old by the arbitrary functions

$$Q_i = Q_i(q_i, p_i, t), \qquad P_i = P_i(q_i, p_i, t), \tag{5-60}$$

the new variables will not in general be canonical. However, it can be shown that if one starts instead with an *arbitrary* differentiable function $F(q_i, P_i, t)$ and uses it to define two new variables Q_j and, implicitly, P_j, and a new function K:

$$p_j \equiv \frac{\partial F(q_i, P_i, t)}{\partial q_j},$$

$$Q_j \equiv \frac{\partial F(q_i, P_i, t)}{\partial P_j}, \tag{5-61}$$

$$K \equiv H + \frac{\partial F(q_i, P_i, t)}{\partial t},$$

then the set of transformation equations (5-60) obtained by solving Eqs. (5-61) for P_i and Q_i results in a canonical transformation in which

$$\dot{Q}_i = \frac{\partial K}{\partial P_i}, \qquad \dot{P}_i = -\frac{\partial K}{\partial Q_i}. \tag{5-62}$$

The function $F(q_i, P_i, t)$ is called the *generating* function of the transformation. The new function $K(Q_i, P_i)$ plays the role of the Hamiltonian in the transformed system.

In the discussion above it was assumed that the generating function F was a function of the original coordinates q_i and the new momenta P_i. It is also possible to use generating functions of the forms $F_1(q_i, Q_i, t)$, $F_2(p_i, P_i, t)$, or $F_3(p_i, Q_i, t)$. With one of these generating functions, the relations determining the transformation, Eq. (5-61), will differ, but can similarly be solved to give transformation equations of the form of Eq. (5-60).

Several important expressions are invariant under a canonical transformation. Most significant to the later development is the Poisson bracket: the Poisson bracket of any two functions is invariant under a canonical transformation. The quantum-mechanical analogue of this will be seen later.

One simple example is provided by the generating function

$$F = \sum_i q_i P_i. \tag{5-63}$$

In this case, equations (5-61) yield

$$p_i = P_i, \qquad Q_i = q_i, \qquad K = H. \tag{5-64}$$

This transformation, which leaves coordinates and momenta unchanged, is the trivial *identity* transformation.

A useful concept is that of an *infinitesimal* canonical transformation. Such a transformation, as the name implies, produces only infinitesimal changes in the variables; the generating function therefore differs from the identity transformation discussed above only by an infinitesimal:

$$F = \sum_i q_i P_i + \epsilon G(q_i, P_i). \tag{5-65}$$

Here ϵ is a constant infinitesimal. While F is the actual generating function, the function G is also at times referred to as the generating function; the term will be used in this book to apply to either F or G. From equations (5–61),

$$p_j = P_j + \epsilon \frac{\partial G(q_i, P_i)}{\partial q_j} \tag{5-66}$$

or

$$\delta p_j \equiv P_j - p_j = -\epsilon \frac{\partial G}{\partial q_i}. \tag{5-67}$$

Similarly, from equations (5–61),

$$Q_j = q_j + \epsilon \frac{\partial G(q_i, P_i)}{\partial P_j} \tag{5-68}$$

or

$$\delta q_j \equiv Q_j - q_j = \epsilon \frac{\partial G}{\partial P_j}. \tag{5-69}$$

Only terms to the first power in ϵ will be of interest: since this is the case, P_j in Eq. (5–69) can be replaced by p_j, giving

$$\delta q_j = \epsilon \frac{\partial G}{\partial p_j}, \tag{5-70}$$

where G is now considered to be a function of q_i and p_i.

The effect of such an infinitesimal canonical transformation is to produce a change δW in any function $W(q_i, p_i)$, given by

$$\delta W = \sum_i \left(\frac{\partial W}{\partial q_i} \delta q_i + \frac{\partial W}{\partial p_i} \delta p_i \right). \tag{5-71}$$

With the use of Eqs. (5–67) and (5–70), this becomes

$$\delta W = \epsilon\{W, G\}. \tag{5-72}$$

Thus the change in any function is given by the Poisson bracket of the function with the generating function G.

5–6 Summary. In this brief review of certain classical formalisms, need for a coordinate system more general than the cartesian was discussed, and it was shown how Newton's second law of motion can be recast in terms of such generalized coordinates to give Lagrange's equations. This was done using variational procedures. The significance of cyclic coordinates in this formalism was pointed out. Then the Hamiltonian formulation of the equations of motion was developed, with the introduction of generalized canonical momenta as independent variables. Some important properties of the Hamiltonian viewpoint were mentioned briefly. Poisson brackets were defined, and several of their properties were tabulated. Finally, canonical transformations that preserve the Hamiltonian form of the equations of motion while altering the choice of independent variables were discussed, and the concept of an infinitesimal canonical transformation was introduced.

CHAPTER 6

OPERATOR FORMALISM

6–1 Postulates of quantum mechanics. It was seen in Chapter 3 that operators play an important role in quantum mechanics. For example, a plane wave, representing a state of a free particle for which the momentum of the particle is definite, satisfies the eigenvalue equation

$$\mathbf{P} \exp [i(\boldsymbol{k} \cdot \boldsymbol{r} - \omega t)] = \boldsymbol{p} \exp [i(\boldsymbol{k} \cdot \boldsymbol{r} - \omega t)], \tag{6–1}$$

where the momentum operator $\mathbf{P} = -i\hbar\boldsymbol{\nabla}$ operates on the eigenfunction, in this case a plane wave, and gives the eigenvalue $\boldsymbol{p} = \hbar\boldsymbol{k}$ times the same eigenfunction. Several important conclusions were drawn from the discussion of this eigenvalue equation:

(1) The observable $\boldsymbol{p}$, a measurable quantity, has associated with it an operator $\mathbf{P}$.

(2) The eigenvalue equation of this operator has as eigenfunctions those wave functions which represent states for which the momentum has some definite value.

(3) The eigenvalue $\boldsymbol{p}$ is the value which would be obtained if the momentum were to be measured.

(4) If the wave function is not some *one* of the possible eigenfunctions but is instead given by a linear superposition of plane waves, it is not possible to predict which of the various momenta associated with the component plane waves would be obtained if a momentum measurement were made. However, it was seen that the square of the amplitude connected with any component plane wave gives a measure of the probability of obtaining the corresponding value for a momentum measurement. This led to Eq. (4–55) as the expression for the average momentum of the particle. Stated exactly, if it be imagined that there is an ensemble of systems all having the same wave function, a momentum measurement on all members would yield different results, with Eq. (4–55) as the average value.

(5) If the momentum of a particle in such a superposition-momentum state is measured, the wave function of the particle must immediately thereafter be a plane wave.

It was found that the energy of a particle is associated with the Hamiltonian operator, and its position with the operator $\boldsymbol{r}$. These ideas will now be established on a formal postulatory basis, and some of the properties of operators and their eigenvalue equations will be derived. The physical reasonableness of the postulates can be seen from the discussions of the earlier chapters.

POSTULATE 1. It is assumed for a system consisting of a particle moving in a conservative field of force (produced by an external potential), that there is an associated wave function, that this wave function determines everything that can be known about the system, and that it is a single-valued function of the coordinates of the particle and of the time.* In general it is a complex function, and may be multiplied by an arbitrary complex number without changing its physical significance.

POSTULATE 2. With every physical observable (the energy of the system, the x-position coordinate of the particle, etc.) there is associated an operator. Denote by Q the operator associated with the observable q. Then a measurement of q gives a result which is one of the eigenvalues of the eigenvalue equation:

$$\mathrm{Q}\psi_n = q_n\psi_n. \tag{6-2}$$

This measurement constitutes an interaction between the system and the measuring apparatus. If the state function was ψ_n prior to the measurement, the result q_n is certain to be obtained from an exact measurement of the observable associated with the operator Q. If initially the wave function is not an eigensolution of Eq. (6-2), it is impossible to predict with certainty which of several possible results will be obtained. However, if the result q_n is obtained, the interaction changes the state of the system to the state described by the function ψ_n. Thus, immediately after a measurement yielding the value q_n, the state function is ψ_n. This is equivalent to the condition that a measurement be repeatable: a measurement giving a result q_n will, if repeated immediately, give with certainty the same result.

Definition 1. An operator Q is *Hermitian* if

$$\int \overline{\psi_a} \mathrm{Q}\psi_b \, dr = \int \overline{\mathrm{Q}\psi_a}\psi_b \, dr, \tag{6-3}$$

where ψ_a and ψ_b are arbitrary normalizable functions. The integration

* Since $|\psi|^2$, and not ψ itself, has been seen to be the quantity of measurable physical significance, the necessity for the assumption of *single-valuedness* is not *a priori* obvious. However, various mathematical difficulties arise if the single-valuedness postulate is abandoned, and so it will be retained for the purposes of this book. For a more detailed discussion of this point see: W. Pauli, *Die allgemeinen Prinzipien der Wellenmechanik*, J. W. Edwards, Ann Arbor, Mich., 1947, p. 126 (reprinted from *Handbuch der Physik*, 2nd ed., vol. 24, part 1); J. M. Blatt and V. F. Weisskopf, *Theoretical Nuclear Physics*, John Wiley and Sons, New York, 1952, Appendix A, footnotes on p. 783 and p. 787.

is assumed to be over the entire three-dimensional space. It is obvious that the operator x associated with the measurement of the x-component of the position of a particle is Hermitian. The operator $P_x = -i\hbar(\partial/\partial x)$ associated with the x-component of the momentum of the particle can also be seen to be Hermitian. This follows from an integration by parts, imposing the condition that the wave function vanishes at infinity.

Since P_x is a Hermitian operator, the square of P_x is also, and so is any power of P_x, as shown by

$$\int \overline{\psi_a} P_x^2 \psi_b \, dr = \int \overline{P_x \psi_a} \cdot P_x \psi_b \, dr = \int \overline{P_x^2 \psi_a} \psi_b \, dr. \tag{6–4}$$

Also, a linear combination of Hermitian operators is a Hermitian operator.

A number of elementary results, which follow directly from the postulates laid down above and which can be expressed in the form of simple theorems, will now be discussed. These theorems, although simple to prove, are fundamental to the whole structure of the quantum-mechanical formalism. First, two theorems will be discussed which relate Hermitian operators to properties of their eigenvalues and to properties of their eigenfunctions, respectively.

THEOREM 1. The eigenvalues of a Hermitian operator are all real.

Proof:

$$Q\psi_n = q_n \psi_n,$$

$$\int \overline{\psi_n} Q \psi_n \, dr = \int \overline{\psi_n} q_n \psi_n \, dr = q_n \int \overline{\psi_n} \psi_n \, dr, \tag{6–5}$$

$$\int \overline{Q\psi_n} \psi_n \, dr = \int \overline{q_n \psi_n} \psi_n \, dr = \overline{q_n} \int \overline{\psi_n} \psi_n \, dr.$$

Therefore

$$\overline{q_n} = q_n, \tag{6–6}$$

and q_n is real. This is an important result in the formalism, inasmuch as the eigenvalues have been interpreted as the results of physical measurements, and such results are real numbers.

Before proceeding with the theorems, a postulate and a few definitions are needed.

POSTULATE 3. Any operator associated with a physically measurable quantity is Hermitian.

Definition 2. Two wave functions are said to be *orthogonal* when

$$\int \overline{\psi_a} \psi_b \, dr = 0, \tag{6–7}$$

the integration being over all space.

Definition 3. A set of functions is *linearly independent* if the linear equation

$$\sum_j c_j \psi_j = 0 \tag{6-8}$$

implies that all $c_j = 0$. If the functions are not linearly independent, they are said to be *linearly dependent.*

Definition 4. An eigenvalue q of an eigenvalue equation is mth-*order degenerate* if there are m linearly independent eigenfunctions corresponding to this eigenvalue.

Consider now another theorem following directly from the Hermitian property of the operator. This concerns the eigenfunctions of Hermitian operators.

THEOREM 2. *Orthogonality.* Two eigenfunctions of an operator are orthogonal to each other if the corresponding eigenvalues are unequal.

Proof:

$$\begin{aligned} \int \overline{\psi_n} Q\psi_m \, dr &= \int \overline{Q\psi_n} \psi_m \, dr = \overline{q_n} \int \overline{\psi_n} \psi_m \, dr \\ &= q_n \int \overline{\psi_n} \psi_m \, dr \\ &= \int \overline{\psi_n} Q\psi_m \, dr = q_m \int \overline{\psi_n} \psi_m \, dr; \end{aligned} \tag{6-9}$$

$$(q_n - q_m) \int \overline{\psi_n} \psi_m \, dr = 0. \tag{6-10}$$

Therefore

$$\int \overline{\psi_n} \psi_m \, dr = 0 \qquad \text{if} \qquad q_n \neq q_m. \tag{6-11}$$

THEOREM 3. If an eigenvalue q of the operator Q is degenerate, any linear combination of the linearly independent eigenfunctions is also an eigenfunction;

$$Q\left(\sum_n c_n \psi_n\right) = q\left(\sum_n c_n \psi_n\right). \tag{6-12}$$

This follows in obvious fashion from the linearity of the equation.

Definition 5. A set of functions constitutes a *complete set* of linearly independent eigenfunctions corresponding to the eigenvalue q if with any other eigenfunction of the eigenvalue q the set is linearly dependent. In other words, the set of functions is *complete* if there is no other function which falls in the set of linearly independent functions.

THEOREM 4. If ψ_j $(j = 1, \ldots, m)$ constitute a complete set of eigenfunctions with the eigenvalue q of mth-order degeneracy for some operator, then any other eigenfunction of this eigenvalue may be expanded in terms of this complete set.

Proof: Let

$$a\psi - \sum_{j=1}^{m} c_j\psi_j = 0. \tag{6–13}$$

If a is equal to zero, then all the c's in this equation must be zero, since these functions are linearly independent. If this were the only possibility, then ψ would constitute a member of the linearly independent set of functions. Since, however, it was assumed that the set of functions ψ_1 through ψ_m was linearly independent and complete, there must be a solution to Eq. (6–13) with a not equal to zero. If a is not equal to zero, then one has

$$\psi = \frac{1}{a}\sum_j c_j\psi_j, \tag{6–14}$$

which constitutes the desired expansion.

THEOREM 5. Linear combinations of the ψ_j may be taken to form a set of m mutually orthogonal functions. These m mutually orthogonal functions are, of course, also linearly independent and can be used to expand any other eigenfunction corresponding to a particular eigenvalue. This theorem can be verified by making use of the Schmidt orthogonalization procedure outlined below.

Schmidt orthogonalization procedure. Designate the set of independent functions corresponding to the eigenvalue q as ψ_j $(j = 1, \ldots, m)$. Choose any one of these functions, say ψ_1, as the first member of a new set u_j $(j = 1, \ldots, m)$:

$$u_1 \equiv \psi_1. \tag{6–15}$$

Designate

$$\int |u_1|^2\, dr \equiv c_{11}, \qquad \int \overline{u_1}\psi_2\, dr \equiv c_{12}. \tag{6–16}$$

Take

$$u_2 \equiv \frac{c_{12}}{c_{11}}\, u_1 - \psi_2. \tag{6–17}$$

Clearly,

$$\int \overline{u_1} u_2\, dr = 0. \tag{6–18}$$

Designate

$$\int |u_2|^2\, dr \equiv c_{22}, \qquad \int \overline{u_1}\psi_3\, dr \equiv c_{13}, \qquad \int \overline{u_2}\psi_3\, dr \equiv c_{23}. \tag{6–19}$$

Take

$$u_3 \equiv \frac{c_{13}}{c_{11}} u_1 + \frac{c_{23}}{c_{22}} u_2 - \psi_3. \tag{6-20}$$

Clearly,

$$\int \overline{u_1} u_3 \, d\tau = \int \overline{u_2} u_3 \, d\tau = 0. \tag{6-21}$$

This procedure can obviously be extended to obtain $u_4, u_5, \ldots, u_m$. As eigenfunctions corresponding to different eigenvalues are already orthogonal, by Eq. (6-11), the above procedure can be used to obtain a complete orthogonal set of eigenfunctions for any Hermitian operator.

Postulate 4. The set of functions ψ_j which are eigenfunctions of the eigenvalue equation

$$Q\psi_j = q_j\psi_j \tag{6-22}$$

form, in general, an infinite set of linearly independent functions. A linear combination of these functions of the form

$$\psi = \sum_j c_j\psi_j \tag{6-23}$$

can be used to express an infinite number of possible functions. It might be expected that this infinite set of linearly independent functions could be used to expand any arbitrary function ψ; actually this assumption is more stringent than is necessary. It will be assumed only that the infinite set of functions formed by the eigenfunctions of any operator playing a role in quantum mechanics can be used to expand a wave function which is a suitable physical wave function. Questions involved in the possibility of expansion of a particularly badly behaved function will not be considered. It is specifically assumed that if ψ is a physically acceptable wave function, it can be expanded in eigenfunctions of any observable of the system.

With the assumption that the complete set of linearly independent eigenfunctions for an operator has been chosen to be orthogonal and with the further assumption that the eigenfunctions are all square-integrable and have been normalized to unity, we have

$$\int \overline{\psi_j}\psi_k \, d\tau = \delta_{jk}. \tag{6-24}$$

Such a set of functions is said to constitute a *complete orthonormal set*. The expansion coefficients c_j in Eq. (6-23) are easily evaluated for such a set by making use of Eq. (6-24):

$$c_j = \int \overline{\psi_j}\psi \, d\tau. \tag{6-25}$$

Definition 6. If there exists a complete set (in the sense of Postulate 4) of linearly independent state functions ψ_j such that ψ_j is an eigenfunction of both of the operators R and S corresponding to physical observables, the corresponding observables are said to be *compatible.*

By "compatible observables" is meant that both R and S are completely predictable for the complete set of states ψ_j. Clearly, position and momentum measurements are not compatible. On the other hand, the three components of the position or the three components of the momentum are simultaneously measurable and hence compatible.

Definition 7. If

$$\mathrm{Q}\psi = \mathrm{R}\psi \tag{6–26}$$

for any arbitrary function in the set of physically permissible wave functions, the operators are *equivalent:*

$$\mathrm{Q} \equiv \mathrm{R}. \tag{6–27}$$

Conversely, the operator equation (6–27) implies Eq. (6–26) for any ψ in the set of acceptable functions.

THEOREM 6. If two observables are compatible, their operators commute.

Proof:

$$\mathrm{S}\psi_j = s_j\psi_j, \qquad \mathrm{R}\psi_j = r_j\psi_j. \tag{6–28}$$

Therefore

$$(\mathrm{RS} - \mathrm{SR})\psi_j = 0 \tag{6–29}$$

and

$$(\mathrm{RS} - \mathrm{SR}) \sum_j c_j\psi_j \equiv (\mathrm{RS} - \mathrm{SR})\psi = 0. \tag{6–30}$$

By the expansion postulate 4, ψ may be any arbitrary function of the class of all wave functions of importance in quantum mechanics. Consequently, Eq. (6–30) implies the commutation of the operators R and S:

$$[\mathrm{R}, \mathrm{S}] \equiv \mathrm{RS} - \mathrm{SR} = 0. \tag{6–31}$$

The expression RS − SR is known as the *commutator* of the operators R and S.

THEOREM 7. If two operators Q and R commute and either Q or R has nondegenerate eigenvalues, its eigenfunctions are also eigenfunctions of the other operator.

Proof:

$$\mathrm{Q}\psi_j = q_j\psi_j, \tag{6–32}$$

where q is assumed to be nondegenerate; then

$$\mathrm{Q}(\mathrm{R}\psi_j) = q_j(\mathrm{R}\psi_j) \tag{6-33}$$

follows directly from Eq. (6–32) by multiplying by the operator R and making use of the commutation relation. On the other hand, Eq. (6–33) states that the function $\mathrm{R}\psi_j$ is an eigenfunction of the operator Q. But the operator Q has been assumed to have only nondegenerate eigenvalues. Consequently, the function $\mathrm{R}\psi_j$ can differ from the original eigenfunction ψ_j by at most a multiplicative constant, and so

$$\mathrm{R}\psi_j = r_j\psi_j. \tag{6-34}$$

This shows that the wave function ψ_j is simultaneously an eigenfunction of both Q and R. Note also that the members of the set of functions ψ_j are orthogonal.

THEOREM 8. If Q and R are operators which commute with each other, there exists a complete set of eigenstates which are simultaneously eigenstates of both Q and R.

The case of the nondegenerate eigenvalue has already been treated. The case of degeneracy is considered here.

Assume that

$$\mathrm{Q}\psi_j = q\psi_j, \tag{6-35}$$

where q is an mth-order degenerate eigenvalue of Q. Operating on Eq. (6–35) with R and making use of the commutation relation leads to

$$\mathrm{Q}(\mathrm{R}\psi_j) = q(\mathrm{R}\psi_j). \tag{6-36}$$

From the form of this equation it is clear that the function $\mathrm{R}\psi_j$ is an eigenfunction of Q, and by an earlier theorem can be expanded in the set of functions ψ_j. Consequently,

$$\mathrm{R}\psi_j = \sum_{k=1}^{m} q_{jk}\psi_k. \tag{6-37}$$

Multiplied by a constant c_j and summed over j, this becomes

$$\mathrm{R}\sum_{j=1}^{m} c_j\psi_j = \sum_{j,k} c_j q_{jk}\psi_k. \tag{6-38}$$

Now assume that

$$\sum_j c_j q_{jk} = rc_k. \tag{6-39}$$

This constitutes a set of m linear equations in the m unknowns c_k that has a nonzero solution for the c_k provided the constant r satisfies the characteristic equation

$$\det (q_{jk} - r\,\delta_{jk}) = 0. \tag{6–40}$$

The determinant is formed from the array of numbers q_{jk} with r subtracted from each diagonal term. Expansion of this determinant leads to an mth-order equation for r which has m roots. With each root r_k there is associated a solution $c_j^{(k)}$ for the c's. Defining

$$u_k \equiv \sum_j c_j^{(k)} \psi_j, \tag{6–41}$$

and substituting into the above equations yields

$$\mathrm{R}u_k = r_k u_k, \qquad \mathrm{Q}u_k = q u_k. \tag{6–42}$$

The m functions given by Eq. (6–41) are linearly independent. The eigenvalues r_k are not necessarily all equal. The above procedure may then be applied to every degenerate or nondegenerate eigenvalue of Q, giving the result

$$\mathrm{R}u_k = r_k u_k, \qquad \mathrm{Q}u_k = q_k u_k. \tag{6–43}$$

Therefore, the functions u_k constitute a complete set of simultaneous eigenfunctions of R and Q. A complete orthonormal set of functions can be obtained from the u_k by using the Schmidt orthogonalization procedure.

In the development thus far, it has been assumed for simplicity that the functions with which we were dealing (the eigenfunctions as well as the wave functions expanded in terms of these eigenfunctions) were all normalizable. It was also assumed that the eigenvalues assumed only discrete values. These assumptions are actually not independent, but go hand in hand. This can be illustrated by a simple example.

Consider sound waves bouncing back and forth inside a cavity resonator. The natural frequencies of oscillation of such a cavity form a discrete set. The volume of the cavity is finite, so an integration of the square of the amplitude over the interior of the cavity leads to a finite number. On the other hand, if the cavity is imagined to expand without limit, the discrete series of natural frequencies for the cavity becomes a continuous distribution of frequencies. At the same time, the integration of the square of the wave amplitude over the interior of the cavity becomes infinite (if the wave amplitude is not everywhere zero). Consequently, for this case the normalization of the eigenfunctions and the discreteness of the eigenvalues are related, one following from the other. A closer investigation shows that this is also true for the general quantum-mechanical case.

As a generalization of the above development, the case of a continuous distribution of eigenvalues will now be considered. Actually, an operator may have a range of values over which the eigenvalues are continuous and a separate range over which the eigenvalues form a discrete set. The case of a continuous distribution of eigenvalues has already been seen in two examples: the operators associated with the measurement of the position of a particle and with the measurement of the momentum of a particle had eigenvalues which took on a continuous range of values. The resulting eigenfunctions, it will be recalled, were unnormalizable. These cases, particularly the case of the momentum eigenfunctions, form a convenient example which can be used as a guide in the discussion of the general case.

The various theorems which have been proved for the discrete case in this section can all be taken over for the case of a continuous distribution of eigenvalues, with only slight modifications. For example, the eigenvalue equation can be written as

$$Q\psi_q = q\psi_q. \tag{6–44}$$

Here the eigenvalue q, which takes on a continuous distribution of values, is also used as a subscript to designate the eigenfunction with which it is associated. The theorem of the orthogonality of eigenfunctions corresponding to different eigenvalues takes the form

$$\int \overline{\psi_{q'}}\psi_q \, dr = 0, \qquad q \neq q'. \tag{6–45}$$

For q' equal to q, the integral is divergent, inasmuch as the wave function is known to be unnormalizable. This suggests that by using a limiting process similar to that used in connection with the discussion of the delta function, we can define the orthogonality integral

$$\int \overline{\psi_{q'}}\psi_q \, dr = \delta(q - q'). \tag{6–46}$$

Here the integral has meaning only by virtue of a limiting process similar to that discussed in Chapter 4.

In a similar manner, the expansion hypothesis for the case of a continuous distribution of eigenvalues can be written as

$$\psi = \int u(q)\psi_q \, dq. \tag{6–47}$$

If, as sometimes happens, there is both a continuous and a discrete range of eigenvalues for the operator Q, the expansion hypothesis is written as

$$\psi = \sum_q u_q\psi_q + \int u(q)\psi_q \, dq, \tag{6–48}$$

where the summation is over the discrete range of the eigenvalues and the integration is over the continuous range of the eigenvalues. If it is assumed that the wave function ψ can be and is normalized to unity,

$$\int |\psi|^2 \, dr = \sum_q |u_q|^2 + \int |u(q)|^2 \, dq = 1. \tag{6-49}$$

This equation will be illustrated with an example for which there is only a continuous range of eigenvalues. Assume that the operator Q corresponds to the momentum in the x-direction of the particle. To avoid difficulties connected with degeneracy, ignore the other two coordinates, y and z. In this particular case, an arbitrary wave function, which will be assumed to be normalized, can be expanded in an integral as in Eq. (6–47). We introduce the normalized momentum eigenfunctions which are normalized in the sense of Eq. (6–46):

$$\psi_p(x) = \left(\frac{1}{2\pi\hbar}\right)^{1/2} \exp\left(i\,\frac{p}{\hbar}\,x\right). \tag{6-50}$$

It is easily shown that Eq. (6–46) is satisfied by these functions. Substituting these functions into Eq. (6–47) gives

$$\psi(x) = \int_{-\infty}^{\infty} u(p)\psi_p(x) \, dp. \tag{6-51}$$

The inverse transformation can then be written as

$$u(p) = \int_{-\infty}^{\infty} \overline{u_p}(x)\psi(x) \, dx. \tag{6-52}$$

If the absolute square of Eq. (6–51) is integrated over all x, one obtains

$$\int_{-\infty}^{\infty} |\psi|^2 \, dx = \int_{-\infty}^{\infty} |u(p)|^2 \, dp = 1. \tag{6-53}$$

From the earlier discussion, the square of the absolute value of u is proportional to the probability per unit momentum of finding a particular value of the momentum if a momentum measurement is made at the time in question. Reference to Eq. (6–53) shows clearly that the function $u(p)$ is in fact correctly normalized to give the probability per unit momentum directly.

The relations of the form of Eq. (6–46) and the corresponding relation for eigenfunctions associated with discrete eigenvalues are analogous to a relation known as the *closure relation.* To obtain this relation, consider the expansion of an arbitrary wave function in terms of eigenfunctions of some particular operation, as in Eq. (6–48):

$$\psi(r) = \sum_q u_q\psi_q + \int u(q)\psi_q \, dq. \tag{6-54}$$

Use of the orthonormal property of these eigenfunctions gives

$$\int \overline{\psi_q}\psi \, dr = u_q \qquad \text{or} \qquad u(q). \tag{6–55}$$

If this is substituted into Eq. (6–54) and the order of integration and summation is interchanged, we obtain

$$\begin{aligned}\psi(r) &= \sum_q \left[\int \overline{\psi_q}\psi \, dr'\right]\psi_q(r) + \int\left[\int \overline{\psi_q}\psi \, dr'\right]\psi_q \, dq \\ &= \int\left[\sum_q \overline{\psi_q}(r')\psi_q(r) + \int \overline{\psi_q}(r')\psi_q(r)\, dq\right]\psi(r')\, dr'.\end{aligned} \tag{6–56}$$

From the form of this equation, it is clear that the term in brackets under the integral is simply a delta function:

$$\sum_q \overline{\psi_q}(r')\psi_q(r) + \int \overline{\psi_q}(r')\psi_q(r)\, dq = \delta(r - r'). \tag{6–57}$$

This is the *closure relation.* Note that if only a continuous range of eigenvalues of Q is considered, this expression is similar to Eq. (6–46), with the role of the variable of integration changed—it being in one case a subscript and in the other the argument of the function.

Postulate 5. If a system is described by a wave function ψ, the expectation value of any observable q with corresponding operator Q is given by

$$\langle q\rangle = \int \overline{\psi} \mathrm{Q}\psi \, dr. \tag{6–58}$$

The reasonableness of this postulate was shown in the previous chapters, in particular, Chapter 5. To see its significance more clearly, we expand the wave function in the eigenfunctions of Q in accordance with the expansion postulate:

$$\psi = \sum_j c_j\psi_j, \qquad \mathrm{Q}\psi_j = q_j\psi_j. \tag{6–59}$$

It is assumed that the wave function ψ is normalizable and is normalized to unity. As has been seen, the eigenfunctions given in Eq. (6–59) are orthogonal to each other, or at least may be chosen so as to be orthogonal; assume that this has been done. Further assume that each of the eigenfunctions is normalizable and has been normalized to unity. The orthonormal character of the functions ψ_j may be expressed, as previously, by

$$\int \overline{\psi_j}\psi_k \, dr = \delta_{jk}. \tag{6–60}$$

Since ψ is normalized, by using Eq. (6–59) one can write

$$\int \bar{\psi}\psi \, d\tau = \sum_{j,k} \bar{c}_j c_k \int \bar{\psi}_j \psi_k \, d\tau = \sum_{j,k} \bar{c}_j c_k \, \delta_{jk} = 1,$$

$$\sum_j |c_j|^2 = 1. \tag{6–61}$$

In a similar manner, Eq. (6–59) can be substituted into Eq. (6–58) to give

$$\langle q \rangle = \sum_j q_j |c_j|^2. \tag{6–62}$$

From these relations, it is evident that $|c_j|^2$ can be, and reasonably is, interpreted as the probability of finding the system in the state designated by the subscript j. Consequently, in a measurement in which q is determined, the probability that the result q_j will be obtained is given by

$$P_j = |c_j|^2. \tag{6–63}$$

If the result q_j is a degenerate eigenvalue, the probability of obtaining this result is found by summing Eq. (6–63) over all subscripts j corresponding to this particular eigenvalue. Use of the orthonormal property of the eigenfunctions ψ_j and Eq. (6–59) makes it easy to obtain an explicit expression for the probability in the form

$$c_j = \int \bar{\psi}_j \psi \, d\tau,$$

$$P_j = |c_j|^2 = \left| \int \bar{\psi}_j \psi \, d\tau \right|^2. \tag{6–64}$$

Postulate 6. The development in time of the wave function ψ, given its form at an initial time and assuming the system is left undisturbed, is determined by the Schrödinger equation

$$\mathrm{H}\psi = i\hbar \frac{\partial}{\partial t} \psi, \tag{6–65}$$

where the Hamiltonian operator H is formed from the corresponding classical Hamiltonian function by substituting for the classical observables their corresponding operators.

Postulate 7. The operators of quantum theory are such that their commutators are proportional to the corresponding classical Poisson brackets according to the prescription

$$[\mathrm{Q}, \mathrm{R}] \equiv (\mathrm{QR} - \mathrm{RQ}) \rightleftharpoons i\hbar\{q, r\}, \tag{6–66}$$

where $\{q, r\}$ is the classical Poisson bracket for the observables q and r.

The variables, if any, in the Poisson bracket are to be replaced by operators.

Two observations should be made in connection with this postulate. The coordinates and momenta must be expressed in cartesian coordinates. Also, in certain cases, ambiguities can arise in the order of noncommuting factors. These can often be resolved by remembering that the operator must be Hermitian. Because of these limitations and ambiguities, this "postulate" must be regarded more as a helpful guide than as a basic postulate of quantum mechanics. When Q and R are functions of r and $\mathbf{P}$ such that Eq. (6–66) yields an ambiguous result, the commutator can be directly evaluated from the basic commutator $[\mathbf{P}, r]$. See Eq. (8–10) for an example of the algebraic technique employed.

An example of an ambiguous operator is offered by a consideration of the Hamiltonian of Eq. (5–52) for a charged particle in an electromagnetic field:

$$\mathrm{H} = \frac{[\mathbf{P} - (q/c)\boldsymbol{A}]^2}{2m} + q\phi. \tag{6–67}$$

Expanded, this becomes

$$\mathrm{H} = \frac{\mathrm{P}^2}{2m} - \frac{q}{mc}\,\mathbf{P}\cdot\boldsymbol{A} + \frac{q^2}{2mc^2}\,A^2 + q\phi. \tag{6–68}$$

The second term could equally well have been written as $-(q/mc)\boldsymbol{A}\cdot\mathbf{P}$; this ambiguity is resolved by writing Eq. (6–68) as

$$\mathrm{H} = \frac{\mathrm{P}^2}{2m} - \frac{q}{2mc}\,(\mathbf{P}\cdot\boldsymbol{A} + \boldsymbol{A}\cdot\mathbf{P}) + \frac{q^2}{2mc^2}\,A^2 + q\phi, \tag{6–69}$$

where it is observed that the operator H is Hermitian, unlike that of Eq. (6–68). Postulate 7 may seem strange. However, note by direct substitution that Postulate 7 is correct for the six components of r and $\mathbf{P}$ taken in any combination, and for any positive integral power of a component of r and a component of $\mathbf{P}$, and vice versa. In Chapter 8, when the time rate of change of the expectation values is considered, it will be found that this postulate represents an important bridge between classical and quantum mechanics. The physical significance of this postulate will be made clear then.

6–2 Algebraic methods. As discussed earlier, the operators encountered in the quantum-mechanical formalism can be manipulated by using the rules of an associative, but noncommutative, algebra. This suggests that operator algebra may play an important role in the development of the quantum formalism, and it is the purpose of this section to investigate this role more fully. Actually, these algebraic ideas are fundamental to the formalism. To illustrate, consider once again the linear harmonic oscillator. The determination of possible energy states by techniques which are almost wholly algebraic will now be demonstrated.

The Hamiltonian operator for the linear harmonic oscillator is expressed by

$$\mathrm{H} = \frac{1}{2m}\,\mathrm{P}_x^2 + \frac{k}{2}\,x^2. \tag{6–70}$$

Once again the motion in the y- and z-directions will be ignored. The energy eigenvalue equation is

$$\mathrm{H}u_n = E_n u_n. \tag{6–71}$$

The Schrödinger time-dependent equation is

$$\mathrm{H}\psi = i\hbar\,\frac{\partial}{\partial t}\,\psi, \tag{6–72}$$

with the general solution

$$\psi = \sum_n c_n u_n \exp\left(-\frac{iE_n}{\hbar}\,t\right). \tag{6–73}$$

The problem under consideration is that of finding the possible eigenvalues of Eq. (6–71) and the corresponding eigenfunctions. Proceed by factoring the operator H into two factors; first define two non-Hermitian operators:

$$\mathrm{R}_\pm \equiv \frac{1}{\sqrt{2m}}\,\mathrm{P}_x \pm i\,\sqrt{\frac{k}{2}}\,x. \tag{6–74}$$

These operators are the Hermitian adjoints of each other; that is, for any reasonably behaved functions u and v, they satisfy the equation

$$\int \bar{u}\mathrm{R}_+ v\,dr = \int \overline{(\mathrm{R}_- u)}v\,dr. \tag{6–75}$$

Multiplying the two operators of Eq. (6–74) together in different orders, we obtain

$$\mathrm{R}_+\mathrm{R}_- + \tfrac{1}{2}\hbar\omega = \mathrm{R}_-\mathrm{R}_+ - \tfrac{1}{2}\hbar\omega = \mathrm{H}, \tag{6–76}$$

where the commutation relation obtained from Eqs. (5–59) and (6–66),

$$[\mathrm{P}_x, x] = -i\hbar, \tag{6–77}$$

has been used. From Eq. (6–76), we obtain the commutation relations

$$[\mathrm{R}_+, \mathrm{R}_-] = -\hbar\omega \tag{6–78}$$

and

$$[\mathrm{H}, \mathrm{R}_\pm] = \pm\hbar\omega\mathrm{R}_\pm. \tag{6–79}$$

It is obvious on physical grounds that any reasonable theory of the simple harmonic oscillator should give energy values for the oscillator which are positive, inasmuch as the energy equals the sum of positive factors times the squares of the momentum and position. It is interesting to note that this result is also obtained from very elementary considerations of the operator algebra. Consider the second term on the right side of Eq. (6–70): x is a Hermitian operator and can have only real eigenvalues. Consequently, the square of x can have only positive real eigenvalues. In the same way, the square of P_x can have only positive real eigenvalues. Consequently, the expectation value of both the kinetic and potential energies and therefore of the Hamiltonian can be only positive. If the expectation value of the Hamiltonian can be only positive, the energy of the simple harmonic oscillator can be only positive (or possibly zero). This implies that there can be no negative energy states for the simple harmonic oscillator.

Since the harmonic oscillator has only positive energy states, possibly including zero, it is clear that there must be a lower bound on the energy of the simple harmonic oscillator. Assume that E_0 represents the lowest energy which the harmonic oscillator can have, and that the corresponding wave function is given by u_0; these quantities satisfy the eigenvalue equation

$$\mathrm{H}u_0 = E_0 u_0. \tag{6–80}$$

It is not known for the moment whether the wave function u_0 is unique; that is, it has not yet been determined whether the energy level of E_0 is degenerate. Operating on the left member of Eq. (6–80) with the operator R_- gives

$$\mathrm{R}_-\mathrm{H}u_0 = E_0 \mathrm{R}_- u_0. \tag{6–81}$$

Making use of the commutation relation Eq. (6–79), we obtain

$$\mathrm{H}(\mathrm{R}_- u_0) = (E_0 - \hbar\omega)(\mathrm{R}_- u_0). \tag{6–82}$$

Note that this is in the form of the eigenvalue equation (6–71), with a new eigenvalue $E_0 - \hbar\omega$, and for which the new eigenfunction is $\mathrm{R}_- u_0$. On the other hand, the assumption that E_0 is the lowest eigenvalue indicates that this can be only a trivial solution to the eigenvalue equation, namely, that the wave function must vanish everywhere. Consequently,

$$\mathrm{R}_- u_0 = 0. \tag{6–83}$$

If this is operated on by R_+, we obtain, by using Eq. (6–76), the relations

$$\mathrm{R}_+\mathrm{R}_- u_0 = 0, \qquad (\mathrm{H} - \tfrac{1}{2}\hbar\omega)u_0 = 0. \tag{6–84}$$

The latter is in the form of an eigenvalue equation, giving the lowest energy eigenvalue E_0:

$$E_0 = \tfrac{1}{2}\hbar\omega. \tag{6-85}$$

In a similar manner, if Eq. (6–80) is operated on by R_+, and the commutation relation Eq. (6–79) is used, one obtains

$$\mathrm{H}(\mathrm{R}_+ u_0) = (E_0 + \hbar\omega)(\mathrm{R}_+ u_0). \tag{6-86}$$

This procedure can be iterated by operating again and again with R_+, which yields

$$\mathrm{H}(\mathrm{R}_+^n u_0) = (E_0 + n\hbar\omega)(\mathrm{R}_+^n u_0). \tag{6-87}$$

This is an eigenvalue equation giving a set of eigenvalues and eigenfunctions of the operator H defined by

$$u_n = c_n \mathrm{R}_+^n u_0, \qquad E_n = (n + \tfrac{1}{2})\hbar\omega, \tag{6-88}$$

where c_n is chosen so as to normalize the eigenfunction u_n. The operators R_+ and R_- are called *ladder operators*, in that they convert an eigenfunction of the Hamiltonian operator to another eigenfunction corresponding to higher or lower eigenvalues, respectively; they generate a whole sequence of eigenvalues. If Eq. (6–83) is written out explicitly, one obtains

$$\left(\frac{d}{dx} + \frac{k}{\hbar\omega}\, x\right) u_0 = 0. \tag{6-89}$$

This is a simple differential equation having the solution

$$u_0 = \left(\frac{k}{\pi\hbar\omega}\right)^{1/4} \exp\left(-\frac{kx^2}{2\hbar\omega}\right). \tag{6-90}$$

The constant factor has been chosen so as to normalize u_0. It should be noted that this solution is unique. Consequently, there is a unique eigenfunction corresponding to the eigenvalue of Eq. (6–85), and this eigenvalue is nondegenerate. In a similar manner, all the eigenvalues given by Eq. (6–88) are nondegenerate, and the corresponding eigenfunctions are generated uniquely by R_+. If this were not so, one could, by successive applications of R_-, generate an eigenfunction associated with E_0 which would be independent of u_0. This would contradict the above result that u_0 is unique. Also, the set of eigenvalues given by Eq. (6–88) is the totality of eigenvalues, for if there were any other eigenvalue not a member of this set, successive applications of the ladder operator R_- to the corresponding eigenfunction would lead to a lower bound to the set of eigenvalues which would differ from that of Eq. (6–85), which has been shown to be unique.

Note that inasmuch as the operator R_+ is an odd operator that changes its sign upon a reflection of x through the origin, and that inasmuch as the function given by Eq. (6–90) is an even function, the functions of Eq. (6–88) are all either even or odd, depending on whether n is even or odd. Since in Eq. (6–88) the constant c_n has been chosen to normalize the wave functions to unity,

$$\int_{-\infty}^{\infty} |u_n|^2 \, dx = 1. \tag{6–91}$$

By means of Eqs. (6–75), (6–76), and (6–88), a purely algebraic technique can be used to evaluate these coefficients, as follows:

$$\begin{aligned} \int_{-\infty}^{\infty} |u_n|^2 \, dx &= 1 \\ &= \left|\frac{c_n}{c_{n-1}}\right|^2 \int_{-\infty}^{\infty} \overline{u_{n-1}} R_- R_+ u_{n-1} \, dx \\ &= n\hbar\omega \left|\frac{c_n}{c_{n-1}}\right|^2 . \end{aligned} \tag{6–92}$$

Therefore,

$$|c_n|^2 = |c_{n-1}|^2 \frac{1}{n\hbar\omega};$$

$$c_0 = 1, \qquad \therefore \quad c_n = \left(\frac{1}{n!}\right)^{1/2} \left(\frac{1}{\hbar\omega}\right)^{n/2} . \tag{6–93}$$

One can also make use of the techniques of operator algebra to evaluate certain expectation values for the linear harmonic oscillator. For example, to calculate the expectation value of the kinetic energy of the oscillator, we make use of the operator

$$\tfrac{1}{4}(R_+^2 + R_-^2) + \tfrac{1}{2}H = \frac{1}{2m} P_x^2. \tag{6–94}$$

When the wave function is u_n, the expectation value of this operator can be written as

$$\left\langle \frac{1}{2m} p_x^2 \right\rangle_n = \int \overline{u_n} [\tfrac{1}{4}(R_+^2 + R_-^2) + \tfrac{1}{2}H] u_n \, dx. \tag{6–95}$$

This integral is of a type which occurs frequently; it is therefore useful to adopt a simpler notation. Such an integral will be written in the shorthand fashion

$$(u, v) \equiv \int_{-\infty}^{\infty} \overline{u} v \, dx. \tag{6–96}$$

This particular definition is easily generalized to an integral over the total space under consideration, which may be one-dimensional, three-dimensional, or even n-dimensional. If we make use of this notation, the expectation value of the kinetic energy of the linear harmonic oscillator for a state designated by the quantum number n can be written as

$$\left\langle \frac{1}{2m}\, p_x^2 \right\rangle_n = (u_n, [\tfrac{1}{4}(\mathrm{R}_+^2 + \mathrm{R}_-^2) + \tfrac{1}{2}\mathrm{H}]u_n). \tag{6–97}$$

The first term on the right can be evaluated as

$$\left(u_n, \frac{1}{4}\, \mathrm{R}_+^2 u_n\right) = \frac{1}{4}\, \frac{c_n}{c_{n+2}}\, (u_n, u_{n+2}) = 0. \tag{6–98}$$

This expression is zero because of the orthogonality of the wave functions u_n. In similar fashion, the second term can also be shown to be equal to zero; consequently Eq. (6–97) reduces to

$$\left\langle \frac{1}{2m}\, p_x^2 \right\rangle_n = \langle \tfrac{1}{2}\mathrm{H} \rangle_n = \tfrac{1}{2}(n + \tfrac{1}{2})\hbar\omega. \tag{6–99}$$

Thus the average value of the kinetic energy of the linear harmonic oscillator is equal to one-half the total energy of the oscillator when it is in a state of definite energy. This corresponds to the result in classical mechanics that the average kinetic energy of the linear harmonic oscillator (in this case a time average) is equal to one-half the total energy. Equation (6–99) was calculated only for a system that is in some definite energy state. It is desirable to calculate the expectation value of the kinetic energy when the oscillator is in a state which is not a state of definite energy, that is, when it is in a *superposition energy state.* In this case, the expectation value is written as

$$\left\langle \frac{1}{2m}\, p_x^2 \right\rangle = \left(\psi, \frac{1}{2m}\, \mathrm{P}_x^2 \psi\right), \tag{6–100}$$

where

$$\psi = \sum_n a_n \exp\,[-i(n + \tfrac{1}{2})\omega t]u_n. \tag{6–101}$$

These equations give

$$\left\langle \frac{1}{2m}\, p_x^2 \right\rangle = \sum_{n,n'} \overline{a_n} a_{n'} \exp\,[i(n - n')\omega t] \left(u_n, \frac{1}{2m}\, \mathrm{P}_x^2 u_{n'}\right). \tag{6–102}$$

If the average over all time is taken, the oscillatory functions all vanish for $n \neq n'$, giving as the time average of the expectation value of the kinetic energy operator

$$\overline{\left\langle \frac{1}{2m}\, p_x^2 \right\rangle} = \sum_n |a_n|^2 \left(u_n, \frac{1}{2m}\, \mathrm{P}_x^2 u_n\right). \tag{6–103}$$

By making use of Eq. (6–99), this can be written as

$$\overline{\left\langle \frac{1}{2m} p_x^2 \right\rangle} = \frac{1}{2} \sum_n |a_n|^2 (u_n, \mathrm{H} u_n)$$

$$= \tfrac{1}{2}\langle \mathrm{H} \rangle. \tag{6–104}$$

This result is again identical to the classical result that the time average of the kinetic energy is equal to one-half the total energy of the oscillator.

In similar fashion, the expectation value of the momentum of a linear harmonic oscillator for a state of definite energy can be evaluated when use is made of the relation

$$\mathrm{P}_x = \sqrt{\frac{m}{2}}\, (\mathrm{R}_+ + \mathrm{R}_-). \tag{6–105}$$

This leads to

$$\langle p_x \rangle_n = 0 \tag{6–106}$$

for the expectation value.

It must be emphasized that the techniques involved in this section for calculation of wave functions and average values for a linear harmonic oscillator have been essentially algebraic in character, involving the algebra of operators. The only differential equation that it was necessary to solve was Eq. (6–89), which was very simple. All other functions were derived from the solution of this equation by ladder-operator techniques, and the evaluation of the expectation values was also carried out algebraically. This indicates the importance of algebraic techniques in quantum mechanics. Unfortunately, however, there are very few problems which can be solved in such a neat, purely algebraic way.

6–3 Many-particle systems. Up to now, the quantum-mechanical development has dealt only with a system consisting of one particle moving in a field of force of some particular type. It is now necessary to extend this development to systems of more than one particle. The extension is straightforward. For example, for two particles of masses m_1 and m_2, one can write a Hamiltonian operator in the form

$$\mathrm{H} = \frac{1}{2m_1} \mathrm{P}_1^2 + V(r_1) + \frac{1}{2m_2} \mathrm{P}_2^2 + V(r_2) + V_{12}(r_1, r_2). \tag{6–107}$$

The momentum operator $\mathbf{P}_1$ involves derivatives with respect to the cartesian coordinates of particle 1, and the operator $\mathbf{P}_2$ involves derivatives with respect to the cartesian coordinates of particle 2. The Hamiltonian operator clearly has a form that one would expect for the total energy of a system of particles, namely, the sum of (a) the kinetic energies of the two particles, (b) the interaction energies V of the individual particles with an external potential, and (c) the interaction energy V_{12} between the two particles. The operator H, since it involves coordinates r_1 and r_2 of the two particles, must clearly operate on a wave function which is a function of the coordinates of the two particles as well as of the time. Hence the wave function has the form

$$\psi = \psi(r_1, r_2, t). \tag{6–108}$$

Note that this function can hardly be interpreted as a physical wave moving in ordinary three-dimensional space. It has the form of a wave moving in a six-dimensional space. Since this is the analogue of the wave function for a one-particle system, it is clear that the physical wavelike properties which a single-particle wave function exhibits are properties which are to be ascribed to one-particle systems only. In other words, ψ is a physical wave only to the extent that it can be associated with the motion of single particles. On the other hand, the wave function given by Eq. (6–108) is as useful for computational purposes as the function defined earlier for a single-particle system. The wave function, therefore, is not to be interpreted as a physical wave running through space, but rather as a function useful in the calculations of the probabilities needed for evaluating expectation values. The natural extension of the one-particle theory requires that the Schrödinger equation be of the form

$$\mathrm{H}\psi = i\hbar\,\frac{\partial\psi}{\partial t}\cdot \tag{6–109}$$

The normalization condition encountered earlier now takes the form

$$\int |\psi|^2\, dr_1\, dr_2 = 1. \tag{6–110}$$

In a similar manner, the condition that two functions be orthogonal takes the form

$$\int \overline{\psi}_a \psi_b\, dr_1\, dr_2 = 0. \tag{6–111}$$

The justification for extending the one-particle formalism to two particles in the manner outlined rests upon the results of the theory. For example, if the rate of change of the average-position coordinate of the wave packet corresponding to one of the particles is computed as

$$\frac{d}{dt}\langle x_1\rangle = \frac{d}{dt}\int \overline{\psi} x_1 \psi\, dr_1\, dr_2, \tag{6–112}$$

it is easily seen, and will be shown explicitly in Chapter 8, that by making use of Eq. (6–109) and the usual commutation rules, the resulting equation of motion for the center of mass of the wave packet agrees with what one would expect from classical theory, at least insofar as this coordinate is concerned. It can be shown in similar fashion that all expectation values obey equations of motion identical to those of the corresponding classical quantities.

If a system containing two particles is such that they do not interact with each other, then the interaction term $V_{12}(r_1, r_2)$ of Eq. (6–107) is absent, and the Hamiltonian can be written as

$$\mathrm{H} = \mathrm{H}_1 + \mathrm{H}_2. \tag{6–113}$$

Here H_1 and H_2 refer to the Hamiltonians for the two particles taken separately. It should be noted that H_1 and H_2 commute with each other:

$$[\mathrm{H}_1, \mathrm{H}_2] = 0. \tag{6–114}$$

This indicates that wave functions may be chosen to be simultaneously eigenfunctions of the two operators, leading to the result that energy eigenfunctions can be written in the form

$$\psi = u_1(r_1)u_2(r_2). \tag{6–115}$$

From this, the eigenvalue equations are

$$\mathrm{H}_1\psi = E_1\psi, \qquad \mathrm{H}_2\psi = E_2\psi, \qquad \mathrm{H}\psi = (E_1 + E_2)\psi. \tag{6–116}$$

It may be noted from the form of Eq. (6–115) that the expectation value of any quantity involving particle 1 is independent of the state of particle 2, and vice versa: the two particles are completely independent. For this type of system, one has the choice of considering the system as a two-particle system or as two separate one-particle systems; the same results are obtained from either consideration.

The two-particle formalism developed above is easily extended to any number of particles, leading to the Schrödinger equation

$$\mathrm{H}\psi = i\hbar \frac{\partial\psi}{\partial t}, \tag{6–117}$$

where the Hamiltonian operator for an N-particle system is given by

$$\mathrm{H} = \sum_{j=1}^{N} \frac{1}{2m_j} \mathrm{P}_j^2 + V(r_1, r_2, \ldots, r_N). \tag{6–118}$$

The wave function is in general a function in a $3N$-dimensional space and a function of time, as indicated by

$$\psi = \psi(r_1, \ldots, r_N, t). \tag{6–119}$$

6–4 Summary. This chapter has been concerned largely with purely formal questions in order to continue the development of the mathematical tools necessary for the further development of quantum mechanics. Perhaps the most interesting physical result which can be drawn from the formal development is that for any of the Hermitian operators Q that are associated with a particular physical quantity, the eigenfunctions correspond to states for which the corresponding physical quantity has a precisely defined value. Any arbitrary function which is a physically meaningful wave function can be expanded in terms of the eigenfunctions of this particular operator, the expansion being particularly easy because the eigenfunctions are all orthogonal to one another.

The physical meaning of such an expansion for an arbitrary wave function in terms of the eigenfunctions of Q is that when the system is not in a state corresponding to some definite well-defined value of the particular physical quantity q, it is in a *superposition* state of this particular variable in which each eigenfunction in the expansion corresponds to a definite possible state resulting from a measurement of q. The probability of obtaining a given result is proportional to the square of the amplitude of the corresponding wave in the superposition. Superposition states therefore correspond to the states of the system for which a given observable is not precisely defined or "sharp."

The importance of algebraic methods in quantum mechanics was illustrated by treating the case of the linear simple harmonic oscillator. Ladder operators were introduced, and the power of the technique involving their use was shown. Finally, a brief discussion was given of the extension of the quantum-mechanical formalism to systems containing many particles.

Problems

6–1. A bead of mass m slides without friction on a straight wire of length a between two rigid walls. (a) What are the energy levels of this system? (b) Show explicitly that the wave functions corresponding to different energies are orthogonal. (c) Calculate the ratio of the probabilities that various energy states are occupied if a measurement indicates that the bead is exactly at the middle of the wire.

A later measurement shows that the bead is not on the right half of the wire. (d) What is the lowest mean energy $\langle H \rangle$ compatible with this measurement? (e) What is the corresponding wave function? (f) For the system in this state of lowest mean energy, what is the probability of finding the system in its lowest energy state?

6–2. (a) Discuss the physical significance of the eigenvalue equation in the quantum-mechanical formalism. (b) What is the significance of the operator? (c) of the eigenvalue? (d) of the eigenfunction? (e) What is the role of the Schrödinger equation in the formalism? (f) What is the significance of an expectation value?

6–3. Show that the general solution to Schrödinger's equation can be written as

$$\psi(x, t) = \sum_n \left[\int \overline{u_n}(x')\psi(x', 0)\, dx' \right] u_n(x) \exp(-i\omega_n t),$$

where $u_n(x)$ is one of an orthonormal set of energy eigenfunctions, and $\omega_n = E_n/\hbar$.

6–4. Normalized energy eigenfunctions for the one-dimensional simple harmonic oscillator can be obtained from Eqs. (6–88), (6–90), and (6–93). The general solution to the Schrödinger equation for the oscillator is

$$\psi(x, t) = \sum_n a_n u_n(x) \exp\left(-\frac{iE_n t}{\hbar}\right).$$

(a) Calculate for this general wave function the expectation value $\langle x \rangle$, expressing the result as a function of the a_n and the time. (b) What is $\langle x \rangle$ for the special case $a_0 = 1/\sqrt{2}$, $a_1 = 1/\sqrt{2}$, $a_n = 0$ for $n > 1$?

6–5. A particle of mass m is confined to move between two infinite plane parallel walls a distance D apart. (a) What is its energy when it is in its lowest energy state? (b) One of the walls is suddenly moved a distance D away from its former position, making the wall separation $2D$. Assume that the wall motion occurs so suddenly that the particle wave function does not have a chance to change during the motion. What is the probability that the particle retains its original energy? (c) What is the probability that the particle has lost some energy? (d) Has the expectation value of the kinetic energy of the particle changed? (e) Interpret these results in terms of a physical model.

6–6. (a) Write a Hermitian operator for the product of the momentum and displacement of a one-dimensional simple harmonic oscillator. (b) Show that the expectation value (average value) of this quantity is zero for any stationary state of the oscillator.

6–7. (a) Show that the ladder operator R_+ of Eq. (6–74) can be written in the form

$$R_+ = u_0^{-1} \frac{P_x}{\sqrt{2m}} u_0,$$

where u_0 is the energy eigenfunction corresponding to the ground state of the simple harmonic oscillator. (b) In similar terms, what are R_- and R_+^n?

6–8. Show that the relation

$$R_- u_0(x + a) = i\sqrt{\frac{k}{2}}\, a u_0(x + a)$$

holds for the lowest energy state of the simple harmonic oscillator. The operator R_- is given by Eq. (6–74).

6–9. A system consists of two particles of masses M_1 and M_2, moving in an unbounded region of constant potential. Their interaction can be described by means of a potential that is a function only of the distance between the particles. (a) Write the Hamiltonian for the system in terms of $\mathbf{r}_1$ and $\mathbf{r}_2$, the position vectors of the two particles. (b) Introduce new coordinates: $\boldsymbol{R}$, the position vector of the center of mass of the system, and $\mathbf{r}$, the position of particle 2 relative to particle 1. Show that the Schrödinger equation can be separated in these new coordinates. (c) Solve the equation for the motion of the center of mass. (d) What is the physical interpretation of these eigenfunctions?

6–10. Show that regardless of the wave function at $t = 0$, the probability density for a simple harmonic oscillator has a periodic motion, with the period equal to the classical oscillation period.

CHAPTER 7

MEASUREMENT

7–1 The meaning of measurement. The role of measurement in physics is that of obtaining information about a system in order to describe its present condition, and also to enable predictions to be made about the future of the system. In classical mechanics, if at a particular time one knows the position and velocity of all the particles making up the system under consideration and furthermore knows the form of the interaction between the particles, it is possible to describe completely the future behavior of the system. So also in quantum mechanics, we expect a measurement to tell something about the condition of the system so as to permit predictions of the future system behavior. In the case of large-scale systems for which classical mechanics constitutes a valid description, a measurement can, in principle, be made sufficiently sensitive so that the interaction of the measuring equipment with the system being measured is negligible: one observes the system without sensibly disturbing it. On the other hand, for small-scale systems, it is usually impossible, *in principle*, at least insofar as our present knowledge extends, to make measurements which do not at the same time disturb the system in a generally unpredictable way. It would seem reasonable to expect that a measurement on a system should be such as to tell something about the present and future state of the system, but not necessarily anything about the past. If we remember that a system is disturbed by a measurement, we can infer the state of a system prior to a certain measurement from the state after the measurement only when the effect of the measurement is completely describable from the result of the measurement. However, the disturbance to a system which results from a measurement is generally not predictable.

This point will be clarified with an example: if the momentum of a particle is measured, the result of the measurement does not necessarily allow an inference to be drawn concerning the momentum prior to the measurement. On the other hand, if the interaction is to be called a measurement, it should say something about the system after the measurement. An immediate repetition of the momentum measurement should give the same value.

The formalism developed earlier satisfies these general conditions. Consider a system described by a wave function which is a superposition of eigenfunctions of the operator Q:

$$\psi = \sum_j c_j\psi_j, \qquad \mathrm{Q}\psi_j = q_j\psi_j. \tag{7–1}$$

For such a system, the observable q is undefined, or uncertain; a measurement of q can yield any of the values q_j for which $|c_j|^2 \neq 0$. If now a measurement of q is made, the measurement will yield a specific one of the possible q's, say q_n. If we assume that this eigenvalue is nondegenerate, it is clear that after the measurement the wave function must be ψ_n, or differ from it by at most a multiplicative constant. It is readily seen, therefore, that the measurement has indeed disturbed the state of the system in a significant way, changing the wave function from ψ to ψ_n. However, the measurement is in principle immediately repeatable, with the certain result that q_n will again be obtained, for now in the expansion of Eq. (7–1) all c_j's are zero, except that $|c_n| = 1$. The condition that the measurement be repeated immediately is usually necessary because in general Q does not commute with the Hamiltonian and hence ψ will deviate from ψ_n as time goes on.

It has been seen earlier that although two different measurements are in general incompatible, certain measurements are compatible; that is, they can be made simultaneously with each other. Compatibility clearly results when the wave function is simultaneously an eigenfunction of two operators. As shown earlier, this occurs only when the two operators commute.

7–2 Photon polarization. It is difficult to discuss the physical problems associated with the notion of measurement in quantum mechanics in relation to the types of measurements described earlier. This is because of the large number of possible results which such measurements can give. For this reason, a simpler type of measurement will be used to discuss the types of physical questions which can arise in connection with the measurement of a physical quantity. Consider a photon and problems related to the measurement of its polarization. In particular, consider two kinds of polarization measurements which can be made on a photon. A photon's "plane polarization" can be measured to determine whether it is plane-polarized vertically or horizontally. This type of measurement will be called a measurement of Q; the device used to make this measurement is illustrated schematically in Fig. 7–1.

In this figure, imagine the box as containing a double-refracting crystal, such as calcite. The photon enters the box from the left and leaves the box in either of two possible light paths, designated as q_1 and q_2, which refer respectively to vertical or horizontal plane polarization. In a similar way, it is possible to determine whether the photon is circularly polarized clockwise or counterclockwise. The device used to make this measurement, which will be designated P, is represented in Fig. 7–2. This can likewise be thought of as a box containing a crystal and, in addition, two quarter-wave plates placed before and after the crystal and so oriented that

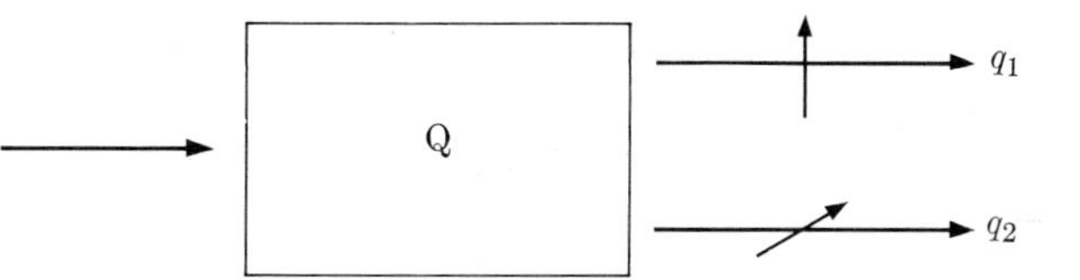

FIG. 7-1. Schematic representation of an apparatus that measures whether a photon is plane polarized vertically or horizontally. The path taken by the photon leaving the apparatus Q depends on its plane-polarization state.

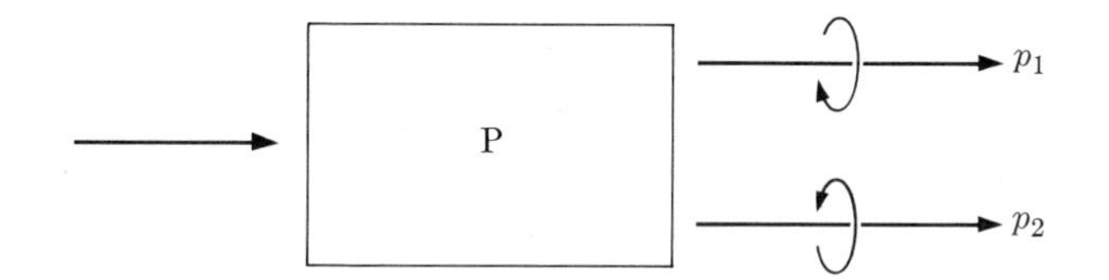

FIG. 7-2. Schematic representation of an apparatus that measures whether a photon is circularly polarized clockwise or counterclockwise. The path taken by the photon leaving the apparatus P depends on its circular-polarization state.

photons leaving in the upper path are circularly polarized as shown and photons leaving in the lower path are circularly polarized in the opposite sense as shown. These two paths are designated p_1 and p_2, respectively.

Note that the measurements Q and P resemble in certain ways the measurements of momentum and position of a particle. These two measurements are incompatible, and are in a sense complementary measurements. It would be very strange indeed if one could say that a photon was plane-polarized in the vertical direction and simultaneously circularly polarized to the right. However, one does not in the same way consider as strange the possibility that an electron is simultaneously in a state of definite momentum and definite position. The difference in apparent "strangeness" can be attributed to a carry-over of classical concepts based on everyday observations.

The measurements of types Q and P satisfy the requirement of being repeatable. As illustrated in Fig. 7-3, if a photon entering the device Q leaves in channel q_1, and is then allowed to pass through another measuring device of this same type, it will again leave in channel q_1. A similar result would be obtained in the case of the measurement P.

That a measurement of this type constitutes not only a determination of the polarization of the particle but also an interaction with the particle in such a way as to affect the polarization can be seen by referring to Fig. 7-4. In this figure, a photon enters from the left. It may be in a state of definite polarization or not, but the polarization is determined by the measurement as being q_1 (the photon leaves the box Q in this channel). In this case, the measurement of Q is followed by a determination of P.

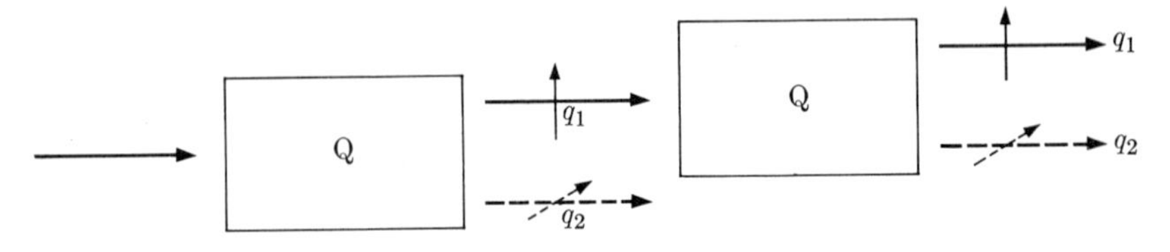

FIG. 7–3. Schematic representation of a repeated measurement Q of the plane-polarization state of a photon.

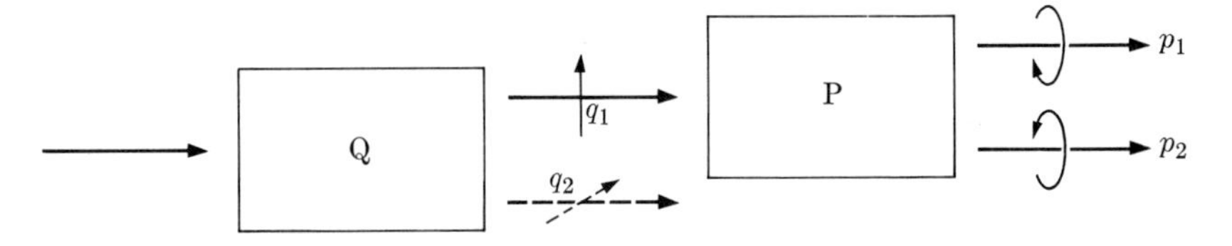

FIG. 7–4. Schematic representation of a measurement P of the circular-polarization state of a photon after a measurement Q has been made of its plane-polarization state.

It is found after making a large number of measurements of this type on similar photons that one cannot predict from which of the two channels of P the photon will emerge. The photon is equally likely to appear in channel p_1 or in p_2. The photon, of course, is never found simultaneously in both channels: one either finds a whole photon or no photon in p_1, and if it is not in p_1, it is certainly found in p_2. In other words, the polarization P is completely unpredictable if a prior measurement of Q has been made. This is quite similar to the problem of the measurement of the momentum of an electron after a measurement of its position has been made.

Now, having determined the polarization P for a particular photon to be p_2, the polarization measurement Q is made again. This time, we find that the photon is equally likely to be discovered in either channel q_1 or q_2. In other words, the measurement of the polarization P that was made as an intermediate step destroyed completely any information that we had about the polarization Q. This also is analogous to the case of momentum and position of a particle. A particle's position can be determined accurately, but if its momentum is then measured, a subsequent measurement of its position is not likely to give the same result as the first position measurement.

The equipment represented in Figs. 7–1 and 7–2 has been described in terms of devices which measure the polarization of a photon. Strictly speaking, this is not quite accurate. There is another element required in order to determine the polarization of a photon. To illustrate what this is, consider Fig. 7–5. The apparatus illustrated here contains another

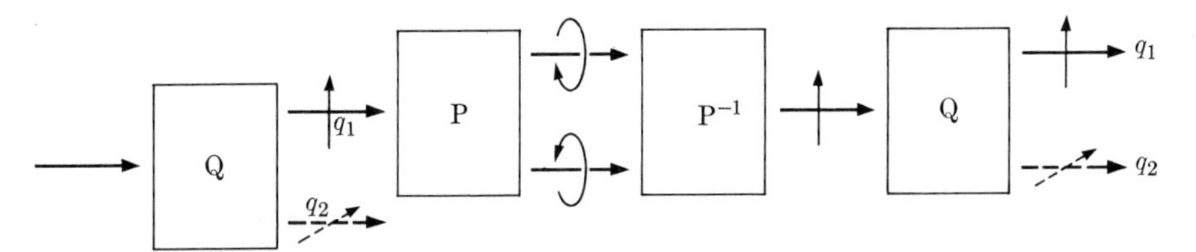

FIG. 7-5. Schematic representation of the effect of apparatus P followed by an inverse apparatus P^{-1} when the apparatuses P and P^{-1} are inserted between two measurements Q of the plane-polarization state of a photon.

element not previously encountered; call this element P^{-1}. This particular element might be thought of as just another box like P but operated in the inverse direction and having a property that P taken in combination with P^{-1} does not affect the polarization of the light at all. It is obvious to anyone with experience in optical matters how the polarization box P can be combined with another similar box to make a device which does not affect the polarization of the light. Consequently, this combination of P and P^{-1} is such that it merely transmits the light, independently of its polarization. In Fig. 7-5 the first box Q can be thought of as measuring the polarization to be in q_1, while the two boxes following, P and P^{-1}, merely transmit the photon to the second box Q with the same polarization, so that the result q_1 is obtained again. Stating it another way, although in Fig. 7-4 the polarization measurement P completely destroyed the previous polarization Q, making it impossible to predict the result of the outcome of a subsequent measurement Q, in Fig. 7-5 the disturbance of the polarization which was effected by the box P is seen to be revocable: if the box P is combined with another box of the right type, the combination can be such as to leave the polarization Q unaffected. However, it should be noted that in this particular case, the first box P in Fig. 7-5 did not really measure the polarization of the photon: no determination was made of the channel (p_1 or p_2) which the photon followed in leaving the box P. It is impossible to predict in which of the two possible paths the photon leaves the box P. In fact, it can be shown that if the photon is determined by some interaction with a photon counter to be, for example, in path p_1, the photon is so disturbed by this interaction that it is no longer true that the final measurement Q is certain to lead to the result q_1: the final measurement Q leads in this case to the results q_1 and q_2 with equal probability.

From this series of experiments, it is seen that more is involved in the measurement of the polarization illustrated in Fig. 7-1 than simply the splitting of the light beam into two paths q_1 and q_2. For a given photon, a determination must be made of the path of the photon before a measurement can be said to have been made. If this determination is

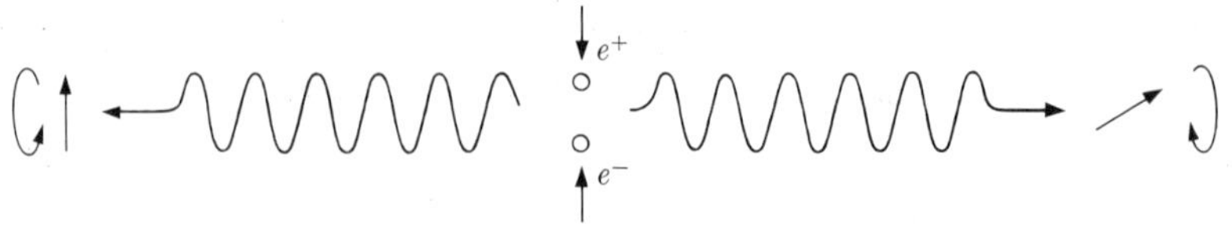

FIG. 7–6. The annihilation of a positron-electron pair in a state of zero angular momentum into two oppositely directed and oppositely polarized gamma rays (high-energy photons).

omitted, then the resulting disturbance to the polarization may be undone. Consequently, one must say that the polarization measurement Q is made only if there is a detector in each of the two paths q_1 and q_2 to indicate the polarization Q of the photon.

A number of paradoxical features are connected with the examples given above. Still another paradox connected with measurement will now be considered, which is in many ways the most difficult of all to reconcile with our usual picture of the physical world. Consider the two photons resulting from the annihilation of an electron and a positron, as shown in Fig. 7–6. In this particular example, the electron and the positron are assumed to be annihilated in a state for which the total angular momentum of the system is zero. Consequently, when the two photons leave the point of annihilation traveling in opposite directions, they must carry away zero total angular momentum: there can be no net angular momentum about an axis in the direction of progagation of the two photons. A photon in a state of circular polarization carries angular momentum. Consequently, if one of the photons is circularly polarized to the left, the other must be circularly polarized to the right in order that the total angular momentum about this axis be zero. We can then say that a circular-polarization measurement made on one of the photons enables us to predict the result of a subsequent circular-polarization measurement made on the other photon. On the other hand, it is known from both theory and experiment that if one of the photons is determined to be plane-polarized, say in a vertical direction, then the other photon is plane-polarized in a horizontal direction. This is rather remarkable, in that a plane-polarization measurement made on one photon enables us to predict that the other photon is plane-polarized and, further, to determine the direction of its polarization. On the other hand, a measurement of the circular polarization of the first photon enables us to predict that the other photon is circularly polarized and what the direction of its circular polarization is.

As the polarization measurement on the first photon is made long after the photons were created, it is very difficult to see how this measurement can be thought of as affecting the polarization of the other photon. The other obvious alternative is, however, equally disturbing: to assume that the photon is both circularly and plane-polarized simultaneously does violence with our usual notions of polarization. It is clear that a situation is encountered here which is inexplicable in terms of a classical model. With any classical model, a description of the system is complete when the polarizations of the photons are each separately described. It is found instead that the photons are correlated in their behavior. If one photon is "forced" into a state of circular polarization, the other must follow. The two photons constitute a *single* dynamical system. Any information obtained about the system is information about both photons. Any interaction on a single photon is an interaction on the system and affects the state of the whole system. The above paradox is very similar to one first discussed by Einstein, Podolsky, and Rosen*, but the paradoxical behavior is made to take a particularly acute form in the above example.

7-3 Summary. A brief discussion has been given of the measurement process, from which it has been seen that any measurement on a physical system has a dual function. First and foremost, a measurement disturbs the system and throws it into a state such that an immediate repetition of the measurement results in no additional disturbance to the system. Second, a measurement gives information to the observer about the resulting state of the system. This information is in the form of a number which represents the value of the quantity measured but which also characterizes the state. The measurement of the polarization of a photon was used as an example to clarify the physical concepts, and it was seen that an irreversible interaction between measuring apparatus and system must occur before a true measurement is made. The polarization of the two photons resulting from positron annihilation was discussed as a final example of the paradoxical behavior that can arise in certain measurements.

---

* A. Einstein, B. Podolsky, and N. Rosen, "Can Quantum-Mechanical Description of Physical Reality Be Considered Complete?" *Phys. Rev.* **47,** 777 (1935).

CHAPTER 8

THE CORRESPONDENCE PRINCIPLE

8–1 The relation of quantum mechanics to classical mechanics. In classical mechanics, the position and momentum of a particle are determined exactly and the equations of motion determine the future values of the position and momentum as functions of the time. In quantum mechanics, it has been seen that it is impossible with any known physical measurement to determine simultaneously both the position and momentum of a particle with arbitrary accuracy. This raises an important point concerning the relationship between classical and quantum mechanics. The wide range of physical phenomena with which classical theory is able to cope indicates that to be a valid physical theory, quantum mechanics must somehow lead to the same predictions as classical mechanics for large-scale "classical" systems. This required correspondence of quantum with classical mechanics in the realm of large objects is so important, in fact, that it has been given a name: the *correspondence principle.**

A clue to the necessary state of a particle for it to be "classical" is given by an examination of the postulates of Chapter 6; in particular, Postulate 7. Such an examination shows that an aspect of quantum theory of the utmost importance is that there are incompatible measurements, expressed by the noncommutativity of the operators associated with certain physical observables. Postulate 7 shows that a quantitative measure of this difference is given by the constant $\hbar$. As seen earlier, this is very small (1.054×10^{-27} erg-sec). A system can be considered "classical," therefore, when the parameters describing it and having the same dimension of action are on a scale large compared with $\hbar$. It is usually only on the submicroscopic level that quantum theory is really required. Exceptions will be noted.

8–2 The transition from quantum mechanics to classical mechanics. The above discussion has indicated under what conditions one might expect classical ideas to hold and when one would expect to need quantum concepts. It was not shown, however, how quantum theory with its strange discontinuities and paradoxical aspects can be applied to macro-

* N. Bohr, "The Quantum Postulate and the Recent Development of Atomic Theory," *Nature* **121,** 580 (1928).

scopic physics to yield a description equivalent to that of classical mechanics. How this merging of concepts can occur will be considered in this section.

It has been seen that it is impossible to determine simultaneously both the position and momentum of a particle with arbitrary accuracy. However, both can be determined simultaneously with limited accuracy. The quantum formulation of just how limited the accuracy must be is discussed later in this chapter. If the position and momentum of a particle are determined with limited accuracy, the resulting wave function is in the form of a wave packet in which the particle is localized to some extent in a certain region. The momentum of the particle is likewise localized within a certain range in momentum space. For quantum mechanics to yield results which are valid in a classical limit, it is necessary for the motion of such a wave packet to be describable in terms of classical equations of motion.

To see how this comes about, one must choose quantities which are analogous to the classically determined position and momentum of the particle. As seen earlier, the expectation values of the position and momentum of the particle associated with the wave packet are a reasonable choice. The position-expectation value is in fact the centroid of the wave packet. Consequently the position, momentum, angular momentum, etc., of the wave packet will be defined to be the corresponding expectation values.

Making use of Postulate 5 of Chapter 6 for the mean value of the position coordinate x of the particle, one obtains for the rate of change for this variable the expression

$$\begin{aligned}\frac{d}{dt}\langle x\rangle &= \frac{d}{dt}\int \bar{\psi}x\psi\,dr\\ &= \int\left[\frac{\partial\bar{\psi}}{\partial t}\,x\psi + \bar{\psi}x\,\frac{\partial\psi}{\partial t}\right]dr. \qquad (8\text{–}1)\end{aligned}$$

This can be taken as representing the velocity of the wave packet.

It is necessary to be careful about the meaning of an equation such as Eq. (8–1). The expectation value $\langle x\rangle$ represents an ensemble average of the results of a *single* measurement of x on each member of the ensemble. The derivative, Eq. (8–1), is the time rate of change of this average. This is physically not the same thing as $\langle p_x/m\rangle$, which is the ensemble average of the results of momentum measurements (divided by the particle mass). It is also not the same as the ensemble average of velocity measurements. In nonrelativistic quantum mechanics, operators for velocity measurements do not occur. To measure the velocity of a particle exactly, its position must be determined and another exact position measurement made at a later time. The first position measurement makes the momentum indeterminate, making a velocity determination based on two successive position measurements meaningless.

The expectation value $\langle dQ/dt \rangle$ is zero unless the operator Q is an explicit function of time. Therefore, usually,

$$\frac{d}{dt}\langle Q\rangle \neq \left\langle \frac{dQ}{dt} \right\rangle. \tag{8–2}$$

In Eq. (8–1), it is assumed that the operator x is not an explicit function of t.

Substituting the Schrödinger equation

$$H\psi = i\hbar \frac{\partial \psi}{\partial t} \tag{8–3}$$

and its complex conjugate into Eq. (8–1) yields

$$\frac{d}{dt}\langle x\rangle = \frac{i}{\hbar}\langle [H, x]\rangle. \tag{8–4}$$

The right side of this equation is $i/\hbar$ times the expectation value of the commutator of H and x.

To put this in a more suitable form for comparison with classical equations, a few commutators must be computed. The commutator of the operators corresponding to the x-component of the momentum and the position coordinates is

$$[P_x, x] = -i\hbar. \tag{8–5}$$

This can be seen from Eq. (5–59) and Postulate 7 of Chapter 6. Also,

$$[P_x, y] = 0. \tag{8–6}$$

From Eq. (8–5),

$$P_x^2 x - P_x x P_x = -i\hbar P_x, \tag{8–7}$$

and

$$P_x x P_x - x P_x^2 = -i\hbar P_x. \tag{8–8}$$

The sum of the last two equations is

$$P_x^2 x - x P_x^2 = [P_x^2, x] = -2i\hbar P_x. \tag{8–9}$$

This is easily generalized to

$$[P_x^n, x] = -ni\hbar P_x^{n-1}. \tag{8–10}$$

This result can also be obtained directly by evaluating the Poisson bracket and using Postulate 7, Chapter 6. For a system whose Hamiltonian is given by

$$\mathrm{H} = \frac{1}{2m}\,\mathrm{P}^2 + V(r), \tag{8–11}$$

by making use of Eqs. (8–4), (8–6), and (8–9), one easily obtains an equation giving the velocity of the wave packet in terms of its momentum:

$$\frac{d}{dt}\,\langle x\rangle = \frac{1}{m}\,\langle p_x\rangle. \tag{8–12}$$

In similar fashion, we can obtain the rate of change of the momentum of the wave packet in terms of the average force acting on the wave packet:

$$\frac{d}{dt}\,\langle p_x\rangle = -\left\langle\frac{\partial V}{\partial x}\right\rangle. \tag{8–13}$$

This is the quantum-mechanical equivalent of Newton's second law of motion, relating the rate of change of the momentum of the wave packet to the average force acting on a particle associated with the wave packet.

The arguments leading to Eqs. (8–12) and (8–13) are easily generalized to give the rate of change with respect to time of the mean value of any physical quantity associated with particles in the wave packet. Let the operator Q correspond to a general physical observable. The expression for the time rate of change of the expectation value of Q for the particles in the wave packet is given by

$$\frac{d}{dt}\,\langle \mathrm{Q}\rangle = \frac{i}{\hbar}\,\langle[\mathrm{H},\mathrm{Q}]\rangle + \left\langle\frac{\partial \mathrm{Q}}{\partial t}\right\rangle. \tag{8–14}$$

This expression, of course, has a very close relationship to the classical expression for the dynamical equations using Poisson brackets. A comparison of the above equation with Eq. (5–55) shows an exact correspondence if the classical observable is replaced by the quantum expectation value and if the Poisson bracket of Eq. (5–55) is replaced with $-i/\hbar$ times the corresponding quantum commutator bracket. This is in conformity with Postulate 7 of Chapter 6. It is an illustration of the close formal connection between the classical and quantum formulations of mechanics mentioned in Chapter 6 in connection with this postulate. In fact, the requirements of the correspondence principle must be met if a valid theory is to be produced.

As a trivial example of the application of Eq. (8–14), it may be noted that the rate of change of the expectation value of the energy of particles in the wave packet is equal to zero for conservative forces for which $\partial H/\partial t = 0$:

$$\frac{d}{dt}\langle H\rangle = 0. \tag{8-15}$$

This is the form which the conservation of energy takes in the classical limit in which quantum mechanics is applied to a wave packet representing a classically described particle.

A more physical picture of the way in which a quantum wave packet can behave like a classical particle can be obtained by considering the one-dimensional simple harmonic oscillator. It was seen in the earlier discussion of the one-dimensional oscillator that the quantum description of the motion of the particle can be very different from that obtained in classical mechanics. (See Chapter 3.) For a state of definite energy, the probability of finding a particle at a given point is independent of the time. Classically, however, the particle of the simple harmonic oscillator oscillates in such a way that the probability that a particle will be in a small volume element at a particular point is quite different from one instant to another. In fact, it is either zero or unity. In the same manner, classically, the momentum of a simple harmonic oscillator is continually changing in time. The description of the momentum according to the quantum-mechanical formalism is such that for a state of definite energy there is a distribution in momenta corresponding to the

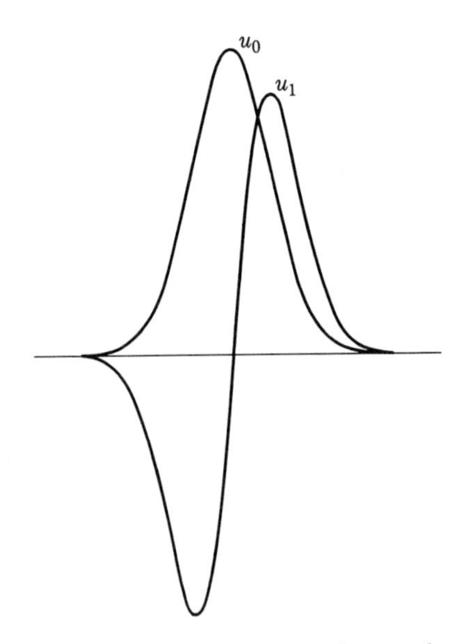

FIG. 8–1. The wave functions u_0 and u_1 for the two lowest energy states of the simple harmonic oscillator.

various plane waves in which the wave function of the oscillator can be expanded. Each plane wave corresponds to a definite state of momentum, the stationary character of the state implying that the probability that a certain momentum will be obtained is constant. The question then arises, how can the classical formalism be said to be equivalent to, or a special case of, the quantum-mechanical formalism?

The connection between the classical and quantum descriptions appears, as has been seen, if one considers the motion of a wave packet. For the case of the simple harmonic oscillator, consider a solution to the Schrödinger equation which is not a state of definite energy but is a superposition of several energy states. The simplest of all examples to consider is the superposition of only two energy states, which we shall take as the state of lowest energy and the first excited-energy state. These wave functions are plotted in Fig. 8–1. The space dependencies of the wave functions are multiplied by their proper time dependencies and combined to give the wave function for the superposition energy state in question:

$$\psi = \frac{1}{\sqrt{2}}\left[\exp\left(-i\,\frac{E_0}{\hbar}\,t\right)u_0 + \exp\left(-i\,\frac{E_1}{\hbar}\,t\right)u_1\right]. \tag{8–16}$$

The absolute square of this wave function is plotted in Fig. 8–2 for several different times.

It can be seen from the figure that this wave function has very much the form of a particle oscillating with simple harmonic motion. Note particularly that the frequency of oscillation is just the simple harmonic

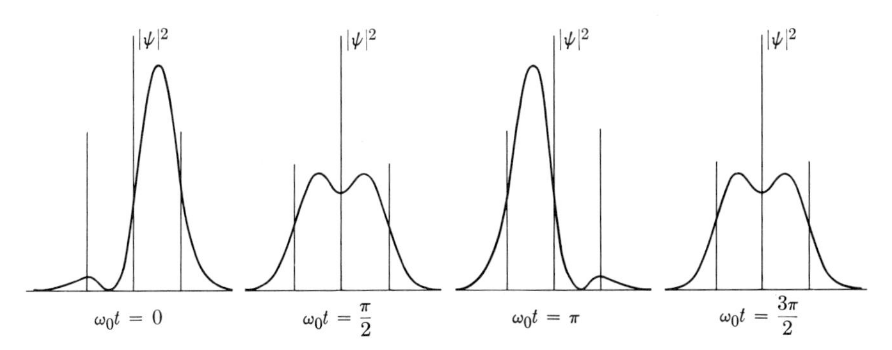

FIG. 8–2. The superposition wave function (Eq. 8–16), composed of equal-amplitude components of the two functions of Fig. 8–1. The wave function is shown for four times, corresponding to equal increments in the relative phases. Note that a strong resemblance to the classical oscillatory behavior of a simple harmonic oscillator is evidenced in even this simple superposition state. The classical limits of the motion are indicated by vertical lines, assuming an energy $E = \langle \mathrm{H} \rangle = \hbar\omega$.

oscillator frequency observed in the case of the corresponding classical oscillation. It therefore appears reasonable that if we were to superpose a large number of energy states, we could more and more closely represent a gaussian wave packet which would oscillate in very much the same way that a classical particle moves. From this point of view, the classical description of the motion of a particle is one for which both the position and momentum of the particle are specified to a certain accuracy, but not to arbitrary accuracy. The state of the system is described by a wave packet whose position more or less accurately specifies the position of the particle and follows classical laws. It is important that the energy not be completely specified, for if the system is in a state of definite energy the wave function cannot describe an oscillatory motion.

The correspondence between the classical and quantum-mechanical descriptions of the simple harmonic oscillator can be seen from yet another point of view. Consider classically the case in which the energy of the oscillator is definite but in which there is no knowledge of the position or momentum of the particle. This means that the classical description is incomplete, for the initial conditions on position and (direction of) momentum are unknown. One can still ask questions about the classically expected behavior of the oscillator, however, and in particular about the "probability density" for finding the particle at any point of its classical path. In classical theory, the probability of finding a particle at a particular point in its path is inversely proportional to its velocity at that point, becoming infinite at the turning points of the motion, where the velocity is zero.

The classical probability density for the oscillator is given by

$$P(x)\,dx = \frac{1}{\pi}\frac{dx}{[(2E/k) - x^2]^{1/2}}, \tag{8-17}$$

where E is the energy of the oscillation, and k is the spring constant. This distribution is shown plotted in Figs. 8-3 and 8-4 along with the corresponding quantum probability densities for two cases, low ($n = 2$) and higher ($n = 10$) quantum numbers. The horizontal scales have been adjusted to give equal classical limits of excursion for the particle. Although the probability distribution for the case $n = 2$ is very different from the classical case, for $n = 10$ the distribution looks, apart from the quantum oscillatory aspect, very much like the classical case. It should be remembered that the higher quantum number case, $n = 10$, still corresponds to an almost infinitesimal motion, for if the classical frequency is one cycle per second, the energy is only about 7×10^{-26} erg. For truly macroscopic motions, the spacing of the quantum nodes of the probability distribution becomes too small to be detected in a practical

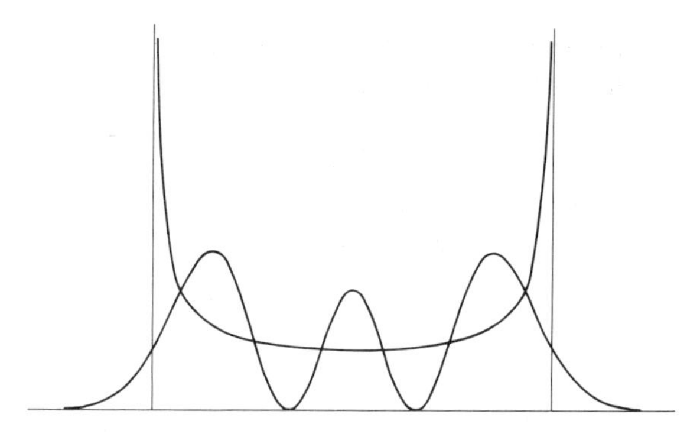

FIG. 8-3. The classical and quantum-mechanical probability distributions for a low-energy ($E = \frac{5}{2}\hbar\omega_0$) simple harmonic oscillator.

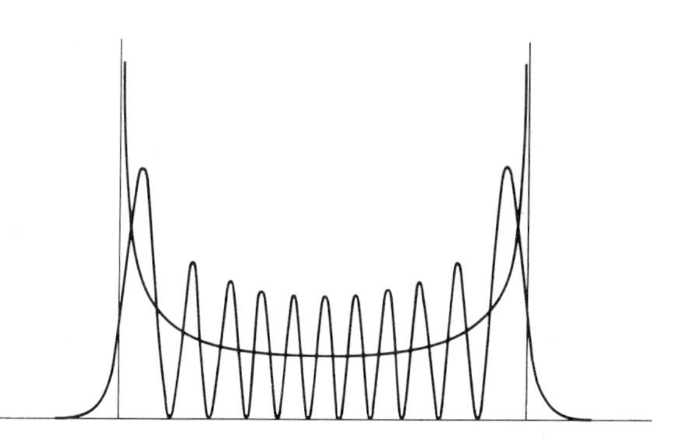

FIG. 8-4. The classical and quantum-mechanical probability distribution for a somewhat more energetic ($E = \frac{21}{2}\hbar\omega_0$) simple harmonic oscillator than that shown in Fig. 8-3.

position measurement, and only the average distribution over a small region of x is of significance. For macroscopic motions, however, such an average is indistinguishable from the classical distribution.

8-3 The correspondence principle and the uncertainty relation. It has been seen that a basic difference between classical and quantum mechanics is that in quantum theory complementary observables cannot be simultaneously measured to arbitrary accuracy. The discussion of Chapter 2 showed that the product of the uncertainties in the measurements of a pair of such variables is of the order of Planck's constant, a small number by macroscopic standards. The previous rather qualitative considerations will now be expressed in more quantitative terms.

The "uncertainty" in the position of a particle must be given some exact meaning: the square of the uncertainty of a particular quantity will be defined to be the mean square deviation from the mean. The deviation from the mean is given by

$$\Delta x \equiv x - \langle x \rangle. \tag{8–18}$$

Consequently, the expectation value of the square of the deviation, or the mean square deviation, is given by

$$\langle \Delta x^2 \rangle = \int \bar{\psi} (\Delta x)^2 \psi \, dx = \int |\Delta x \psi|^2 \, dx. \tag{8–19}$$

With a similar definition for the square of the uncertainty in the momentum, the product Π of the squares of the uncertainties is given by

$$\Pi \equiv \langle \Delta x^2 \rangle \langle \Delta p_x^2 \rangle. \tag{8–20}$$

In the following development, use is made of the well-known *Schwartz inequality*. This can be written as

$$\int |f|^2 \, dx \cdot \int |g|^2 \, dx \geq \left| \int \bar{f} g \, dx \right|^2 \cdot \tag{8–21}$$

When the Schwartz inequality is applied to the product of the two uncertainties of Eq. (8–20), we obtain

$$\langle \Delta x^2 \rangle \langle \Delta p_x^2 \rangle \geq \left| \int \bar{\psi} \, \Delta x \, \Delta \mathrm{P}_x \psi \, dx \right|^2 = |\langle \Delta x \, \Delta p_x \rangle|^2. \tag{8–22}$$

The operator appearing in the integral on the right of this equation can be expressed in the form

$$\begin{aligned} \Delta x \, \Delta \mathrm{P}_x &= \tfrac{1}{2}[\Delta x, \Delta \mathrm{P}_x] + \tfrac{1}{2}(\Delta x \, \Delta \mathrm{P}_x + \Delta \mathrm{P}_x \, \Delta x) \\ &= \frac{i\hbar}{2} + \tfrac{1}{2}(\Delta x \, \Delta \mathrm{P}_x + \Delta \mathrm{P}_x \, \Delta x). \end{aligned} \tag{8–23}$$

Consequently, the right side of Eq. (8–22) can be written as

$$|\langle \Delta x \, \Delta p_x \rangle|^2 = \frac{\hbar^2}{4} + \tfrac{1}{4} \langle \Delta x \, \Delta p_x + \Delta p_x \, \Delta x \rangle^2. \tag{8–24}$$

This follows because the two terms on the right of Eq. (8–23) have expectation values which are purely imaginary and real, respectively. (The second term is a Hermitian operator with real eigenvalues, and consequently has an expectation value which is real.)

The second term on the right of Eq. (8–24) must be positive and, as shown below, may be zero, leading to the inequality

$$\langle \Delta x^2 \rangle \langle \Delta p_x^2 \rangle \geq \frac{\hbar^2}{4} \cdot \tag{8–25}$$

This represents an exact statement of the uncertainty principle, namely, that the product of the mean square deviation of a coordinate x and the mean square deviation of the conjugate momentum is greater than or equal to $(\hbar/2)^2$.

8–4 The minimum-uncertainty wave function. It is interesting to determine the conditions for which the inequality in Eq. (8–25) becomes an equality. There are two conditions that must be simultaneously imposed: first, that the Schwartz inequality of Eq. (8–22) be an equality, and second, that the second term on the right of Eq. (8–24) vanish. The condition that the Schwartz inequality become an equality is given by

$$f = \alpha g, \tag{8–26}$$

with α being any complex number. As applied to Eq. (8–22), this condition becomes

$$\Delta x \psi = \alpha \, \Delta P_x \psi. \tag{8–27}$$

The condition that the second term on the right side of Eq. (8–24) vanish can be written as

$$\int \bar{\psi}(\Delta x \, \Delta P_x + \Delta P_x \, \Delta x)\psi \, dx = 0. \tag{8–28}$$

Combining these leads to

$$(\bar{\alpha} + \alpha) \int \bar{\psi}(\Delta P_x)^2 \psi \, dx = 0. \tag{8–29}$$

Because the integral in this last expression must be positive-definite (greater than zero), α must be purely imaginary. With this condition,

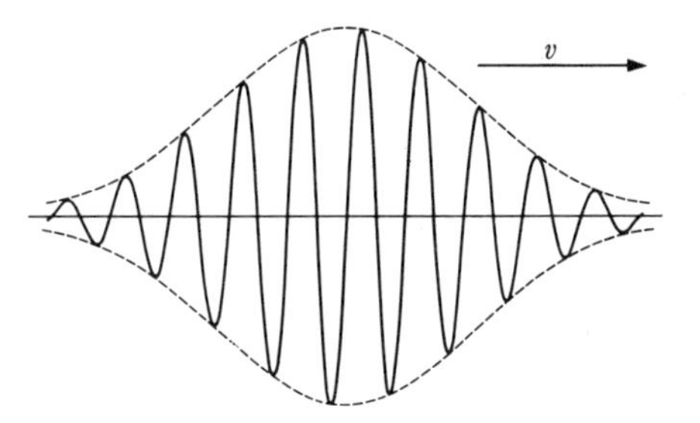

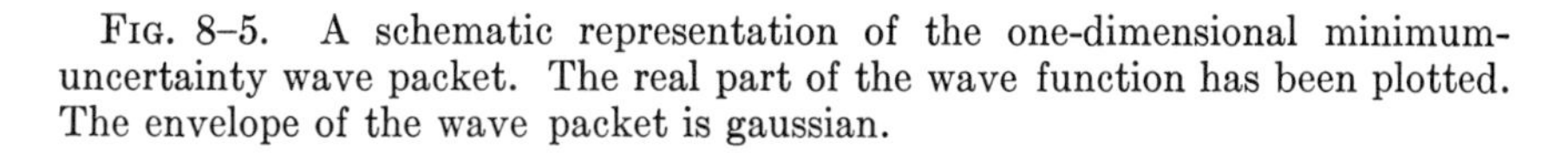

FIG. 8–5. A schematic representation of the one-dimensional minimum-uncertainty wave packet. The real part of the wave function has been plotted. The envelope of the wave packet is gaussian.

Eq. (8–27) can be integrated to give the normalized result

$$\psi(x) = \left[\frac{1}{2\pi\langle\Delta x^2\rangle}\right]^{1/2} \exp\left[-\frac{(x - \langle x\rangle)^2}{4\langle\Delta x^2\rangle} + \frac{i\langle p_x\rangle x}{\hbar}\right]. \tag{8–30}$$

The wave function for which a minimum exists in the product of the uncertainty of position and momentum is a gaussian wave packet. That is, the envelope of the wave packet, the function which multiplies a purely periodic plane wave, is the gaussian function. This is illustrated schematically in Fig. 8–5.

8–5 The uncertainty principle and the simple harmonic oscillator. The above results will now be applied to the case of the one-dimensional simple harmonic oscillator and in particular to its ground state. It has been seen that the lowest energy state of the linear harmonic oscillator has an energy of $\frac{1}{2}\hbar\omega$. In view of the uncertainty principle, this nonzero lowest energy is a result which should be expected. If the simple harmonic oscillator were to have an energy of zero, its potential and kinetic energies would have to be separately zero, since both of these energies are positive. But the case in which the potential energy is equal to zero would correspond to knowing definitely that the position of the particle is at the equilibrium point. This would correspond to knowing the position with arbitrary accuracy and would imply that the momentum is completely uncertain. But this complete uncertainty in the momentum would imply that the mean value of the kinetic energy would be infinite. On the other hand, for the kinetic energy to be zero, the potential energy would need to be infinite. Consequently, from just the uncertainty principle it is clear that the lowest energy of the simple harmonic oscillator must be nonzero. In fact, simply by using the uncertainty principle together with other reasonable arguments, one can calculate the ground-state energy of the oscillator. This will now be done.

It was shown in Chapter 6 that for a simple harmonic oscillator the average value of the potential energy is equal to the average value of the kinetic energy. Writing this out explicitly, we have

$$\overline{\langle \tfrac{1}{2}kx^2\rangle} = \overline{\left\langle\frac{1}{2m}\, p_x^2\right\rangle} = \frac{E_0}{2}. \tag{8–31}$$

On the other hand, the uncertainty principle is

$$\langle(\Delta x)^2\rangle\langle(\Delta p_x)^2\rangle \geq \frac{\hbar^2}{4}. \tag{8–32}$$

In the case of the simple harmonic oscillator, it is clear that the mean

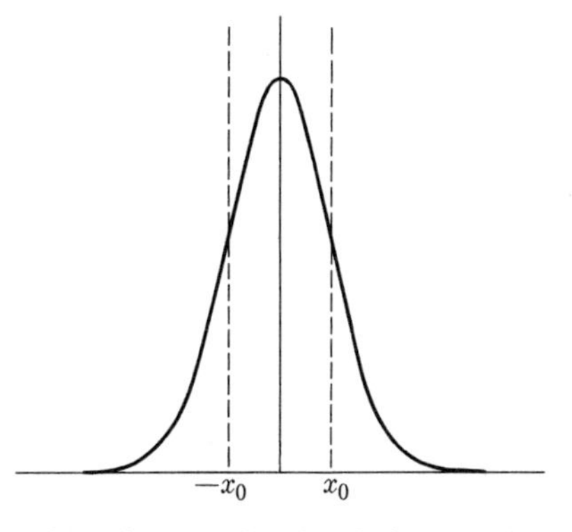

FIG. 8-6. The wave function for the simple harmonic oscillator in its ground state. The classical limits of the motion are indicated by the broken vertical lines at $\pm x_0$.

values for x and p_x are both zero, and consequently,

$$\overline{\langle x^2 \rangle} = \langle (\Delta x)^2 \rangle, \qquad \overline{\langle p_x^2 \rangle} = \langle (\Delta p_x)^2 \rangle. \tag{8-33}$$

Combining these equations, we obtain

$$\sqrt{\frac{1}{2m}\,\overline{\langle p_x^2 \rangle}\,\frac{k}{2}\,\overline{\langle x^2 \rangle}} = \tfrac{1}{2}E_0 \geq \tfrac{1}{4}\hbar\omega. \tag{8-34}$$

If we assume that for the lowest energy state this inequality is to be taken as an equality, we obtain the correct result for the ground-state energy of the simple harmonic oscillator:

$$E_0 = \tfrac{1}{2}\hbar\omega. \tag{8-35}$$

The wave function of the simple harmonic oscillator for its ground state is plotted in Fig. 8-6 as a function of position with two broken lines being placed at the coordinates $-x_0$ and $+x_0$, the classical limits of the motion. x_0 is given by

$$\tfrac{1}{2}kx_0^2 = \tfrac{1}{2}\hbar\omega. \tag{8-36}$$

Classically, a particle having the energy of the ground state would be able to oscillate between the limits $+x_0$ and $-x_0$, but the particle could not move beyond these limits, inasmuch as its potential energy would exceed its total energy if it were to be found outside these limits. On the other hand, from the probability interpretation of the wave function, it is clear that the probability density for the position of the particle is nonzero outside these limits in quantum-mechanical formalism. There thus arises a question of how the law of conservation of energy can be maintained if it is possible to observe the particle in a region for which its potential energy exceeds its total energy. One possibility that immediately comes to mind, the possibility of the existence of a negative kinetic energy, does not seem to be particularly feasible, as this would imply that the momentum of the particle could take on imaginary values.

The paradox can be resolved by noting that a measurement made to determine whether the particle is in the classically excluded region entails an interaction with the particle which in general changes its energy. After making a measurement which localizes the particle in a classically excluded region, we find that the region is in general no longer an excluded region: the particle can now have energies sufficiently large to make this a classically allowed region.

8–6 Summary. This chapter has considered the correspondence principle and its connection with the commutation relations for the operators of the quantum-mechanical formalism. The expectation values associated with quantum-mechanical wave packets were seen to satisfy equations of motion identical to those satisfied by the corresponding classical quantities. It was found that the time derivative of the expectation value of an operator is directly related to the commutation relation between this operator and the Hamiltonian of the particle. Consequently, the commutation relations are intimately connected with the classical equations of motion and are also a useful guide in selecting the correct operators.

The motion of a wave packet in a simple harmonic oscillator was discussed as an example of what is meant by the "classical" description of a particle in quantum-mechanical formalism. A quantitative discussion of the uncertainty relation was then given, with rigorous definitions being given to the position and momentum uncertainties. It was shown that a gaussian wave packet corresponds to the case of minimum uncertainty. Finally, the uncertainty principle was used to obtain the energy of the ground state of the one-dimensional simple harmonic oscillator.

Problems

8–1. A one-dimensional simple harmonic oscillator is in a state for which a measurement of energy would yield either $\frac{1}{2}\hbar\omega_0$ or $\frac{3}{2}\hbar\omega_0$, each with a probability of one-half. A measurement of the momentum of the particle at time $t = 0$ gives a mean value which is as large a positive value as can be obtained subject to the above energy condition. (a) Calculate the following mean values as functions of time: $\langle \mathrm{H}\rangle$, $\langle p^2/2m\rangle$, $\langle \frac{1}{2}kx^2\rangle$, $\langle p\rangle$, and $\langle x\rangle$. (b) Compare these results with those obtained from classical mechanics for an oscillator with an energy $\frac{1}{2}\hbar\omega_0$. Note the effects of the zero-point energy $\frac{1}{2}\hbar\omega_0$.

8–2. Prove *Ehrenfest's theorem* for the case of a particle in an electromagnetic field; i.e., from

$$\frac{d}{dt}\langle \mathrm{F}\rangle = \frac{i}{\hbar}\langle [\mathrm{H}, \mathrm{F}]\rangle + \left\langle \frac{\partial \mathrm{F}}{\partial t}\right\rangle,$$

$$\mathrm{H} = \frac{1}{2m}\mathbf{\Pi}\cdot\mathbf{\Pi} + e\phi, \qquad \mathbf{\Pi} \equiv \mathbf{P} - \frac{e}{c}A,$$

show that

$$\frac{d}{dt}\langle r\rangle = \left\langle \frac{1}{m}\mathbf{\Pi}\right\rangle,$$

$$\frac{d}{dt}\langle \mathbf{\Pi}\rangle = \langle \text{Lorentz force}\rangle.$$

8–3. A particle of mass m is constrained to move along an infinite wire without friction. Assume that a measurement on the system at $t = 0$ shows that the wave function is

$$\psi = A\exp(-ax^2).$$

(a) Compute $\langle \Delta x^2\rangle\langle \Delta p_x^2\rangle$ as a function of time. (b) How does this depend on a?

8–4. One interesting property of the simple harmonic oscillator is the existence of wave functions in the form of wave packets which oscillate without a change in shape. This appears to be a unique property of the harmonic oscillator. Show that the wave function having the initial form

$$\psi(x, 0) = u_0(x + a), \qquad t = 0,$$

is such a wave-packet solution. Here $u_0(x)$ is the ground-state energy eigenfunction of the oscillator. [*Hint:* (a) As a preliminary, show that

$$u_0(x + a) = u_0^{-1}(0)u_0\left(\frac{a}{\sqrt{2}}\right)u_0^{-1}(x)\exp\left(\frac{i\mathrm{P}a}{2\hbar}\right)u_0^2(x),$$

where the operator $\exp(i\mathrm{P}a/2\hbar)$ is defined through the series expansion

$$\exp\left(\frac{i\mathrm{P}a}{2\hbar}\right) \equiv 1 + \frac{i\mathrm{P}a}{2\hbar} + \frac{1}{2!}\left(\frac{i\mathrm{P}a}{2\hbar}\right)^2 + \cdots$$

(b) Make use of the result of Problem 6–7 and Eqs. (6–73) and (6–88) to show that

$$\psi(x, t) = u_0^{-1}(0)u_0\left(\frac{a}{\sqrt{2}}\right) \exp\left(-\tfrac{1}{2}i\omega t\right)u_0^{-1}(x) \exp\left[i\,\frac{\mathrm{P}a}{2\hbar} \exp\left(-i\omega t\right)\right]u_0^2(x).$$

(c) Compute this function explicitly, and show that it represents a wave packet which oscillates without a change of shape of the envelope function. Plot the function roughly for $t = 0$ and $t = \pi/2\omega$. Note that the particle wave number k oscillates periodically.]

8–5. Use the wave function of Problem 8–4 to compute the expectation values of the observables H, P, x, $\mathrm{P}^2/2m$, and $\frac{1}{2}kx^2$. Compare these results with those of a classical oscillator having an amplitude a.

CHAPTER 9

ANGULAR MOMENTUM

9–1 Orbital angular-momentum operators. In the preceding development, angular momentum has not been discussed, nor has the form that the angular-momentum operators must take to give a formalism consistent with quantum theory as developed thus far. In classical mechanics, the z-component of the orbital angular momentum of a particle about an axis is related to the position and linear momentum of the particle by

$$L_z \equiv xp_y - yp_x. \tag{9–1}$$

The other cartesian components of orbital angular momentum can be obtained from the expression by repeated application of the cyclic permutation given by $x \to y$, $y \to z$, $z \to x$.

To find quantum-mechanical operators for angular momentum, use is made of the requirement that the correspondence principle must be satisfied. Thus any relation which appears in classical mechanics must be valid as a relation between expectation values. It should be remembered that one particular way in which the requirements of the correspondence principle are introduced into quantum mechanics is through the requirement that commutators be given by the classical Poisson brackets, from Postulate 7, Chapter 6.

It is also evident that classical relations between the expectation values of operators will be obtained if the relations between the operators are the classical ones. Thus one possible set of expressions for angular-momentum operators is obtained by taking the usual classical expressions in terms of position and momentum and replacing the classical quantities by the corresponding operators. As an example, the resulting expression for the z-component of orbital angular momentum is

$$\mathrm{L}_z = x\left(-i\hbar\,\frac{\partial}{\partial y}\right) - y\left(-i\hbar\,\frac{\partial}{\partial x}\right) = -i\hbar\left(x\,\frac{\partial}{\partial y} - y\,\frac{\partial}{\partial x}\right). \tag{9–2}$$

This method of obtaining operators breaks down if, because of ambiguity introduced by noncommuting factors, the resulting operator is not uniquely defined. The operator given by Eq. (9–2) has no noncommuting factors and is hence unambiguous. As a check on the correctness of Eq. (9–2), the commutation relations [obtained from Eqs. (9–2)]

$$\begin{aligned} [\mathrm{L}_z, x] &= i\hbar y, & [\mathrm{L}_z, \mathrm{P}_x] &= i\hbar \mathrm{P}_y, \\ [\mathrm{L}_z, y] &= -i\hbar x, & [\mathrm{L}_z, \mathrm{P}_y] &= -i\hbar \mathrm{P}_x \end{aligned} \tag{9–3}$$

can be compared with the corresponding classical equations using Poisson brackets. The above method of obtaining the angular-momentum operators is seen to be in harmony with Postulate 7 of Chapter 6.

The commutation relations among the various components of the angular momentum can be obtained from Eq. (9–3):

$$\begin{aligned} [\mathrm{L}_x, \mathrm{L}_y] &= i\hbar \mathrm{L}_z, & [\mathrm{L}_y, \mathrm{L}_x] &= -i\hbar \mathrm{L}_z, & [\mathrm{L}_z, \mathrm{L}_x] &= i\hbar \mathrm{L}_y, \\ [\mathrm{L}_x, \mathrm{L}_z] &= -i\hbar \mathrm{L}_y, & [\mathrm{L}_y, \mathrm{L}_z] &= i\hbar \mathrm{L}_x, & [\mathrm{L}_z, \mathrm{L}_y] &= -i\hbar \mathrm{L}_x. \end{aligned} \tag{9–4}$$

Note that the operators for the three components of angular momentum do not commute with one another, and, from the results of Section 6–1, they are not simultaneously measurable.

Another physical quantity of considerable interest is the square of the magnitude of the angular momentum, or the sum of the squares of the three components of the angular momentum. The corresponding operator is defined through

$$\mathrm{L}^2 \equiv \mathrm{L}_x^2 + \mathrm{L}_y^2 + \mathrm{L}_z^2. \tag{9–5}$$

From Eqs. (9–4), L^2 commutes with all three of the components of the angular momentum:

$$[\mathrm{L}^2, \mathrm{L}_x] = [\mathrm{L}^2, \mathrm{L}_y] = [\mathrm{L}^2, \mathrm{L}_z] = 0. \tag{9–6}$$

These relations can be written in vector notation as

$$[\mathrm{L}^2, \mathbf{L}] = 0. \tag{9–7}$$

Since the z-component of the angular momentum and the square of the angular momentum commute with each other, it is possible to choose eigenfunctions which are simultaneously eigenfunctions of both operators. We then have

$$\mathrm{L}^2\psi = a\psi, \tag{9–8}$$

$$\mathrm{L}_z\psi = b\psi. \tag{9–9}$$

From Eq. (9–5) it is clear that the expectation values of L^2 and L_z^2 satisfy the relation

$$\langle \mathrm{L}^2 \rangle \geq \langle \mathrm{L}_z^2 \rangle. \tag{9–10}$$

From this it follows that

$$a \geq b^2. \tag{9–11}$$

It is useful at this point to define two operators which play a role similar to that of the ladder operators used in the problem of the simple harmonic oscillator. They are

$$L_{\pm} \equiv L_x \pm iL_y. \tag{9–12}$$

It is easily verified by direct multiplication, making use of the commutator Eqs. (9–4), that

$$L_{\pm}L_{\mp} = L^2 - L_z^2 \pm \hbar L_z. \tag{9–13}$$

By making use of the other angular-momentum commutators, it can be shown that

$$[L_z, L_{\pm}] = \pm\hbar L_{\pm}. \tag{9–14}$$

This equation says that the operators L_+ and L_- play the role of ladder operators with regard to the eigenvalue Eq. (9–9): if we multiply the left side of Eq. (9–9) by L_+ and use Eq. (9–14), we obtain

$$L_z(L_+\psi) = (b + \hbar)(L_+\psi). \tag{9–15}$$

This is a new eigenvalue equation with a new eigenvalue $(b + \hbar)$ and a new eigenfunction $(L_+\psi)$. Because L^2 commutes with all three components of **L**, it is evident that by multiplying Eq. (9–8) by L_+, we obtain

$$L^2(L_+\psi) = a(L_+\psi). \tag{9–16}$$

Thus the operator L_+ operating on an eigenfunction which is a simultaneous eigenfunction of L_z and L^2 generates a new simultaneous eigenfunction of these two operators for which the eigenvalue of L^2 is left unchanged but for which the eigenvalue of L_z is increased by $\hbar$. The eigenvalue b has an upper bound; otherwise, the inequality of Eq. (9–11) would be violated. Therefore, if we assume that b is the largest eigenvalue compatible with Eq. (9–11), then Eq. (9–15) can be satisfied only for the trivial case in which the eigenfunction vanishes everywhere:

$$L_+\psi = 0. \tag{9–17}$$

If we multiply the left side of this equation by L_- and use Eq. (9–13), the result is

$$L_-L_+\psi = (L^2 - L_z^2 - \hbar L_z)\psi = 0. \tag{9–18}$$

From this and Eqs. (9–8) and (9–9), we obtain

$$a = b(b + \hbar). \tag{9–19}$$

In a similar manner, if we multiply the left side of Eq. (9–9) by the operator L_- and use Eq. (9–14), we obtain, after iterating n times,

$$L_z(L_-^n\psi) = (b - n\hbar)(L_-^n\psi). \qquad (9\text{–}20)$$

This is again in the form of an eigenvalue equation, which can be written as

$$L_z\psi' = (b - n\hbar)\psi', \qquad (9\text{–}21)$$

with

$$\psi' \equiv L_-^n\psi. \qquad (9\text{–}22)$$

Clearly, the square of this eigenvalue $(b - n\hbar)$ can be made to increase without limit by making n sufficiently large. Hence, there must be a largest value of n for which the inequality of Eq. (9–11) can be satisfied. Assume that n is this largest value. If this is the case, then the application of the operator L_- to ψ' must give zero:

$$L_-\psi' = 0. \qquad (9\text{–}23)$$

If we multiply the left side of this equation by L_+ and use Eq. (9–13), the result is

$$\begin{aligned} L_+L_-\psi' &= (L^2 - L_z^2 + \hbar L_z)\psi' \\ &= [a - (b - n\hbar)^2 + (b - n\hbar)\hbar]\psi' = 0. \end{aligned} \qquad (9\text{–}24)$$

From this,

$$a = (b - n\hbar)^2 - (b - n\hbar)\hbar. \qquad (9\text{–}25)$$

If we combine this with Eq. (9–19), a can be eliminated to give

$$0 = -2bn\hbar - 2b\hbar + n\hbar^2 + n^2\hbar^2, \qquad (9\text{–}26)$$

which in turn can be factored to give

$$2b(n + 1) = n(n + 1)\hbar. \qquad (9\text{–}27)$$

Since n must be positive, this can be written as

$$b = \tfrac{1}{2}n\hbar \equiv l\hbar. \qquad (9\text{–}28)$$

From this, l is positive and either an integer or a half-integer, depending on whether n is even or odd. It will be shown shortly* that for the orbital angular momentum which is being considered here, l takes on only integral

---

* See also the footnote on p. 91.

values:

$$l = 0, 1, 2, 3, \ldots \tag{9–29}$$

The significance of odd n-values will be discussed later. Substituting the value for b from Eq. (9–28) into Eq. (9–19), one obtains as the eigenvalue for the square of the angular momentum:

$$a = l\hbar(l\hbar + \hbar) = l(l + 1)\hbar^2. \tag{9–30}$$

The above development can be summarized by writing Eqs. (9–8) and (9–30), and (9–9) and (9–28), as

$$\mathrm{L}^2\psi_{lm_l} = l(l + 1)\hbar^2\psi_{lm_l}, \tag{9–31}$$

$$\mathrm{L}_z\psi_{lm_l} = m_l\hbar\psi_{lm_l}. \tag{9–32}$$

Here the notation has been changed slightly to give the wave function two indices l and m_l corresponding to the eigenvalues of L^2 and L_z. l can take on positive integral values only, $l = 0, 1, 2, \ldots$, and m_l can take on positive or negative integral values such that $l \geq |m_l|$. Equations (9–31) and (9–32) result directly from the commutation relations of the angular momentum, and hence follow from only the algebraic properties of the operators.

Note that only one component of the angular momentum may be precisely specified at a time, for the operators for the components are noncommuting. The choice of L^2 and L_z as mutually commuting operators is hence arbitrary. That these wave functions single out a particular direction in space for special consideration means merely that a measurement of this particular component is needed before the system can be known to be in one of these states. L_x or L_y could equally well have been used in place of L_z in Eq. (9–32).

Although a simultaneous knowledge of two components of the angular momentum is impossible, it is possible to say something about the other components. For example, for the particle in the angular-momentum state given by Eqs. (9–31) and (9–32), the expectation values of L_x and L_y are

$$\langle \mathrm{L}_x \rangle = \langle \mathrm{L}_y \rangle = 0. \tag{9–33}$$

This is seen by writing

$$\mathrm{L}_x = \tfrac{1}{2}(\mathrm{L}_+ + \mathrm{L}_-) \tag{9–34}$$

and computing $\langle \mathrm{L}_x \rangle$. Also,

$$\langle \mathrm{L}_x^2 \rangle = \langle \mathrm{L}_y^2 \rangle = \tfrac{1}{2}\langle \mathrm{L}^2 - \mathrm{L}_z^2 \rangle = \tfrac{1}{2}[l(l + 1) - m^2]\hbar^2. \tag{9–35}$$

Note that when the angular momentum is "parallel" to the z-axis ($m = l$), the x- and y-components are still not zero.

It is helpful to visualize the results of this section with the aid of a geometrical model. Consider the length of the angular-momentum vector $\boldsymbol{L}$ to be $\sqrt{l(l+1)}\,\hbar$. The $2l + 1$ allowed projections of this on the z-axis are given by $m_l\hbar$, with $m_l = 0, \pm 1, \pm 2, \ldots, \pm l$. Note that the projection on the z-axis never exceeds the length of the vector. The angular-momentum vector thus may be visualized as lying on the surface of a cone having the z-axis for its axis and an altitude of $m_l\hbar$. All positions in the surface are assumed to be equally likely. This model clearly is in agreement with Eqs. (9–33) and (9–35).

9–2 Orbital angular-momentum wave functions.* Consider now the orbital angular-momentum wave functions which are simultaneously eigenfunctions of L^2 and L_z. It is helpful to introduce spherical coordinates for the particle in the usual fashion:

$$\begin{aligned} x &= r \sin\theta \cos\phi, \\ y &= r \sin\theta \sin\phi, \\ z &= r \cos\theta. \end{aligned} \tag{9–36}$$

In terms of these spherical coordinates, the operator for the z-component of orbital angular momentum of a particle takes on the form

$$\mathrm{L}_z = -i\hbar \frac{\partial}{\partial\phi}\cdot \tag{9–37}$$

When the operator L_z in this form is substituted into Eq. (9–32), the resulting partial differential equation is readily solved:

$$\psi_{lm_l} = \exp(im_l\phi) f(r, \theta), \tag{9–38}$$

where m_l must take on integral values if the resulting function is to be single-valued.† Inasmuch as this assumption has been made (Postulate 1, Chapter 6), it is necessary that m_l, and consequently l, take on integral values in the case of orbital angular momentum. This justifies the assumption made earlier in connection with Eq. (9–29). The ladder operators

* Notation and techniques similar to those used in this section are to be found in E. U. Condon and G. H. Shortley, *Theory of Atomic Spectra*, Cambridge University Press, Cambridge, 1951, Chapter 3.

† See the footnote on p. 91 on this point.

defined in Eq. (9–12) become, in terms of spherical coordinates,

$$\mathrm{L}_{\pm} \equiv \mathrm{L}_x \pm i\mathrm{L}_y = \hbar \exp(\pm i\phi)\left(\pm \frac{\partial}{\partial\theta} + i \cot\theta \frac{\partial}{\partial\phi}\right). \tag{9–39}$$

In a similar manner, the operator for L^2 is easily calculated from this expression for $\mathrm{L}_{\pm}$, from Eq. (9–37) for L_z, and from Eq. (9–13), which relates L^2 to $\mathrm{L}_{\pm}$ and L_z. The result is

$$\mathrm{L}^2 = -\hbar^2\left[\frac{1}{\sin\theta}\frac{\partial}{\partial\theta}\left(\sin\theta\frac{\partial}{\partial\theta}\right) + \frac{1}{\sin^2\theta}\frac{\partial^2}{\partial\phi^2}\right]. \tag{9–40}$$

By comparing this with the expression for the Laplacian operator in spherical coordinates,

$$\nabla^2 \equiv \left(\frac{1}{r}\frac{\partial}{\partial r} r\right)^2 + \frac{1}{r^2}\left[\frac{1}{\sin\theta}\frac{\partial}{\partial\theta}\left(\sin\theta\frac{\partial}{\partial\theta}\right) + \frac{1}{\sin^2\theta}\frac{\partial^2}{\partial\phi^2}\right], \tag{9–41}$$

it can be seen that the operator for the square of the angular momentum is essentially the angular part of the Laplacian operator. Consequently, the operator for kinetic energy in the case of three-dimensional motion, expressed in terms of the Laplacian, becomes

$$-\frac{\hbar^2}{2m}\nabla^2 = \frac{1}{2m}\mathrm{P}_r^2 + \frac{\mathrm{L}^2}{2mr^2}. \tag{9–42}$$

This expression has a simple interpretation in terms of classical mechanics. In classical mechanics, it is possible to express the kinetic energy of the particle as a sum of the kinetic energy associated with motion in a radial direction and the kinetic energy associated with motion at right angles to the radius vector. The kinetic energy of the angular part of the motion takes on the value of the second term of the right side of Eq. (9–42), whereas the kinetic energy associated with radial motion can be expressed in terms of a radial operator defined by

$$\mathrm{P}_r = -i\hbar\frac{1}{r}\frac{\partial}{\partial r} r. \tag{9–43}$$

This is *not* the r-component of the particle momentum.

If m_l takes on its maximum allowed value for a given l, namely $m_l = l$, then the ladder operator L_+ when applied to the corresponding eigenfunction must give zero:

$$(\mathrm{L}_x + i\mathrm{L}_y)\psi_{ll} = 0 = \hbar\exp(i\phi)\left(\frac{\partial}{\partial\theta} + i\cot\theta\frac{\partial}{\partial\phi}\right)\exp(il\phi)\Theta_{ll}(\theta). \tag{9–44}$$

In this equation, since the angular-momentum operators are functions only of the angle variables, the dependence on r has been omitted. The form of the angular dependence is given by Eq. (9–38). In general, the wave function contains some function of r as a factor, in addition to a term having this angular dependence. Equation (9–44) is readily reduced to the ordinary differential equation

$$\frac{d\Theta_{ll}}{d\theta} = l \cot \theta \Theta_{ll}, \tag{9–45}$$

which has the solution

$$\Theta_{ll} = (-1)^l \sqrt{\frac{(2l+1)!}{2}} \frac{1}{2^l l!} \sin^l \theta. \tag{9–46}$$

The numerical coefficient on the right of this equation has been chosen to normalize Θ_{ll} so that

$$\int_0^\pi |\Theta_{ll}(\theta)|^2 \sin \theta \, d\theta = 1. \tag{9–47}$$

If we substitute this function into the original expression for the wave function, we obtain a general form of the wave function when it is characterized by a total angular-momentum quantum number l and a z-component of angular momentum with a quantum number $m_l = l$:

$$\psi_{ll} = \frac{1}{\sqrt{2\pi}} \exp(il\phi) \Theta_{ll}(\theta) f(r). \tag{9–48}$$

The form of the function of r is still undetermined and can be determined only by other considerations, since the angular momentum concerns only the angular variables. The coefficient in front of this equation is so chosen as to normalize the ϕ-dependence of the wave function in accordance with

$$\int_0^{2\pi} \left| \frac{1}{\sqrt{2\pi}} \exp(il\phi) \right|^2 d\phi = 1. \tag{9–49}$$

The angular part of Eq. (9–48) is defined to be a *spherical harmonic* and is given the notation

$$Y_{ll}(\theta, \phi) = \frac{1}{\sqrt{2\pi}} \exp(il\phi) \Theta_{ll}(\theta). \tag{9–50}$$

By making use of Eq. (9–22), we can also write other spherical harmonics which are simultaneous eigenfunctions of L^2 and L_z. For example, if we apply the operator L_- once, we have

$$cL_-Y_{ll}(\theta, \phi) = Y_{l,l-1}(\theta, \phi). \tag{9–51}$$

Here the constant c is included so that the spherical harmonic with indices $l, l-1$ will be normalized as was the spherical harmonic with the indices l, l:

$$\int |Y_{ll}|^2 \, d\Omega = \int_{\phi=0}^{2\pi} \int_{\theta=0}^{\pi} |Y_{ll}|^2 \sin\theta \, d\theta \, d\phi = 1. \tag{9–52}$$

By iterating this procedure, one can generate the spherical harmonic with indices l and m (here m_l has been replaced by m):

$$Y_{lm} = c_{lm} L_-^{l-m} Y_{ll}. \tag{9–53}$$

An iterative procedure can also be used to calculate the normalizing constants by making use of

$$Y_{lm} = \frac{c_{lm}}{c_{l,m+1}} L_- Y_{l,m+1} \tag{9–54}$$

and the normalizing relation

$$\int_{\phi=0}^{2\pi} \int_{\theta=0}^{\pi} \overline{Y_{lm}} Y_{lm} \sin\theta \, d\theta \, d\phi = (Y_{lm}, Y_{lm}) = 1. \tag{9–55}$$

By remembering that L_+ is the Hermitian adjoint of L_-, one can obtain

$$\left|\frac{c_{lm}}{c_{l,m+1}}\right|^2 (Y_{l,m+1}, L_+L_-Y_{l,m+1}) = 1. \tag{9–56}$$

From Eq. (9–13), this becomes

$$\left|\frac{c_{lm}}{c_{l,m+1}}\right|^2 (Y_{l,m+1}, [L^2 - L_z^2 + \hbar L_z] Y_{l,m+1}) = 1. \tag{9–57}$$

Here the operators operating on their eigenfunctions generate their eigenvalues; hence Eq. (9–57) reduces to

$$\left|\frac{c_{lm}}{c_{l,m+1}}\right|^2 (l - m)(l + m + 1)\hbar^2 = 1. \tag{9–58}$$

By defining the c's in Eq. (9–53) to be positive and real, one obtains

$$L_-Y_{l,m+1} = \sqrt{(l - m)(l + m + 1)}\, \hbar Y_{lm}, \tag{9–59}$$

from which, by iteration,

$$Y_{lm} = \sqrt{\frac{(l+m)!}{(2l)!(l-m)!}}\,\frac{1}{\hbar^{l-m}}\,L_-^{l-m}Y_{ll}. \tag{9–60}$$

This spherical harmonic can, of course, be written as a product of a function of ϕ and a function of θ:

$$Y_{lm} = \frac{1}{\sqrt{2\pi}}\exp(im\phi)\,\Theta_{lm}(\theta). \tag{9–61}$$

The iterative operation which occurs in Eq. (9–60) can be performed in a simple way by substituting a new variable for $\cos\theta$. The resulting generation of the function of θ of Eq. (9–61) can be written as

$$\Theta_{lm}(\theta) = (-1)^l\sqrt{\frac{(2l+1)(l+m)!}{2(l-m)!}}\,\frac{1}{2^l l!}\,\frac{1}{\sin^m\theta}\left(\frac{d}{d\cos\theta}\right)^{l-m}\sin^{2l}\theta. \tag{9–62}$$

In the case of the subscript $m = 0$, this equation becomes

$$\Theta_{l0}(\theta) = \sqrt{\frac{2l+1}{2}}\,\frac{1}{2^l l!}\left(\frac{d}{d\cos\theta}\right)^l(\cos^2\theta - 1)^l. \tag{9–63}$$

Thus $\Theta_{l0}(\theta)$ is simply a Legendre polynomial:

$$\Theta_{l0}(\theta) = \sqrt{\frac{2l+1}{2}}\,P_l(\cos\theta). \tag{9–64}$$

Equation (9–63) for the generation of Legendre polynomials is known as *Rodrigues' formula.*

The other spherical harmonics can be generated from those with $m = 0$ by applying the operators L_+ and L_-. When this is done, the function of θ, Eq. (9–62), can be expressed in terms of Legendre polynomials as

$$\begin{aligned}\Theta_{lm} &= (-1)^m\sqrt{\frac{(2l+1)(l-m)!}{2(l+m)!}}\sin^m\theta\left(\frac{d}{d\cos\theta}\right)^m P_l(\cos\theta), \qquad m>0\\ &= \sqrt{\frac{(2l+1)(l-|m|)!}{2(l+|m|)!}}\sin^{|m|}\theta\left(\frac{d}{d\cos\theta}\right)^{|m|} P_l(\cos\theta), \qquad m<0.\end{aligned} \tag{9–65}$$

The resulting functions, plotted in Fig. 9–1 for $\phi = 0$, are known as

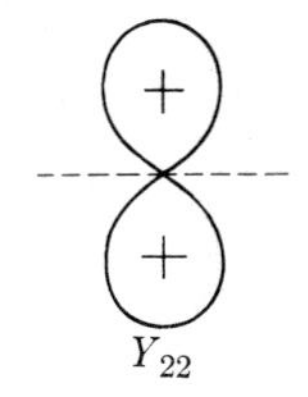

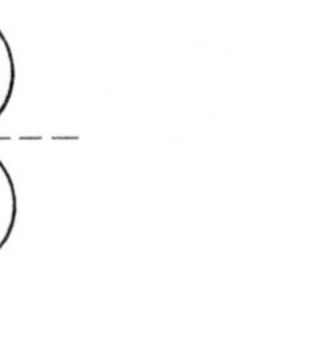

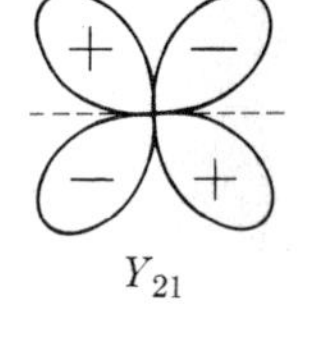

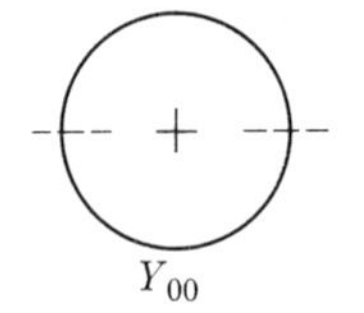

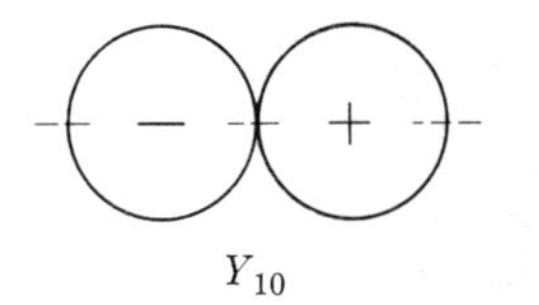

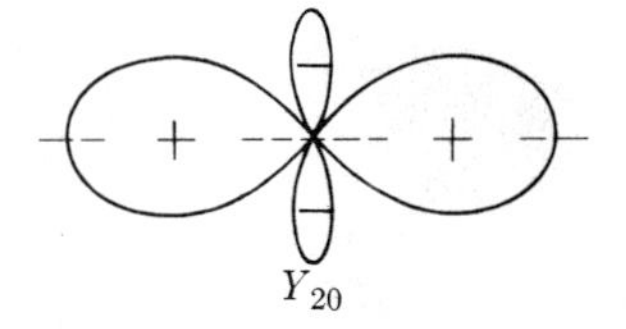

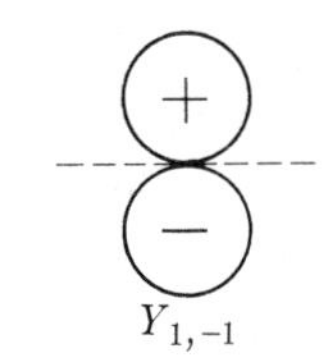

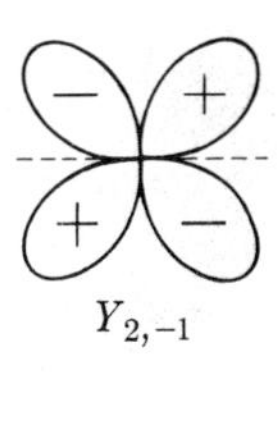

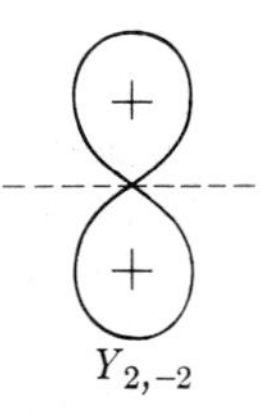

FIG. 9–1. Polar plots of the spherical harmonics for $l = 0, 1, 2$ for all values of the index m, at $\phi = 0$. Note that in this figure the polar axis is horizontal.

associated Legendre functions. The spherical harmonics for small values of l and m are given below:

$$
\begin{aligned}
Y_{00} &= \frac{1}{\sqrt{4\pi}}, \\
Y_{11} &= -\sqrt{\frac{3}{8\pi}} \sin\theta \exp(i\phi), \\
Y_{10} &= \sqrt{\frac{3}{4\pi}} \cos\theta, \\
Y_{1,-1} &= \sqrt{\frac{3}{8\pi}} \sin\theta \exp(-i\phi), \\
Y_{22} &= \sqrt{\frac{15}{32\pi}} \sin^2\theta \exp(2i\phi), \\
Y_{21} &= -\sqrt{\frac{15}{8\pi}} \cos\theta \sin\theta \exp(i\phi), \\
Y_{20} &= \sqrt{\frac{5}{16\pi}} (3\cos^2\theta - 1), \\
Y_{2,-1} &= \sqrt{\frac{15}{8\pi}} \cos\theta \sin\theta \exp(-i\phi), \\
Y_{2,-2} &= \sqrt{\frac{15}{32\pi}} \sin^2\theta \exp(-2i\phi).
\end{aligned}
\tag{9-66}
$$

When a particle is in a state for which the orbital angular momentum is known and characterized by the quantum number $l = 0, 1, 2, 3, \ldots$, it is said to be respectively in an S-, P-, D-, F-, ... state: $l = 0$ characterizes S-states, $l = 1$ characterizes P-states, $l = 2$, D-states, etc. The origin of this nomenclature is optical spectroscopy, where these letters ($S \rightarrow$ sharp, $P \rightarrow$ principle, $D \rightarrow$ diffuse, $F \rightarrow$ fine) were used to characterize spectroscopic series by the appearance of spectroscopic lines.

9–3 Angular momentum in general. Thus far, only orbital angular momentum has been dealt with explicitly. However, it was seen that the formalism based on commutation relations permitted either half-integral or integral values for l: the restriction to integral l-values resulted from an explicit form of the operator and the requirement of a single-valued wave function. The possible half-integral result followed directly from the commutation relations for the angular-momentum components; if corresponding elements can be found in nature, this would suggest that these commutators represent a more fundamental aspect of angular momentum than do Eq. (9–1) and the single-valuedness postulate for the wave functions.

Experiment has confirmed that this is indeed the case and that there exist elements of reality corresponding to the previously excluded half-integral l-values. These are related to the *spin angular momentum* of the particle. It is clear from the earlier developments that if this generalization is to be admitted, new coordinates must also be admitted or the requirement of single-valuedness cannot be met. The new coordinates represent internal degrees of freedom of the particle.

For spin angular momentum, it is found empirically that the quantum numbers may take on *either* integral or half-integral values. The relations obtained so far have all been derived, as noted above, from the commutators. We therefore have the result that the simultaneous eigenfunctions of the square of the spin angular momentum, designated S^2, and the z-component of the spin, designated S_z, are given by

$$\begin{aligned} \mathrm{S}^2\psi_{sm_s} &= s(s+1)\hbar^2\psi_{sm_s}, \\ \mathrm{S}_z\psi_{sm_s} &= m_s\hbar\psi_{sm_s}, \end{aligned} \tag{9–67}$$

where s and m_s may take on either integral or half-integral values, depending upon the nature of the spin of the particle under discussion. In the case of an atomic nucleus, the spin momentum is commonly designated by the symbol I, and the relations for nuclear angular momentum are written in the form of Eq. (9–67) with the substitution of I^2 and I_z for S^2 and S_z, and I and m_I for s and m_s.

9–4 Addition of angular momenta. In this section, the problem of the addition of two different kinds of angular momentum, the orbital angular momentum and spin angular momentum, of an electron will be considered. The relations which will be obtained, however, are valid for any two angular momenta. The total angular momentum of an electron can be written as a sum of the orbital and the spin angular momenta:

$$\mathbf{J} = \mathbf{L} + \mathbf{S}, \tag{9–68}$$

where $\mathbf{J}$ has the components

$$\mathrm{J}_x = \mathrm{L}_x + \mathrm{S}_x, \qquad \mathrm{J}_y = \mathrm{L}_y + \mathrm{S}_y, \qquad \mathrm{J}_z = \mathrm{L}_z + \mathrm{S}_z. \tag{9–69}$$

The commutation relations for $\mathbf{J}$ are the same as for the individual angular momenta $\mathbf{L}$ and $\mathbf{S}$. Therefore J^2 and J_z commute. The eigenvalues and simultaneous eigenfunctions of J^2 and J_z are

$$\begin{aligned} J^2\psi_{jm_j} &= j(j+1)\hbar^2\psi_{jm_j}, \\ J_z\psi_{jm_j} &= m_j\hbar\psi_{jm_j}, \end{aligned} \tag{9-70}$$

where $j \geq |m_j|$ and is positive and integral or half-integral, depending on whether s is integral or half-integral.

The square of the total angular momentum is given by

$$J^2 = L^2 + S^2 + 2\mathbf{L}\cdot\mathbf{S}. \tag{9-71}$$

Inasmuch as the operators **L** and **S** operate on different variables, namely, position and spin variables, the vector operator **L** commutes with all three components of the operator **S**, and

$$[L^2, \mathbf{L}\cdot\mathbf{S}] = 0. \tag{9-72}$$

Also, since L^2 commutes with S^2,

$$[L^2, J^2] = 0 \tag{9-73}$$

and

$$[S^2, J^2] = 0. \tag{9-74}$$

It is thus apparent that the three operators J^2, L^2, S^2 mutually commute with one another. It is also clear from consideration of the form of the operator J_z that it commutes with L^2 and S^2. Consequently, the four operators J^2, L^2, S^2, J_z all commute with one another, and the corresponding observables are all simultaneously measurable. For reasons indicated above, **S** and **L** commute with each other, and the set of operators L^2, L_z, S^2, S_z is also a mutually commuting set. Therefore there are at least these two alternative sets of four angular-momentum operators which are mutually commuting.

To consider the possible eigenvalues of J^2 associated with the first set of four operators, it is convenient to consider first the second set, namely L^2, L_z, S^2, S_z. It is assumed for the moment that l and s are known and fixed. There is a total of $(2l+1)\cdot(2s+1)$ possible orientation states of m_l and m_s for fixed values of the quantum numbers l and s. The largest value of the z-component of the total angular momentum, m_j, occurs when both m_l and m_s take on their maximum value; this largest value of m_j is given by

$$(m_j)_{\max} = l + s. \tag{9-75}$$

This largest value of $J_z = L_z + S_z$ implies that $(j)_{\max}$ must also take on this value:

$$(j)_{\max} = l + s. \tag{9-76}$$

For a fixed l and s, this largest value of m_j can occur in only one way: the eigenvalue $m_j = j$ is nondegenerate. The next lowest value of the z-component of the angular momentum occurs when m_j is given by

$$m_j = l + s - 1, \tag{9-77}$$

since it has been seen that the complete set of states can be generated by means of ladder operators that change the z-component of momentum by an integral amount. The state for $m_j = l + s - 1$ can occur in two different ways: either by decreasing m_l by one unit or decreasing m_s by one unit. One state with this value of m_j is associated with the quantum number j given by Eq. (9-76), inasmuch as for this value of j all $2j + 1$ orientations of the spin are possible. The other value must therefore be associated with the value of j given by

$$j = l + s - 1. \tag{9-78}$$

It is evident that this state, $j = m_j = l + s - 1$, is also nondegenerate. This argument can be iterated to show that j can take on all values between the limits set by the inequality

$$(l + s) \geq j \geq |l - s|, \tag{9-79}$$

and there are $2j + 1$ nondegenerate states for each value of j. These $2j + 1$ states correspond to the $2j + 1$ possible orientations of the

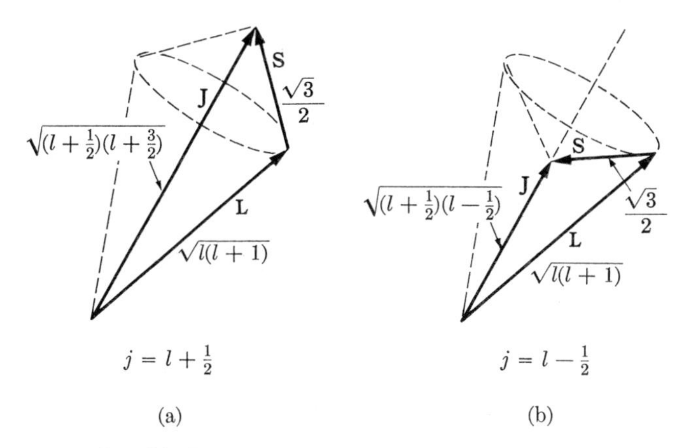

FIG. 9-2. Graphical representation of the addition of an orbital angular momentum $\boldsymbol{L}$ to a spin angular momentum $\boldsymbol{S}$ to give a total angular momentum $\boldsymbol{J}$, for the case $s = \frac{1}{2}$, $l \neq 0$. The two cases of $\boldsymbol{S}$ (a) "parallel" to $\boldsymbol{L}$ and (b) "antiparallel" to $\boldsymbol{L}$ are shown.

angular momentum with respect to the axis of quantization (the z-axis). If the numbers of all these states are added, since there are $2j + 1$ possible states for each j, the total number of possible orientations of the resultant angular momentum vector has the value $(2l + 1) \cdot (2s + 1)$. This same value was previously found from consideration of the two angular-momentum vectors as being oriented independently of each other. For the case of spin one-half, the possible values of j are given by

$$j = l + \tfrac{1}{2}, \qquad j = l - \tfrac{1}{2}, \qquad l \neq 0. \tag{9–80}$$

The addition of the angular momenta can be shown graphically as in Fig. 9–2 for the case of spin one-half. One can picture the spin angular momentum as being pointed either "parallel" or "antiparallel" to the orbital angular momentum, with the resulting total $\mathbf{J}$ taking on $2j + 1$ orientations relative to some fixed direction in space. However, as in Fig. 9–2, because of the fluctuation effects related to the uncertainty principle which lead to a spin vector for spin one-half having a length greater than $\frac{1}{2}\hbar$ and to an orbital angular-momentum vector having a length greater than $l\hbar$, the vectors add as shown.

9–5 Class T operators. In considering problems connected with angular momentum, it is useful to define a class of operators that have certain commutation relations in common. This group of operators is here designated as operators of "class $\mathbf{T}$"; they have the following commutators with any angular momentum operator such as $\mathbf{J}$:

$$\begin{aligned} [\mathrm{J}_x, \mathrm{T}_x] &= 0, \\ [\mathrm{J}_x, \mathrm{T}_y] &= i\hbar \mathrm{T}_z, \\ [\mathrm{J}_x, \mathrm{T}_z] &= -i\hbar \mathrm{T}_y, \end{aligned} \tag{9–81}$$

$$[\mathbf{J}, \mathbf{T}_1 \cdot \mathbf{T}_2] = 0. \tag{9–82}$$

The vectors $\boldsymbol{r}$, $\mathbf{P}$, $\mathbf{J}$, and any of their cross products fall into the class $\mathbf{T}$. In fact, any vector which transforms under a proper coordinate rotation as $\boldsymbol{r}$ does falls in this class.

As a special case of the commutation relation given by Eq. (9–82), we have

$$[\mathbf{J}, \mathrm{T}^2] = 0. \tag{9–83}$$

It is convenient to introduce the operator

$$\mathrm{T}_+ = \mathrm{T}_x + i\mathrm{T}_y, \tag{9–84}$$

which has the commutation relation with J_z given by

$$[J_z, T_+] = \hbar T_+. \tag{9–85}$$

It may be verified directly that it also satisfies the commutation relation

$$[J^2, T_+] = 2\hbar[T_+J_z - T_zJ_+] + 2\hbar^2 T_+. \tag{9–86}$$

By comparison of Eq. (9–85) with the commutation relation Eq. (9–14), it is seen that this operator is a ladder operator that has the effect of increasing the z-component of angular momentum whenever it is applied to a wave function. Furthermore, it may be verified by the use of Eq. (9–86) that whenever T_+ acts on a wave function for which m is equal to j, it not only increases the m-index by one unit but also increases the j-index by one unit:

$$T_+\psi_{jj} \sim \psi_{j+1,j+1}. \tag{9–87}$$

To verify this, consider

$$J^2\psi_{jj} = j(j+1)\hbar^2\psi_{jj}. \tag{9–88}$$

Multiply the left member of this equation by the operator T_+ and make use of the commutation relation Eq. (9–86) to rearrange terms:

$$[J^2T_+ - 2\hbar(T_+J_z - T_zJ_+) - 2\hbar^2T_+]\psi_{jj} = j(j+1)\hbar^2T_+\psi_{jj}. \tag{9–89}$$

Inasmuch as

$$J_+\psi_{jj} = 0, \tag{9–90}$$

Eq. (9–89) can be reduced to

$$J^2(T_+\psi_{jj}) = (j+1)(j+2)\hbar^2(T_+\psi_{jj}). \tag{9–91}$$

On the other hand, by making use of the ladder property given by the commutation relation Eq. (9–85) and multiplying the eigenvalue equation for J_z by the operator T_+, we find

$$J_z(T_+\psi_{jj}) = (j+1)\hbar(T_+\psi_{jj}). \tag{9–92}$$

From these latter two equations, it is seen that the effect of the operator T_+ acting on a wave function for which m_j is equal to j is to increase both indices:

$$T_+\psi_{jj} = \text{constant}\cdot\psi_{j+1,j+1}. \tag{9–93}$$

Also, by reference to Eq. (9–83), it is clear that operation with the square of the operator **T** has no effect on the two indices: the wave function is still an eigenfunction of J^2 and J_z with the same eigenvalue.

As a trivial example of the usefulness of vectors of the class **T**, note that, except for normalization, the spherical harmonics can be generated in the following way. The vector r is of the class **T**. Hence

$$(x + iy)Y_{ll} = f(r)Y_{l+1,l+1}. \tag{9-94}$$

Consequently,

$$Y_{lm}(\theta, \phi) = \text{const} \cdot (\mathrm{L}_x - i\mathrm{L}_y)^{l-m}\left(\frac{x + iy}{r}\right)^l \cdot 1. \tag{9-95}$$

Note that when the number 1 is considered to be a function of r it is a function with $l = m = 0$.

9–6 Summary. This chapter has dealt with angular momentum, deriving the eigenvalues and (orbital) eigenfunctions of angular-momentum operators using primarily algebraic techniques. It was found that in quantum mechanics the concept of angular momentum is best defined in relation to certain commutation relations; these were seen to be sufficient to find the eigenvalues of both the square and individual components of the angular momentum. It should be emphasized that the commutation relations of Eqs. (9–4) are properties of angular momentum *in general* and that the results derived from these commutation relations hold for all types of angular momentum. Thus, Eqs. (9–4) through (9–28), (9–30) through (9–35), (9–59), (9–60), and (9–68) through (9–80) are applicable to angular momentum in general. (From symmetry, the eigenvalues of J_x and J_y must be the same as those of J_z, which have been computed.) It was shown that the corresponding operators commute and that they can therefore be measured simultaneously. Only one component of angular momentum can be known exactly at one time, however. The relation of orbital angular-momentum wave functions to spherical harmonics was pointed out. The addition of two angular momenta was discussed, and a simple vector model given for such addition. Finally, a class of operators **T** was defined, and some formal properties of operators of this class were presented.

PROBLEMS

9–1. (a) What is the energy-eigenvalue equation for a rotator consisting of two equal point masses M held relatively rigidly a distance d apart by a massless rod? (b) What are the eigenvalues? (c) What are the eigenfunctions? (Neglect the effects of vibration involving a stretching of the rod.)

9–2. Assume that a one-particle system has an orbital angular momentum with a z-component of $m\hbar$ and a square magnitude of $l(l+1)\hbar^2$. (a) Show that

$$\langle \mathrm{L}_x \rangle = \langle \mathrm{L}_y \rangle = 0.$$

(b) Show that

$$\langle \mathrm{L}_x^2 \rangle = \langle \mathrm{L}_y^2 \rangle = \frac{l(l+1)\hbar^2 - m^2\hbar^2}{2}.$$

A measurement of a component making an angle θ with the z-axis is made. (c) Calculate the mean value and mean square value for this measurement. (d) Assuming that $l = 1$, calculate the probabilities of obtaining $m' = \pm 1, 0$ for this component. (e) Having made this measurement, what is the probability of obtaining the result $m\hbar$ in a repetition of the measurement of L_z? [*Hint:* Introduce the operators $\mathrm{L}_{\pm} = \mathrm{L}_x \pm i\mathrm{L}_y$.]

9–3. For a two-particle system, show that regardless of the type of force field acting on the particles, it is possible to measure simultaneously either of the following sets of four quantities but not both:

$$\mathrm{L}_1^2,\ \mathrm{L}_{1z},\ \mathrm{L}_2^2,\ \mathrm{L}_{2z}; \qquad \mathrm{L}_1^2,\ \mathrm{L}_2^2,\ \mathrm{L}^2,\ \mathrm{L}_z.$$

9–4. The operator associated with a measurement of the product of the x- and y-components of angular momentum of a particle is $\frac{1}{2}(\mathrm{L}_x\mathrm{L}_y + \mathrm{L}_y\mathrm{L}_x)$. (a) Show that this operator is Hermitian. (b) For a state for which the z-component of angular momentum has the value $m\hbar$ and the total angular momentum squared has the value $l(l+1)\hbar^2$, calculate the mean value of this operator. (c) Calculate the mean value of the square of this product. [*Hint:* Express the above product operator in terms of the $\mathrm{L}_{\pm}$ operators.]

9–5. The wave function of a particle of mass m moving in a potential well is, at a particular time,

$$\psi = (x + y + z) \exp\left(-\alpha\sqrt{x^2 + y^2 + z^2}\right).$$

Calculate the probability of obtaining for a measurement of L^2 and L_z the results $2\hbar^2$ and 0 respectively.

9–6. Two different observers are looking at the same atomic system, which they agree has an angular momentum $j = 1$. Each man assumes that the component of angular momentum in the direction of his axis of quantization is $\pm\hbar$ or 0. (a) Discuss the compatibility of these assumptions for various angles between the two axes of quantization. (b) In what sense are the men both correct and incorrect? (c) Under what circumstances are both men correct?

CHAPTER 10

CENTRAL FORCES

10–1 Qualitative behavior with an attractive potential. This chapter considers problems in which the only forces acting upon a particle are central forces, that is, those for which the potential energy is a function only of the radial distance from the origin. In this case, the Hamiltonian operator can be written as

$$\mathrm{H} = \frac{1}{2m}\mathrm{P}^2 + V(r). \tag{10–1}$$

Since r and $\mathbf{P}$ are class $\mathbf{T}$ operators, it is apparent from Eq. (9–82) that for central forces the angular-momentum operators L_x, L_y, and L_z all commute with the Hamiltonian; consequently, L^2 also commutes with the Hamiltonian. Thus the three operators H, L^2, and L_z constitute a set of operators which commute, and it is possible to choose wave functions which are simultaneously eigenfunctions of these three operators:

$$\psi_{Elm} = R_{Elm}(r)Y_{lm}(\theta, \phi). \tag{10–2}$$

The angular dependence of this wave function is the proper and unique dependence we associate with eigenvalues of L^2 and L_z, characterized by the quantum numbers l and m. Using Eq. (9–42) to express the kinetic-energy operator in the Hamiltonian of Eq. (10–1), one obtains the energy-eigenvalue equation

$$\left[\frac{1}{2m}\mathrm{P}_r^2 + \frac{\mathrm{L}^2}{2mr^2} + V(r)\right]\psi_{Elm} = E\psi_{Elm}. \tag{10–3}$$

Inasmuch as ψ_{Elm} is an eigenfunction of the operator L^2, this becomes

$$\left[\frac{1}{2m}\mathrm{P}_r^2 + \frac{l(l+1)\hbar^2}{2mr^2} + V(r)\right]R_{El} = ER_{El}. \tag{10–4}$$

Note that R_{El} does not depend on the quantum number m. This is an equation in the variable r only and can be put into formal correspondence with the problem of one-dimensional motion by making use of the substitution

$$u_{El} \equiv rR_{El}. \tag{10–5}$$

With this substitution, one obtains

$$\left[\frac{1}{2m}\left(-i\hbar\frac{d}{dr}\right)^2 + \frac{l(l+1)\hbar^2}{2mr^2} + V(r)\right]u_{El} = Eu_{El}. \tag{10–6}$$

This equation is identical in form to that of a one-dimensional problem (with motion in the r-direction). However, it has significance only for positive values of r, and by referring to Eq. (10–5) we see that the boundary condition to be satisfied by the function u at the point $r = 0$ is that u should vanish; otherwise, the radial function R would be divergent at the origin. The boundary condition that u should vanish for $r = 0$ is equivalent to the assumption that the potential energy should be infinite at the point $r = 0$; thus the solution to Eq. (10–6) can be put into an exact correspondence with the solution to a one-dimensional motion problem by taking the potential energy to jump to infinity at the origin but otherwise taking the form of the second and third terms in the bracket on the left of the equation. The form of the second and third terms in the bracket of Eq. (10–6) is plotted separately in Fig. 10–1 as a function of r, assuming a specific attractive form for $V(r)$. In Fig. 10–2, the sum of these two expressions is plotted. This can be considered as an *effective potential* for the one-dimensional motion, consisting of the real potential energy $V(r)$ and a centrifugal-force potential energy $l(l + 1)\hbar^2/2mr^2$. The form

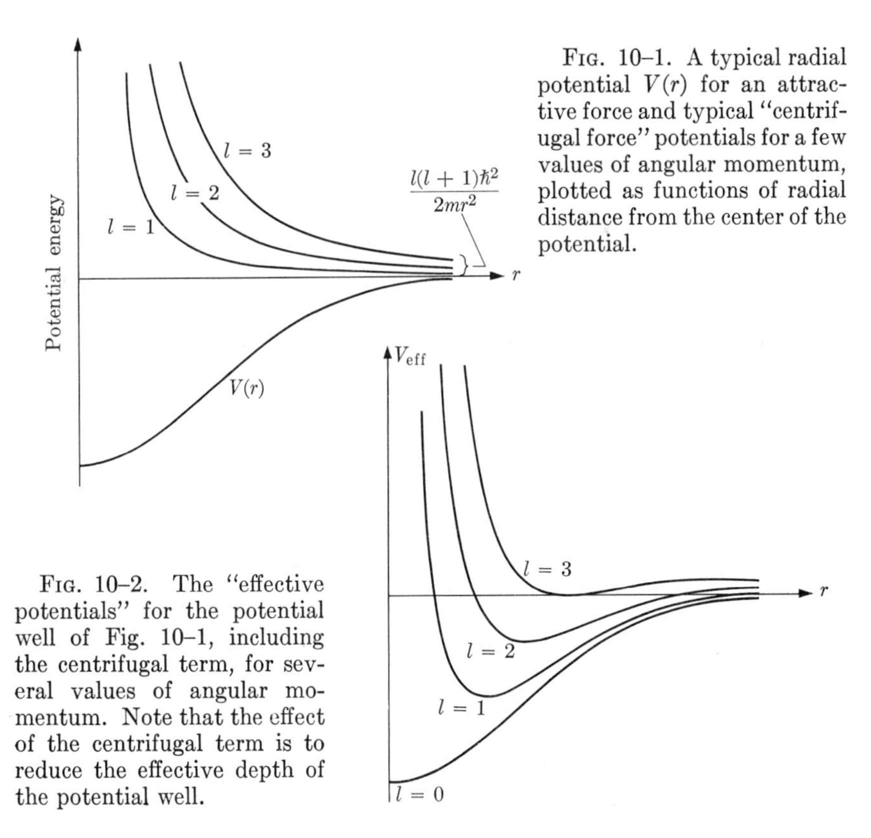

FIG. 10–1. A typical radial potential $V(r)$ for an attractive force and typical "centrifugal force" potentials for a few values of angular momentum, plotted as functions of radial distance from the center of the potential.

FIG. 10–2. The "effective potentials" for the potential well of Fig. 10–1, including the centrifugal term, for several values of angular momentum. Note that the effect of the centrifugal term is to reduce the effective depth of the potential well.

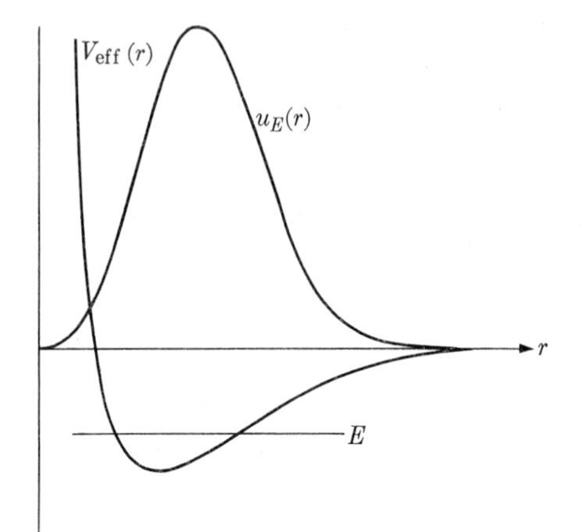

FIG. 10–3. A radial function $u(r)$ associated with the $l = 1$ effective potential well of Fig. 10–2.

of a radial function $u(r)$ associated with the motion in the potential well given by the effective potential V_{eff} of Fig. 10–2 is indicated in Fig. 10–3. In many cases it is thus possible to obtain a rough notion of the form of the wave function simply by observing the form of the equivalent potential function; this qualitative behavior of the wave function may be sufficient to answer a physical question without calculations. The fact that one is dealing with central forces greatly simplifies the problem.

10–2 The hydrogenic atom. As a problem for which an exact calculation of the radial function can be made, we will consider the hydrogen atom, or more generally, a hydrogenic atom for which the charge on the nucleus may be any multiple of the electronic charge. For the hydrogenic atom, the Hamiltonian takes the form

$$\mathrm{H} = \frac{1}{2m}\mathrm{P}^2 - \frac{Ze^2}{r}. \tag{10–7}$$

(Here, and throughout this book, the electronic charge will be taken as $-e$, so that $e = 4.80 \times 10^{-10}$ statcoulomb is a *positive* number.) The effective potential energy V_{eff} for hydrogen is plotted in Fig. 10–4 for several values of l. With a potential-energy function of this form, for the case of negative energy of the particle one obtains only bound solutions, as discussed in Chapter 3. A possible form for a bound-state wave function would be that given in Fig. 10–5. In the case of the hydrogenic atom, Eq. (10–6) takes the form

$$-\frac{\hbar^2}{2m}\frac{d^2u}{dr^2} + \frac{l(l+1)\hbar^2}{2mr^2}u - \frac{Ze^2}{r}u = Eu. \tag{10–8}$$

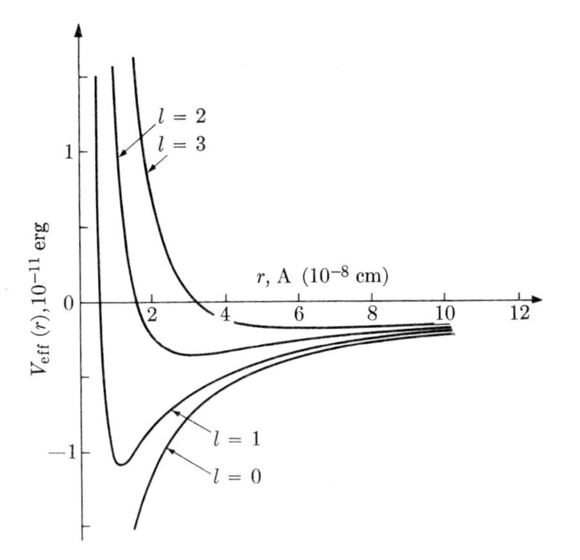

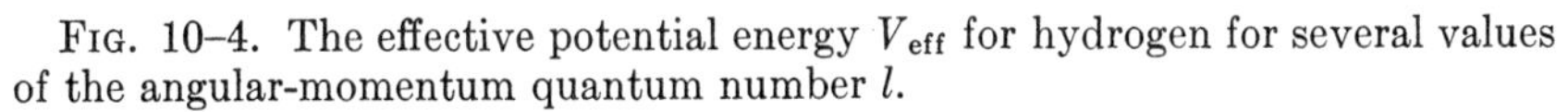
Fig. 10–4. The effective potential energy V_{eff} for hydrogen for several values of the angular-momentum quantum number l.

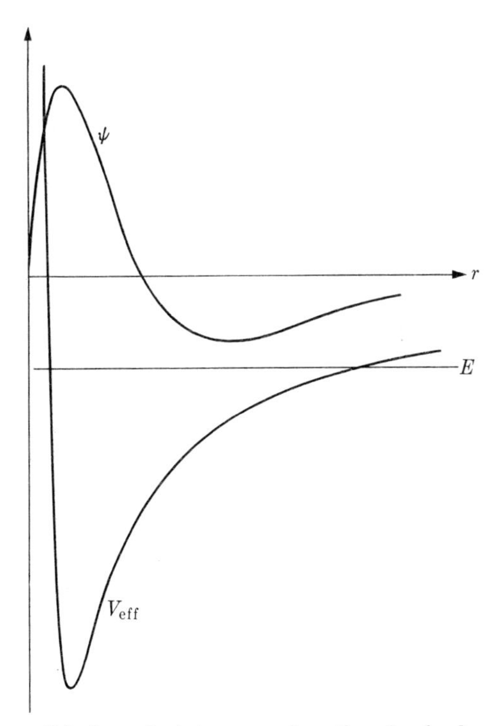

Fig. 10–5. A possible bound-state wave function for hydrogen. The wave function shown corresponds to the $l = 1$ effective potential of Fig. 10–4.

This can be simplified by using a new measure of length,

$$\rho \equiv \frac{\sqrt{8m|E|}}{\hbar}\, r, \tag{10–9}$$

and a new measure of the binding energy of the particle,

$$\lambda \equiv \sqrt{\frac{m}{2|E|}} \cdot \frac{Ze^2}{\hbar}. \tag{10–10}$$

With these substitutions, Eq. (10–8) becomes

$$\frac{d^2u}{d\rho^2} - \frac{l(l+1)}{\rho^2}\, u + \left(\frac{\lambda}{\rho} - \frac{1}{4}\right) u = 0. \tag{10–11}$$

As in the discussion of the differential equation for the simple harmonic oscillator, consider first the asymptotic dependence of the solution. The asymptotic behavior of the solution is clearly

$$u \sim \exp\left(\pm \frac{\rho}{2}\right), \tag{10–12}$$

where the minus sign must be taken, since u must be everywhere finite. Again, because of the dominance of the exponential dependence, one can multiply the exponential by a polynomial and still preserve the asymptotic behavior. This suggests that we look for a solution which is finite everywhere in the form of a polynomial multiplying the exponential of Eq. (10–12):

$$u = F \exp\left(-\tfrac{1}{2}\rho\right). \tag{10–13}$$

If we apply this assumption, Eq. (10–11) becomes

$$\frac{d^2F}{d\rho^2} - \frac{dF}{d\rho} + \left[\frac{\lambda}{\rho} - \frac{l(l+1)}{\rho^2}\right] F = 0, \tag{10–14}$$

where

$$F = \sum_{k=1}^{\infty} A_k \rho^k. \tag{10–15}$$

This automatically fulfills the condition that F vanish at $\rho = 0$. Substituting this expression into Eq. (10–14) and equating coefficients of like powers of ρ to zero gives the relationships

$$\begin{aligned} l(l+1)A_1 &= 0, \\ (\lambda - 1)A_1 + [2 - l(l+1)]A_2 &= 0 \end{aligned} \tag{10–16}$$

and the recursion formula

$$[k(k+1) - l(l+1)]A_{k+1} + (\lambda - k)A_k = 0, \qquad k \geq 2. \quad (10\text{–}17)$$

If the series of Eq. (10–15) does not terminate, i.e., is infinite, the ratio of succeeding terms is, from Eq. (10–17),

$$\frac{A_{k+1}}{A_k} = \frac{k - \lambda}{k(k+1) - l(l+1)}, \qquad k \geq 2. \quad (10\text{–}18)$$

The limit of this ratio as k increases without limit is

$$\frac{A_{k+1}}{A_k} \xrightarrow[k\to\infty]{} \frac{1}{k+1}. \quad (10\text{–}19)$$

This is the same ratio of coefficients as in the power-series expansion of $\exp \rho$; the series of Eq. (10–15) thus has the asymptotic behavior $\exp \rho$ if it is nonterminating. Clearly, the result is then that u has an asymptotic dependence $\exp(\frac{1}{2}\rho)$, which violates the condition that the wave function be everywhere finite. A physically acceptable solution to Eq. (10–14) of the form of Eq. (10–15) must therefore have only a finite number of terms.

If λ is nonintegral, it is clear from the recursion relation Eq. (10–17) that if any A_k is nonzero, the series cannot terminate, since both k and l must be integral. The only acceptable solution for λ nonintegral is therefore the trivial solution in which all $A_k = 0$, or $F = 0$.

Considering, then, only integral values for λ, we can similarly show that there are no physically acceptable solutions either for $\lambda = 0$ or for $\lambda = l$. This leaves the case $\lambda = n$, where $n \neq l$ is an integer. From the relations of Eqs. (10–16) and (10–17), it can be shown that

$$A_k = 0, \qquad k \leq l, \quad (10\text{–}20)$$

must hold. From this result it follows that the case of $\lambda = n < l$ leads to a nonterminating series and hence must be rejected. The case

$$\lambda = n > l \quad (10\text{–}21)$$

leads to a terminating series. This can be seen from Eq. (10–17), which shows that in this case

$$A_k = 0 \quad \text{for} \quad k \geq n + 1. \quad (10\text{–}22)$$

The resulting polynomials, which can be designated by the two indices n and l, are closely related to the *associated Laguerre polynomials:*

$$u_{ln} = \left(\sum_{k=l}^{n} A_k \rho^k\right) \exp\left(-\tfrac{1}{2}\rho\right). \tag{10–23}$$

If we use Eq. (10–21) in conjunction with the definition of λ, Eq. (10–10), we obtain an expression for the possible bound-energy states of the hydrogenic atom:

$$E_n = -\tfrac{1}{2} mc^2 \alpha^2 \frac{Z^2}{n^2}, \qquad n > l, \tag{10–24}$$

where

$$\alpha \equiv \frac{e^2}{\hbar c} \tag{10–25}$$

is known as the *fine-structure constant.* The expression for the energy eigenvalues does not contain l as a parameter. There is usually more than one value of l for a given energy. This is an accidental degeneracy which is peculiar to the coulomb potential.

TABLE 10–1

SEVERAL RADIAL WAVE FUNCTIONS FOR HYDROGENIC ATOMS

$R_{nl}(r) \equiv \dfrac{1}{r} u_{nl}$
$R_{10}(r) = \left(\dfrac{Z}{a_0}\right)^{3/2} \cdot 2 \exp\left(-\dfrac{Zr}{a_0}\right)$
$R_{20}(r) = \left(\dfrac{Z}{2a_0}\right)^{3/2} \cdot 2\left(1 - \dfrac{1}{2}\dfrac{Zr}{a_0}\right) \exp\left(-\dfrac{1}{2}\dfrac{Zr}{a_0}\right)$
$R_{21}(r) = \left(\dfrac{Z}{2a_0}\right)^{3/2} \cdot \dfrac{1}{\sqrt{3}}\dfrac{Zr}{a_0} \exp\left(-\dfrac{1}{2}\dfrac{Zr}{a_0}\right)$
$R_{30}(r) = \left(\dfrac{Z}{3a_0}\right)^{3/2} \cdot 2\left[1 - \dfrac{2}{3}\dfrac{Zr}{a_0} + \dfrac{2}{27}\left(\dfrac{Zr}{a_0}\right)^2\right] \exp\left(-\dfrac{1}{3}\dfrac{Zr}{a_0}\right)$
$R_{31}(r) = \left(\dfrac{Z}{3a_0}\right)^{3/2} \cdot \dfrac{4\sqrt{2}}{3}\dfrac{Zr}{a_0}\left(1 - \dfrac{1}{6}\dfrac{Zr}{a_0}\right) \exp\left(-\dfrac{1}{3}\dfrac{Zr}{a_0}\right)$
$R_{32}(r) = \left(\dfrac{Z}{3a_0}\right)^{3/2} \cdot \dfrac{2\sqrt{2}}{27\sqrt{5}}\left(\dfrac{Zr}{a_0}\right)^2 \exp\left(-\dfrac{1}{3}\dfrac{Zr}{a_0}\right)$

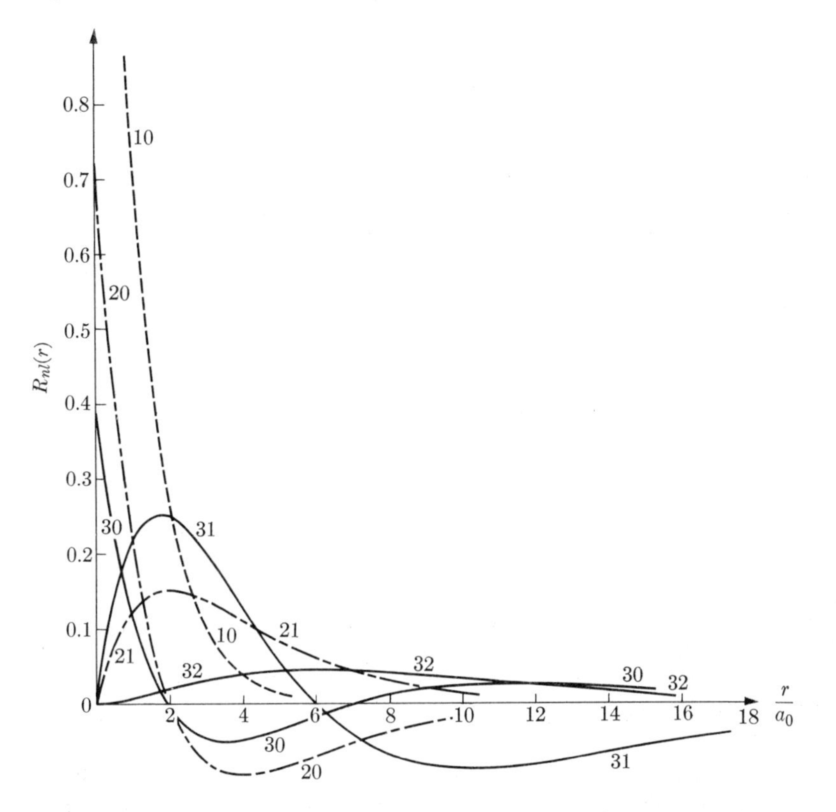

FIG. 10–6. The radial wave functions $R_{nl}(r)$ for hydrogenic atoms for $n = 1, 2, 3$. Each curve is labeled with two integers, representing the corresponding n and l values. Note the effect of the centrifugal force in "pushing out" the wave function from the center of the atom. Note also that the functions have $n - l - 1$ nodes.

In Table 10–1 a few of the simpler radial wave functions are tabulated; these are plotted in Fig. 10–6. In the expressions for these functions,

$$a_0 \equiv \frac{\hbar^2}{me^2} \tag{10–26}$$

is the *Bohr radius* for the hydrogen atom. It should be noted that these radial functions have $n - l - 1$ nodes.

In Fig. 10–7 an energy-level diagram for the hydrogen atom is shown, with the relevant quantum numbers associated with the various energy states. Spectroscopic notation for the various levels is also given, at the top of the figure.

In the above treatment of the hydrogen atom, we made one important implicit assumption that deserves further consideration. The hydrogen

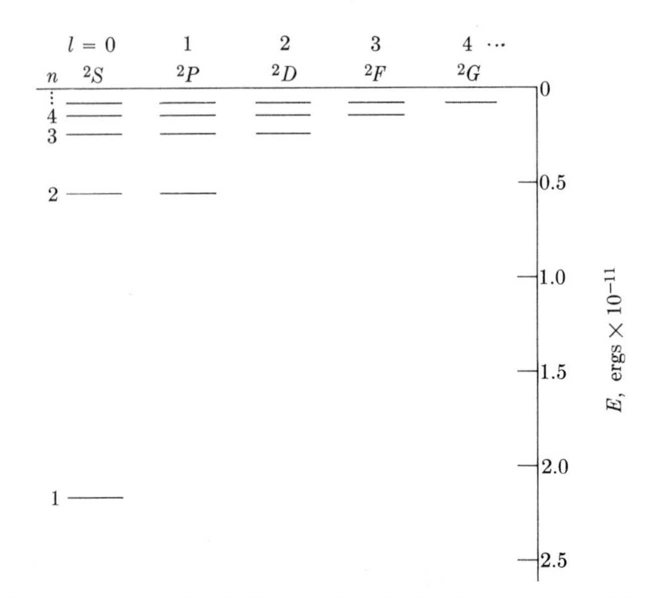

FIG. 10–7. An energy-level diagram for the hydrogen atom. The principal quantum numbers n are indicated at the left of the figure, and the spectroscopic notation for the various terms is given at the top. Compare these energy levels with Fig. 10–4.

atom was treated like a single-particle system by the implicit assumption of Eq. (10–1) that a single electron moves about a *fixed* attractive center. Because of the much greater mass of a hydrogen nucleus (proton) compared with the electronic mass, this is a reasonable approximation. Modifications in the above development which are required by not regarding the proton simply as a center of force around which the electron moves, but instead as a member of a two-body dynamical system, will now be considered. In this case, the Hamiltonian can be written as

$$\mathrm{H} = \frac{1}{2m_1}\mathrm{P}_1^2 + \frac{1}{2m_2}\mathrm{P}_2^2 - \frac{e^2}{r_{12}}, \tag{10–27}$$

where the subscript 1 refers to the electron and the subscript 2 to the proton. Here the denominator of the potential-energy term is given by

$$r_{12} \equiv |\boldsymbol{r}_1 - \boldsymbol{r}_2|. \tag{10–28}$$

It is useful to replace the position variables $\boldsymbol{r}_1$ and $\boldsymbol{r}_2$ of the two particles by other coordinates describing the locations of the particles. We introduce the position of the electron relative to the proton $\boldsymbol{r}$ by

$$\boldsymbol{r} \equiv \boldsymbol{r}_1 - \boldsymbol{r}_2, \tag{10–29}$$

and also introduce the coordinates of the center of mass of the system of two particles:

$$\boldsymbol{R} \equiv \frac{m_1 \boldsymbol{r}_1 + m_2 \boldsymbol{r}_2}{m_1 + m_2}. \tag{10–30}$$

The corresponding momentum operators are defined by

$$\begin{aligned} \mathbf{p} &\equiv -i\hbar \boldsymbol{\nabla}_r, \\ \mathbf{P} &\equiv -i\hbar \boldsymbol{\nabla}_R. \end{aligned} \tag{10–31}$$

We further introduce symbols for the total mass and the reduced mass of the atom:

$$\begin{aligned} M &\equiv m_1 + m_2, \\ \mu &\equiv \frac{m_1 m_2}{m_1 + m_2}. \end{aligned} \tag{10–32}$$

Substituting these various expressions into the Hamiltonian of Eq. (10–27), we obtain

$$\mathrm{H} = \frac{1}{2M} \mathrm{P}^2 + \frac{1}{2\mu} \mathrm{p}^2 - \frac{e^2}{r}. \tag{10–33}$$

The advantage of this transformation is that the momentum associated with the motion of the center of mass, which is simply the total translational momentum of the atom, now involves coordinates independent of the potential energy of the atom, and consequently the momentum operator P commutes with the Hamiltonian:

$$[\mathrm{H}, \mathrm{P}] = 0. \tag{10–34}$$

The energy of the atom can then be separated into two parts, the internal energy, given by

$$\mathrm{H}_0 \equiv \frac{1}{2\mu} \mathrm{p}^2 - \frac{e^2}{r}, \tag{10–35}$$

and the first term on the right side of Eq. (10–33), representing the energy associated with the translational motion of the atom as a whole. Since the momentum operator P of Eq. (10–31) and the internal energy operator H_0 commute with each other, we can choose wave functions which are simultaneous eigenfunctions of these two operators. The operator H_0 is identical in form to the operator we considered earlier for the hydrogen atom when the dynamical properties of the proton were ignored and the proton was regarded merely as a center of force. Consequently, the solution to the eigenvalue equation will be identical to the earlier solution, the only difference being that the electron mass is here replaced by the reduced mass of the atom. The wave function, which is simultaneously an eigenfunction of the translational energy of the atom and the internal energy, is of the form

$$\psi = \exp\left(\frac{i\boldsymbol{P}\cdot\boldsymbol{R}}{\hbar}\right) u_{n\,lm_l}(r). \tag{10-36}$$

The energy eigenvalue associated with this wave function is easily seen to represent the energy of translation of the atom plus the internal energy; for the internal energy, we have

$$E_n = -\tfrac{1}{2}\mu c^2\alpha^2 \frac{1}{n^2}\cdot \tag{10-37}$$

The correctness of this particular form for the internal energy of the atom has been verified by comparing the spectra of hydrogen, deuterium, and tritium, for which the reduced masses are measurably different.

10-3 The three-dimensional oscillator. As a second example of the type of problem encountered in the case of motion of a particle under the influence of central forces, we consider the isotropic three-dimensional oscillator. In this case, the Hamiltonian can be written as

$$\mathrm{H} = \frac{1}{2\mu}\mathrm{P}^2 + \tfrac{1}{2}kr^2. \tag{10-38}$$

One has the choice of choosing eigenfunctions to be simultaneously eigenfunctions of H, L^2, and L_z because of the central force under which the particle is moving or, alternatively, one can choose eigenfunctions that are simultaneous eigenfunctions of the mutually commuting operators H_x, H_y, H_z, defined through

$$\mathrm{H}_x \equiv \frac{1}{2\mu}\mathrm{P}_x^2 + \tfrac{1}{2}kx^2, \quad \text{etc.} \tag{10-39}$$

In terms of these, the Hamiltonian can be expressed as

$$\mathrm{H} = \mathrm{H}_x + \mathrm{H}_y + \mathrm{H}_z. \tag{10-40}$$

Since H_x, H_y, and H_z commute and each operates on a different variable from the others, it is possible to write the eigenfunctions as

$$\psi_{qrs} = \psi_q(x)\psi_r(y)\psi_s(z), \tag{10-41}$$

where

$$\begin{aligned} \mathrm{H}_x\psi_q(x) &= (q+\tfrac{1}{2})\hbar\omega\psi_q(x), \\ \mathrm{H}_y\psi_r(y) &= (r+\tfrac{1}{2})\hbar\omega\psi_r(y), \\ \mathrm{H}_z\psi_s(z) &= (s+\tfrac{1}{2})\hbar\omega\psi_s(z), \end{aligned} \tag{10-42}$$

Table 10–2

Degeneracies of the Energy States of a Three-Dimensional Oscillator

Energy state	Degeneracy
$n = 0$	1
$n = 1$	3
$n = 2$	6
$n = 3$	10
$\vdots$	$\vdots$

from the earlier discussion of the one-dimensional oscillator (Chapter 3). Here the quantum numbers q, r, and s are associated respectively with the x-, y-, and z-motions of the particle. The simultaneous eigenfunction which appears in Eq. (10–41) is clearly an eigenfunction of the Hamiltonian H, the eigenvalue equation for which is

$$\mathrm{H}\psi_{qrs} = (q + r + s + \tfrac{3}{2})\hbar\omega\psi_{qrs} = (n + \tfrac{3}{2})\hbar\omega\psi_{qrs}. \qquad (10\text{–}43)$$

A reason for considering this set of simultaneous eigenfunctions is to count the degeneracy of the various energy states of the three-dimensional oscillator. Note that the ground state with $n = 0$ can be achieved in only one way, by setting q, r, and s all equal to zero. On the other hand, the first excited state $n = 1$ can be obtained by setting any one of the quantum numbers q, r, or s equal to one and the others to zero; there are three ways this can occur, and consequently the degeneracy of the state $n = 1$ is 3. In a similar way, one can count the degeneracies of the other energy states of the three-dimensional oscillator, which will yield the results given in Table 10–2.

One reason it is convenient to know the degeneracies of the three-dimensional oscillator is that in considering the problem of finding simultaneous eigenstates of H, L^2, and L_z, it is useful to have a criterion to determine when the set of wave functions is complete. With this new set of commuting observables, choose a new set of wave functions characterized by an index n for the energy, l for the total angular momentum, and m for the z-component of angular momentum. The energy-eigenvalue equation must be

$$\mathrm{H}\psi_{nlm} = (n + \tfrac{3}{2})\hbar\omega\psi_{nlm}. \qquad (10\text{–}44)$$

It is clearly desirable to find a ladder operator which will not only generate states of various energies but also states of various angular momenta; we introduce the vector operator **R** defined by

$$\mathbf{R} \equiv \frac{1}{\sqrt{2\mu}}\mathbf{P} + i\sqrt{\frac{k}{2}}\,\mathbf{r}. \tag{10–45}$$

A comparison with Eq. (6–74) shows that each component of this vector is a ladder operator for generating higher energy states from lower energy states: every time it is applied to a wave function, it gives a new wave function for which the energy is greater. Since the vector **R** defined by Eq. (10–45) is a linear combination of two class **T** vectors, it also is in class **T**. Consequently we can define the operator R_+:

$$\mathrm{R}_+ \equiv \mathrm{R}_x + i\mathrm{R}_y, \tag{10–46}$$

which will serve as a ladder operator for generating states of higher angular momentum from those of lower angular momentum. From Eq. (6–79), the operator R_+ satisfies the commutation relation with the Hamiltonian given by

$$[\mathrm{H}, \mathrm{R}_+] = \hbar\omega \mathrm{R}_+. \tag{10–47}$$

The lowest energy state of the three-dimensional oscillator, since it is nondegenerate, can be written directly, as in Eq. (10–41), simply as a product of the three lowest-state wave functions for the simple harmonic oscillator in the x-, y-, and z-directions. This is, when normalized to unity,

$$\psi_{000} = \left(\frac{k}{\pi\hbar\omega}\right)^{3/4} \exp\left(-\frac{1}{2}\frac{kr^2}{\hbar\omega}\right). \tag{10–48}$$

Operating on this wave function s times with the operator R_+ gives

$$\mathrm{R}_+^s\psi_{000} = \psi_{sss}. \tag{10–49}$$

The ladder property of the operator R_+ with respect to increasing energy and angular momentum increases all three indices by one unit.

On the other hand, from Eq. (9–83), the operator R^2 obtained by squaring Eq. (10–45), when applied to a wave function which is simultaneously an eigenfunction of L^2 and L_z, does not change the eigenvalues corresponding to these two operators, but merely increases the energy. Thus it is a ladder operator for increasing the energy of the state without changing angular momentum. Since the vector **R** itself increases the energy by one unit, the operator R^2 increases the energy by two units: when this operator is iteratively applied to the wave function of Eq. (10–48), the

TABLE 10–3

DEGENERACIES OF THE ENERGY EIGENSTATES OF A THREE-DIMENSIONAL OSCILLATOR

Energy eigenstates			Degeneracy
$n = 0$	$l = 0$	$m = 0$	1
$n = 1$	$l = 1$	$m = 1, 0, -1$	3
$n = 2$	$l = 0, 2$	$m = 0; 2, 1, 0, -1, -2$	6
$n = 3$	$l = 1, 3$	$m = 1, 0, -1; 3, 2, 1, 0, -1, -2, -3$	10
$\vdots$	$\vdots$	$\vdots$	$\vdots$

result is

$$(\mathrm{R}^2)^s\psi_{000} = \psi_{2s,0,0}. \tag{10–50}$$

It is clear that by applying first the operator R^2, then the operator R_+, and finally the orbital angular-momentum ladder operator L_-, one can obtain the expression for the general wave function which is simultaneously an eigenfunction of H, L^2, and L_z:

$$\psi_{nlm} = \mathrm{L}_-^{l-m}\mathrm{R}_+^l(\mathrm{R}^2)^{(n-l)/2}\psi_{000}. \tag{10–51}$$

Since the power of R^2 must be integral, n and l must be both even or odd, and $n \geq l$.

No attempt has been made in the above formalism to preserve the normalization of the wave function, so Eq. (10–51) is not properly normalized. On the other hand, by using techniques very similar to those employed in Chapter 9, it is easy to calculate the proper constant by which to multiply Eq. (10–51) so that the resulting function is normalized to unity. Equation (10–51) represents a set of functions which are simultaneously eigenfunctions of the three operators H, L^2, and L_z; however, there still exists the possibility that this set of functions may not be complete. To check this, the degeneracy of each energy eigenstate will be calculated. The degeneracies are enumerated in Table 10–3. It is seen by comparing Table 10–3 with Table 10–2 that the degeneracies are the same, and hence the set of eigenfunctions given by Eq. (10–51) is complete.

10–4 The free particle. A free particle has already been discussed in terms of motion characterized by a plane wave when the energy and the linear momentum of the particle were well-defined, i.e., known. The plane wave was then a simultaneous eigenstate of the Hamiltonian and the linear momentum of the particle. On the other hand, a free particle can also be considered to be a particle which is moving in a central field of force, the trivial case in which no force is present. Consequently, the Hamiltonian, L^2, and L_z are three simultaneously commuting operators, and it is possible to choose eigenfunctions which are simultaneously eigenfunctions of these three operators. Such a set of functions cannot be plane waves, inasmuch as the linear-momentum operator does not commute with the angular-momentum operators. The eigenvalue equations for energy, total angular momentum, and the z-component of angular momentum are

$$\begin{aligned} \mathrm{H}\psi_{klm} &= E\psi_{klm} = \frac{\hbar^2 k^2}{2\mu}\psi_{klm}, \\ \mathrm{L}^2\psi_{klm} &= l(l+1)\hbar^2\psi_{klm}, \\ \mathrm{L}_z\psi_{klm} &= m\hbar\psi_{klm}. \end{aligned} \tag{10–52}$$

With the definition

$$\psi \equiv \frac{1}{r}u, \tag{10–53}$$

the radial equation for the free particle in the case of $l = 0$ takes the form

$$-\frac{\hbar^2}{2\mu}\frac{d^2u}{dr^2} - \frac{\hbar^2k^2}{2\mu}u = 0. \tag{10–54}$$

This is a simple differential equation which can be solved to give

$$\psi_{k00} = \frac{\sin kr}{kr}. \tag{10–55}$$

This wave function is not normalized to unity, nor is it normalizable.

Instead of considering the radial differential equation for states other than $l = 0$, one can find a way of generating all the other wave functions from the state of $l = 0$ given in Eq. (10–55). The momentum operator $\mathbf{P}$ belongs to the class of vector operators $\mathbf{T}$; we introduce the operator P_+:

$$\mathrm{P}_+ \equiv \mathrm{P}_x + i\mathrm{P}_y. \tag{10–56}$$

Since P_+ is simply the sum of two components of the linear momentum of the particle, P_+ commutes with the Hamiltonian. As such, a wave function which is an energy eigenfunction will remain an energy eigenfunction of the same energy after being operated on by P_+. On the other hand, from Eq. (9–87), the effect of the operator P_+ on a wave function with $l = m$ is that of increasing both l and m by one. Consequently, the operation of P_+ on the wave function of Eq. (10–55) must generate the wave function

$$P_+\psi_{k00} \sim \psi_{k11}. \tag{10–57}$$

This procedure may be iterated l times to generate the wave function

$$P_+^l\psi_{k00} \sim \psi_{kll}. \tag{10–58}$$

Making use of the angular-momentum ladder operator, one can then generate the general wave function for the free particle with quantum numbers k, l, and m:

$$L_-^{l-m}P_+^l\psi_{k00} \sim \psi_{klm}. \tag{10–59}$$

To see in somewhat more detail the effect of operating on a function with an operator of the form P_+, consider the effect of this operator on any general function of r:

$$P_+f(r) = -i\hbar\left(\frac{x+iy}{r}\right)\frac{d}{dr}f(r). \tag{10–60}$$

Using the result of Problem 10–7, this operation may be iterated to give

$$P_+^l f(r) = (-i\hbar)^l(x+iy)^l\left(\frac{1}{r}\frac{d}{dr}\right)^l f(r). \tag{10–61}$$

Except for a proportionality constant, this equation can be written as

$$P_+^l f(r) \sim Y_{ll}r^l\left(\frac{1}{r}\frac{d}{dr}\right)^l f(r). \tag{10–62}$$

From this and Eqs. (10–55) and (10–58), the radial function for the free particle can be written in the form

$$R_{kl}(r) \equiv j_l(kr) = (-1)^l\left(\frac{r}{k}\right)^l\left(\frac{1}{r}\frac{d}{dr}\right)^l\left(\frac{\sin kr}{kr}\right). \tag{10–63}$$

This radial function is a *spherical Bessel function.* These functions will be discussed in detail in Chapter 16. Combining this radial function with the spherical harmonic gives as the wave function for a free particle

$$\psi_{klm} = Y_{lm}(\theta, \phi)R_{kl}(r). \tag{10–64}$$

10–5 Parity. Thus far, the operators that have been investigated have been associated with well-known physical quantities that have significance in large-scale physics. There are, however, operators which do not correspond to the physical observables of large-scale physics. For example, it was found that the wave functions for the simple harmonic oscillator could be catalogued as being either even or odd. We could have introduced an operator which, operating on an even function, would give the eigenvalue 1 and operating on an odd function would give the eigenvalue -1. Such an operator might be thought of in some sense as corresponding to something physically measurable, it being uniquely given in this particular case by the energy of the particle. There are, in fact, numerous operators which can be associated with physically measurable things on an atomic level, yet which have no correspondence in large-scale classical physics. One of these is the *parity operator.* The parity operator has the property

$$\mathrm{P}\psi = \psi(-r_1, -r_2, \ldots), \tag{10–65}$$

namely, that in operating on a function, it changes each of the position variables into its negative. The eigenvalue equation for the parity operator is

$$\mathrm{P}\psi = \gamma\psi. \tag{10–66}$$

If this equation is operated on by the parity operator again, one obtains

$$\mathrm{P}^2\psi = \gamma^2\psi. \tag{10–67}$$

However, from Eq. (10–65) it is apparent that if one applies the parity operator to a function twice, the function is converted back into itself. Consequently, the square of the parity operator must be the identity operator:

$$\mathrm{P}^2 \equiv \mathrm{I}, \tag{10–68}$$

where

$$\mathrm{I}\psi = 1 \cdot \psi. \tag{10–69}$$

Therefore γ^2 must be equal to 1, and γ must be one of the two roots of 1:

$$\gamma = \pm 1. \tag{10–70}$$

An eigenfunction corresponding to the eigenvalue $+1$ for the parity operator is said to be a *function of even parity;* one having the eigenvalue -1 is said to be a *function of odd parity.* When a wave function is of even parity, the system is said to be in a *state of even parity;* for a function of odd parity, the system is said to be in a *state of odd parity.*

If there are no external forces acting on a system of particles, then the potential energy is a function only of the positions of the particles relative to one another. If it is furthermore assumed that the potential energy is a function only of the distance between particles, the Hamiltonian can be written as

$$\mathrm{H} = \sum_{ij} \frac{1}{2m_j} \mathrm{P}_j^2 + V(r_{ij}), \tag{10–71}$$

where

$$r_{ij} = |r_i - r_j|. \tag{10–72}$$

It is easily seen that for a Hamiltonian of the form of Eq. (10–71), the Hamiltonian and the parity operator commute:

$$[\mathrm{H}, \mathrm{P}] = 0. \tag{10–73}$$

It is also easily seen that the parity operator is Hermitian. Choosing simultaneous eigenstates of the Hamiltonian and the parity, we can characterize the various states of different energy by their parity. Also, inasmuch as the wave function for a state of even parity is very different from that for a state of odd parity, it would be an accident if the two states of different parity were to have the same energy.

An example of such a rare accident occurs in the case of the hydrogen atom, where the energy states of $n = 2, 3, 4, \ldots$ are degenerate and contain components of different parity. (However, when relativistic effects are included, the degeneracy is removed.) The states with l even are states of even parity, and states with l odd are states of odd parity. There are also numerous examples of molecules that have states of different parity lying very close to one another, but these energy states of different parity, strictly speaking, do not coincide. When more complex interactions with the electromagnetic field are taken into account, hydrogen has energy states of definite parity. For a complex system, the total angular momentum of the system and the z-component of the angular momentum, as well as the parity and the Hamiltonian, are all mutually commuting observables and can be simultaneously measured, provided, of course, that the Hamiltonian is of the form shown in Eq. (10–71).

An important example of the application of parity is its application to nuclear energy states.* These states can be characterized by the specification of the values of energy, angular momentum, and parity. It is interesting to note that parity is a useful, and in certain cases measurable, quantity in describing nuclear states even though the nuclear wave functions themselves are not known.

---

* The importance of the parity concept in nuclear physics is discussed by J. M. Blatt and V. F. Weisskopf, *Theoretical Nuclear Physics*, John Wiley and Sons, New York, 1952.

As a further example of the application of the parity concept, consider the electric dipole moment associated with a group of particles. An operator for the electric dipole moment of a system of particles can be written as

$$\mathbf{M} = \sum_j q_j r_j, \tag{10–74}$$

where q_j refers to the charge of the jth particle in the system, and the sum is over all the particles of the system. This dipole moment has an expectation value which is zero if it is computed for a state of definite parity. This follows from the fact that the vector $\boldsymbol{M}$ changes sign under a reflection of all the coordinates:

$$\langle \boldsymbol{M} \rangle_{\pm} = (\psi_{\pm}, \mathbf{M}\psi_{\pm}) = (\mathrm{P}\psi_{\pm}, \mathbf{M}\mathrm{P}\psi_{\pm}). \tag{10–75}$$

Since P is Hermitian,

$$\langle \boldsymbol{M} \rangle_{\pm} = (\psi_{\pm}, \mathrm{P}\mathbf{M}\mathrm{P}\psi_{\pm}), \tag{10–76}$$

and since

$$\mathrm{P}\mathbf{M} = -\mathbf{M}\mathrm{P}, \tag{10–77}$$

$$\langle \boldsymbol{M} \rangle_{\pm} = -(\psi_{\pm}, \mathbf{M}\mathrm{P}^2\psi_{\pm}) = -(\psi_{\pm}, \mathbf{M}\psi_{\pm}) = -\langle \boldsymbol{M} \rangle_{\pm}. \tag{10–78}$$

Therefore

$$\langle \boldsymbol{M} \rangle_{\pm} = 0. \tag{10–79}$$

The vanishing of the expectation value of the electric dipole moment of a collection of particles can be interpreted as meaning that the average value of the dipole moment of the collection of particles is zero whenever the particles are in some state of definite energy (and hence, from above, of definite parity), assuming, of course, the absence of accidental degeneracy of states of different parity.

The questions raised by the nonconservation of parity in β-decay are outside the scope of this text and have been deliberately ignored.

10–6 Summary. In this chapter, the central-force problem has been discussed, and it has been shown how a separation of variables in the Schrödinger equation leads to an equivalent one-dimensional (radial) problem. The angular dependence gives rise to a centrifugal term in the effective potential for the radial motion. The hydrogenic atom was considered, with both a qualitative and analytical discussion of the radial wave functions being given, and a few functions were plotted. The treatment of the motion of the proton in a hydrogen atom was also presented, leading to a slight modification of the "infinite-mass nucleus" energy levels.

The three-dimensional harmonic oscillator was the next example studied. Here ladder-operator techniques again demonstrated their value in generating a complete set of wave functions. A free particle, previously treated as a force-free particle, was then considered as a particle acted on by a central force of vanishing strength, ladder operators again being used. Finally the concept of parity was discussed and was used to show that, under quite general conditions, a collection of particles in a state of definite energy has a vanishing expectation value for its electric dipole moment.

Problems

10–1. Assuming a potential-energy function for a diatomic molecule of the form

$$V(r) = \frac{C}{r^3} - \frac{D}{r^2},$$

calculate an integer l_0 such that the quantum number l is less than l_0 for all bound states.

10–2. Prove that the parity operator is Hermitian.

10–3. Prove that if a particle moves in a central potential for which there is at least one bound state, the lowest energy state is an S-state.

10–4. Find the energy levels of a free particle enclosed in a spherical box with perfectly reflecting walls in terms of the roots of appropriate functions.

10–5. Discuss the motion of a particle of mass m in the spherically symmetric potential

$$V = -\frac{\hbar^2}{2m}\frac{\beta}{r^2},$$

where β is a positive constant. [*Hint:* Consider the behavior of the wave function near the origin, remembering the requirement that the wave function be normalizable.]

10–6. Find the appropriate normalization factor for Eq. (10–51).

10–7. Show that:

$$[\mathrm{P}_+, (x + iy)] \equiv (\mathrm{P}_x + i\mathrm{P}_y)(x + iy) - (x + iy)(\mathrm{P}_x + i\mathrm{P}_y) = 0.$$

CHAPTER 11

MATRIX REPRESENTATIONS

11–1 Matrix representations of wave functions and operators. In previous chapters, it was shown that a complete description of the state of a dynamical system is provided by the wave function $\psi(r_1, r_2, \ldots)$ for the state. This chapter is concerned with various ways of representing the wave function and hence the state. This leads to alternate forms of the quantum-mechanical formalism.*

To begin, we choose a complete orthonormal set of functions $u_j(r_1, r_2, \ldots)$; these satisfy the equations

$$(u_j, u_k) \equiv \int \overline{u_j} u_k \, dr_1 \, dr_2 \cdots = \delta_{jk}. \tag{11–1}$$

For simplicity, assume that the set u_j is discrete and finite. Usually, an infinite set of orthonormal functions is required for the expansion of an arbitrary wave function. However, a finite set may be sufficient for the expansion of a limited class of functions. The development will be generalized later to include the cases of infinite sets with or without a continuous range of eigenvalues. Since the u_j form a complete set, any physically admissible wave function ψ can be expanded in terms of them:

$$\psi = \sum_j a_j u_j, \tag{11–2}$$

where

$$a_j = (u_j, \psi). \tag{11–3}$$

The set of numbers a_j constitutes a complete description of the state, since the functions u_j are assumed to be given and known. This set of numbers a_j is said to form a *representation* of the wave function ψ. A type of equation frequently met in quantum-mechanical formalism is of the form

$$Q\psi = \psi', \tag{11–4}$$

---

* Historically, the matrix formulation of quantum mechanics was presented slightly earlier than the wave-mechanical formalism used thus far: W. Heisenberg, "Über quantentheoretische Umdeutung kinematischer und mechanischer Beziehungen," *Z. Physik* **33,** 879 (1925); M. Born and P. Jordan, "Zur Quantenmechanik," *Z. Physik* **34,** 858 (1925); M. Born, W. Heisenberg, and P. Jordan, "Zur Quantenmechanik II," *Z. Physik* **35,** 557 (1925). The equivalence of the wave and matrix formalisms was shown by Schrödinger in 1926: E. Schrödinger, "Über das Verhältnis der Heisenberg-Born-Jordanschen Quantenmechanik zu der meinen," *Ann. Physik* **79,** 734 (1926).

where Q is a differential operator. Upon expansion of both ψ and ψ' in terms of the u_j, as in Eq. (11–2), this becomes

$$Q \sum_j a_j u_j = \sum_j a'_j u_j. \tag{11–5}$$

Multiplication of both sides by $\overline{u_k}$ and integration over all space leads to

$$\sum_j Q_{kj} a_j = a'_k, \tag{11–6}$$

where

$$Q_{kj} = (u_k, Qu_j) \equiv \int \overline{u_k} Q u_j \, dr_1 \, dr_2 \cdots \tag{11–7}$$

Q_{kj} is known as a *matrix element* of Q. It is convenient to express Eq. (11–6) in matrix notation; the elements Q_{kj} can be arranged in a square array:

$$\mathbf{Q} \equiv \begin{bmatrix} Q_{11} & Q_{12} & Q_{13} & \cdots \\ Q_{21} & Q_{22} & Q_{23} & \cdots \\ Q_{31} & Q_{32} & Q_{33} & \cdots \\ \vdots & & & \end{bmatrix}. \tag{11–8}$$

This array is defined to be the matrix $\mathbf{Q}$. In a similar way, the numbers a_j and a'_j can be arranged in linear arrays known as *column vectors* (or *column matrices*):

$$\mathbf{a} \equiv \begin{bmatrix} a_1 \\ a_2 \\ a_3 \\ \vdots \end{bmatrix}; \qquad \mathbf{a}' \equiv \begin{bmatrix} a'_1 \\ a'_2 \\ a'_3 \\ \vdots \end{bmatrix}. \tag{11–9}$$

In matrix notation, Eq. (11–6) becomes

$$\mathbf{Qa} = \mathbf{a}', \tag{11–10}$$

where the law of matrix multiplication is given by Eq. (11–6).

11–2 Matrix algebra. In addition to the case of the multiplication of a square matrix and a column vector, more general algebraic operations can be performed with matrices. This section deals with these algebraic properties of matrices. It has been seen above that matrices need not be square arrays, e.g., the column vector $\mathbf{a}$. If two matrices have equal dimensions, i.e., the number of rows are equal and the number of columns are equal, it is possible to define matrix addition:

$$\mathbf{R} + \mathbf{S} = \mathbf{T}. \tag{11–11}$$

The addition rule is

$$R_{ij} + S_{ij} = T_{ij}. \tag{11–12}$$

The general law for the multiplication of two matrices

$$\mathbf{RS} = \mathbf{T} \tag{11–13}$$

is given by

$$\sum_k R_{ik}S_{kj} = T_{ij}. \tag{11–14}$$

From this it can be seen that a necessary requirement for matrix multiplication is that the number of rows of the matrix $\mathbf{S}$ be equal to the number of columns of the matrix $\mathbf{R}$. The resultant product matrix will have the number of rows of the matrix $\mathbf{R}$ and the number of columns of the matrix $\mathbf{S}$.

The above rules for matrix addition and multiplication imply several general algebraic relations that are often taken to be postulates of matrix algebra:

(1) Multiplication is associative:

$$\mathbf{A}(\mathbf{BC}) = (\mathbf{AB})\mathbf{C}. \tag{11–15}$$

(2) There exists a square identity matrix $\mathbf{I}$ such that

$$\mathbf{IA} = \mathbf{A}. \tag{11–16}$$

It is clear that

$$I_{jk} = \delta_{jk}. \tag{11–17}$$

(3) The distributive law holds:

$$\mathbf{A}(\mathbf{B} + \mathbf{C}) = \mathbf{AB} + \mathbf{AC}. \tag{11–18}$$

(4) A square matrix *may* have an inverse:

$$\mathbf{AA}^{-1} = \mathbf{I} = \mathbf{A}^{-1}\mathbf{A}. \tag{11–19}$$

If it does, it is said to be *nonsingular*.

(5) In general, multiplication is noncommutative:

$$\mathbf{AB} \neq \mathbf{BA}. \tag{11–20}$$

If $\mathbf{AB} = \mathbf{BA}$, the matrices are said to commute.

A few definitions are useful. The *transpose* of the matrix $\mathbf{A}$ is written $\widetilde{\mathbf{A}}$ and has elements

$$\widetilde{A}_{ij} \equiv A_{ji}. \tag{11–21}$$

The *Hermitian adjoint* of a matrix A is written A^* and has elements

$$A^*_{ij} \equiv \overline{A_{ji}}. \tag{11-22}$$

The Hermitian adjoint of the *product* of two matrices is equal to the product of their Hermitian adjoints taken in *inverse* order:

$$(\mathsf{AB})^* = \mathsf{B}^*\mathsf{A}^*. \tag{11-23}$$

If a matrix is equal to its transpose, it is *symmetric*:

$$A_{ij} = \tilde{A}_{ij} = A_{ji}. \tag{11-24}$$

A matrix is *Hermitian* if it is equal to its Hermitian adjoint:

$$A_{ij} = A^*_{ij} = \overline{A_{ji}}. \tag{11-25}$$

A matrix is *unitary* if its inverse is equal to its Hermitian adjoint:

$$A^{-1}_{ij} = A^*_{ij}. \tag{11-26}$$

A matrix representation of a Hermitian operator is Hermitian, for

$$\begin{aligned}\overline{Q_{jk}} &\equiv \overline{(u_j, \mathrm{Q}u_k)} \\ &= (\mathrm{Q}u_k, u_j) \\ &= (u_k, \mathrm{Q}u_j) \\ &\equiv Q_{kj}.\end{aligned} \tag{11-27}$$

The third step depends on the Hermitian character of Q.

The matrix of the product of two operators is the product of the corresponding matrices. This is shown by making use of the closure relation derived in Chapter 6, Eq. (6–57):

$$\sum_j \overline{u_j}(r_1, r_2, \ldots)u_j(r'_1, r'_2, \ldots) = \delta(r_1 - r'_1)\,\delta(r_2 - r'_2)\cdots \tag{11-28}$$

To simplify the notation, assume in the following that the system is describable by the coordinates r. The product of two matrices is given, as above, by

$$\begin{aligned}\sum_k Q_{jk}P_{kl} &= \sum_k (u_j, \mathrm{Q}u_k)(u_k, \mathrm{P}u_l) \\ &\equiv \sum_k \int \overline{u_j}\mathrm{Q}u_k\,dr \int \overline{u_k}\mathrm{P}u_l\,dr'.\end{aligned} \tag{11-29}$$

From the closure relation, Eq. (11–28), this is equal to

$$\begin{aligned}\sum_k Q_{jk}P_{kl} &= \int \overline{u_j}\mathrm{Q}\,\delta(r - r')\mathrm{P}u_l\,dr\,dr' \\ &= \int \overline{\mathrm{Q}u_j}\,\delta(r - r')\mathrm{P}u_l\,dr\,dr' \\ &= \int \overline{\mathrm{Q}u_j}\mathrm{P}u_l\,dr \\ &= \int \overline{u_j}\mathrm{QP}u_l\,dr \\ &\equiv [\mathsf{QP}]_{jl}. \end{aligned} \tag{11–30}$$

From this, it follows that the matrices of commuting operators are commuting, and that the matrix of an operator that is inverse to Q is the matrix inverse to Q; the algebraic properties of the differential operators are mirrored in their matrices.

It is generally desirable to take the set of functions u_k used as the base of the matrix representation to be the eigenfunctions of some quantum-mechanical operator. For example, the u_k may be the eigenfunctions of the Hamiltonian:

$$\mathrm{H}u_k = E_k u_k. \tag{11–31}$$

Then

$$H_{ij} \equiv (u_i, \mathrm{H}u_j) = (u_i, E_j u_j) = E_j\,\delta_{ij}. \tag{11–32}$$

In this case, H has nonzero elements only along the diagonal of the matrix. Such a matrix is said to be *diagonal*. If the orthonormal set of base functions is simultaneously a set of eigenfunctions of several commuting operators, the matrices of all these operators are diagonal.

11–3 Types of matrix representation. If the orthonormal set of base functions is time-independent, the Schrödinger equation is left unchanged in form upon transforming to a matrix representation. Let the expansion coefficients be represented by $\psi_n(t)$:

$$\psi(r, t) \equiv \sum_n \psi_n(t)u_n(r). \tag{11–33}$$

Substituting this expression into the Schrödinger equation yields

$$\mathsf{H}\psi = i\hbar\,\frac{d}{dt}\,\psi. \tag{11–34}$$

The right side of this equation needs some explanation: the time derivative of the matrix ψ with elements ψ_j represents the matrix having the elements

ψ_j. A representation of this type, in which the base functions are time-independent (thus making the wave vector ψ time-dependent), is known as a *Schrödinger representation.*

Another type of representation, known as the *Heisenberg representation,* is sometimes useful. Consider a set of functions u_n of both r and t that is an orthonormal set at $t = 0$ and satisfies Schrödinger's equation. The set continues to be orthonormal at all times, as is seen below:

$$\mathrm{H}u_n = i\hbar \frac{\partial u_n}{\partial t} \cdot \tag{11-35}$$

Then

$$(u_m, \mathrm{H}u_n) = i\hbar \left(u_m, \frac{\partial}{\partial t} u_n\right) \cdot \tag{11-36}$$

Alternatively,

$$(u_n, \mathrm{H}u_m) = i\hbar \left(u_n, \frac{\partial}{\partial t} u_m\right) \tag{11-37}$$

or

$$(\mathrm{H}u_m, u_n) = -i\hbar \left(\frac{\partial}{\partial t} u_m, u_n\right) \cdot \tag{11-38}$$

Since H is Hermitian, Eq. (11-36) can be written as

$$(\mathrm{H}u_m, u_n) = +i\hbar \left(u_m, \frac{\partial}{\partial t} u_n\right) \cdot \tag{11-39}$$

Subtracting Eq. (11-38) from Eq. (11-39) gives

$$\begin{aligned} 0 &= i\hbar \left[\left(u_m, \frac{\partial}{\partial t} u_n\right) + \left(\frac{\partial}{\partial t} u_m, u_n\right)\right] \\ &= i\hbar \frac{d}{dt} (u_m, u_n). \end{aligned} \tag{11-40}$$

This implies that the orthonormality of the set of functions u_n does not change with time.

Since

$$(u_m, u_n) = \delta_{mn} \tag{11-41}$$

for all time, the functions u_n can be used to obtain a matrix representation. Let

$$\psi \equiv \sum_n \psi_n u_n(r, t). \tag{11-42}$$

Each term in the sum satisfies the Schrödinger equation; the sum with constant coefficients ψ_n will therefore also satisfy this equation, and the representation of the wave function ψ, which is a solution to Schrödinger's equation, is time-independent. (The coefficients ψ_n, which are the representation, are time-independent.)

On the other hand, an operator in this representation is usually time-dependent; consider an operator with matrix elements

$$Q_{ij} = (u_i, \mathrm{Q}u_j). \tag{11–43}$$

The time derivative of this matrix has elements

$$\dot{Q}_{ij} = \left(\frac{\partial u_i}{\partial t}, \mathrm{Q}u_j\right) + \left(u_i, \mathrm{Q}\,\frac{\partial u_j}{\partial t}\right) + \left(u_i, \frac{\partial \mathrm{Q}}{\partial t}\,u_j\right). \tag{11–44}$$

From Eq. (11–35), this can be written as

$$\begin{aligned}\dot{Q}_{ij} &= \frac{i}{\hbar}\,[(\mathrm{H}u_i, \mathrm{Q}u_j) + (u_i, \mathrm{QH}u_j)] + \left(u_i, \frac{\partial \mathrm{Q}}{\partial t}\,u_j\right)\\ &= \frac{i}{\hbar}\,(u_i, [\mathrm{HQ} - \mathrm{QH}]u_j) + \left(u_i, \frac{\partial \mathrm{Q}}{\partial t}\,u_j\right),\end{aligned} \tag{11–45}$$

since H is Hermitian. Thus the matrix relation

$$\dot{\mathbf{Q}} = \frac{i}{\hbar}\,[\mathbf{H}, \mathbf{Q}] + \frac{\partial \mathbf{Q}}{\partial t} \tag{11–46}$$

holds. From the connection between the quantum-mechanical commutator and the classical Poisson bracket postulated in Chapter 6 (see Postulate 7 and the following discussion), the classical analogue of this equation is

$$\dot{Q} = \{Q, H\} + \frac{\partial Q}{\partial t}. \tag{11–47}$$

In other words, any matrix $\mathbf{Q}$ has a time dependence such that it obeys the classical equation of motion derived in Chapter 5, Eq. (5–55).

The type of representation discussed above, known as the *Heisenberg representation*, has all its time dependence connected only with the operators; this dependence can be obtained from classical equations of motion. This is yet another example of the very close formal ties between classical and quantum formulations.

A further type of representation, the *interaction representation*, is also frequently used. Assume that the Hamiltonian can be divided into two parts, H_0 and H_1. The physical situation of interest will make clear what division is appropriate for any given problem. Choose an orthonormal set of base functions which satisfy the Schrödinger equation with H_0 as the Hamiltonian:

$$\mathrm{H}_0 u_k = i\hbar\,\frac{\partial u_k}{\partial t}. \tag{11–48}$$

If we expand the wave function ψ in terms of the functions u_k,

$$\psi = \sum_k \psi_k u_k, \tag{11-49}$$

the complete Schrödinger equation, with $\mathrm{H} = \mathrm{H}_0 + \mathrm{H}_1$, becomes

$$\mathrm{H} \sum_k \psi_k u_k = i\hbar \frac{\partial}{\partial t} \sum_k \psi_k u_k. \tag{11-50}$$

Since the u_k satisfy Eq. (11-48), this becomes

$$\mathrm{H}_1 \sum_k \psi_k u_k + i\hbar \sum_k \psi_k \frac{\partial}{\partial t} u_k = i\hbar \frac{\partial}{\partial t} \sum_k \psi_k u_k \tag{11-51}$$

or

$$\mathrm{H}_1 \sum_k \psi_k u_k = i\hbar \sum_k \frac{\partial \psi_k}{\partial t} u_k. \tag{11-52}$$

If we multiply each side of this equation on the left by $\overline{u_m}$ and integrate over all space, it becomes the matrix equation

$$\mathsf{H}_1 \psi = i\hbar \frac{\partial}{\partial t} \psi. \tag{11-53}$$

In this interaction representation (so named because H_1 is generally taken as the term in the Hamiltonian representing the interaction between distinct systems), the equations of motion of any time-independent matrix operator Q are

$$\dot{\mathsf{Q}} = \frac{i}{\hbar} [\mathsf{H}_0, \mathsf{Q}]. \tag{11-54}$$

It should be noted that Eqs. (11-53) and (11-54) reduce to those of a Heisenberg representation, i.e., time-independent ψ and $\dot{\mathsf{Q}}$, given by Eq. (11-46) when $\mathsf{H}_1 = 0$. The interaction representation is particularly useful when H_1 is small, that is, when H_1 affects the eigenvalues of H only slightly. Under these conditions, approximation methods known as *perturbation techniques* can be employed. These will be discussed in Chapter 14.

It should be noted that there is no unique representation which can be characterized as the Schrödinger, the Heisenberg, or the interaction representation, since the orthonormal set of base functions is not uniquely specified. However, with a Heisenberg representation it is occasionally convenient to place a restriction on the representation by requiring that the energy (Hamiltonian) be diagonal. It may be usefully restricted further by requiring that a complete set of operators which commute with the

Hamiltonian be simultaneously diagonal, along with the Hamiltonian. The choice of a complete set of operators uniquely specifies the representation except for the ordering of the rows and columns and for an arbitrary phase factor exp $(i\delta_k)$ by which each of the base functions u_k can be multiplied. Perhaps the easiest way to see this is to consider the eigenfunctions of H when all the eigenvalues are nondegenerate. As was seen in the discussion of Theorem 8 in Chapter 6, the eigenfunctions of the set of mutually commuting operators form a complete unique set up to an arbitrary multiplicative factor, which from the requirements of normality must be of the form exp $(i\delta_k)$.

11–4 Infinite matrices. Thus far, the discussion has been limited to the case of finite-dimensional spaces with a finite discrete set of base functions u_j. In general, physically interesting situations will require the use of an infinite set of base functions to represent them properly. It will be assumed that the results of the finite-dimensional theory discussed above can be directly applied to the infinite-dimensional case; a rigorous treatment of this matter is outside the scope of this book.

Even thus expanding our treatment to include infinite-dimensional spaces, the assumption that the base functions form a discrete set implies that the quantum-mechanical system is confined in a (very large, perhaps) box, for it can be shown that with an unbounded system the eigenfunctions will in general include a continuous range of functions. For simplicity in treating this more complex situation the discussion will be limited to a single-parameter continuous set. Assume a complete set of functions $u_q(r)$, where q takes on all values between $-\infty$ and $+\infty$. The functions are assumed to be orthonormal in the sense that

$$(u_q, u_{q'}) = \delta(q - q') \tag{11–55}$$

[see the discussion in connection with Eq. (6–46)]. This is very similar to the closure relation

$$\int_{-\infty}^{\infty} u_q^*(r)u_q(r')\,dq = \delta(r - r'), \tag{11–56}$$

except that the spaces of integration are interchanged.

Since the set $u_q(r)$ is complete, any physically allowable wave function $\psi(r)$ can be expanded in the form

$$\psi(r) = \int_{-\infty}^{\infty} \psi(q)u_q(r)\,dq. \tag{11–57}$$

Note that

$$\int |\psi(r)|^2\,dr = \int |\psi(q)|^2\,dq. \tag{11–58}$$

A special case of this latter relation has already been met in Eq. (4-48), where the general continuous variable q of the above discussion was the propagation vector $\boldsymbol{k}$. The function $\psi(q)$ defined by Eq. (11-57) can be considered to be the matrix representation of ψ. In fact, $\psi(\boldsymbol{r})$ can itself be considered to be a matrix representation, with the base vectors $\delta(\boldsymbol{r} - \boldsymbol{r}')$:

$$\psi(\boldsymbol{r}) = \int \psi(\boldsymbol{r}')\, \delta(\boldsymbol{r} - \boldsymbol{r}')\, d\boldsymbol{r}'. \tag{11-59}$$

This is sometimes known as the *r-representation.*

If we use the orthogonal basis provided by the $u_q(\boldsymbol{r})$, the representation $\psi(q)$ is obtained. Using Eq. (11-57) and the orthonormality relation of Eq. (11-55), we obtain

$$\begin{aligned}(u_q, \psi) \equiv \int \overline{u_q}(\boldsymbol{r})\psi(\boldsymbol{r})\, d\boldsymbol{r} &= \iint \psi(q')\overline{u_q}(\boldsymbol{r})u_{q'}(\boldsymbol{r})\, d\boldsymbol{r}\, dq' \\ &= \int \psi(q')\, \delta(q' - q)\, dq' \\ &= \psi(q).\end{aligned} \tag{11-60}$$

By analogy with Eq. (11-7), the matrix representation of a Hermitian operator Q is

$$Q_{q'q} \equiv \int \overline{u_{q'}} \mathrm{Q} u_q\, d\boldsymbol{r}. \tag{11-61}$$

Note that if the u_q are eigenfunctions of Q, then

$$Q_{q'q} = q\, \delta(q - q'), \tag{11-62}$$

and the matrix is diagonal.

The elements of the product of two Hermitian matrices are given by

$$(\mathbf{QP})_{q'q''} = \int Q_{q'q} P_{qq''}\, dq. \tag{11-63}$$

This relation is analogous to Eq. (11-14) for the discrete case.

In similar fashion, the equation

$$\psi' = \mathrm{Q}\psi \tag{11-64}$$

becomes, in a matrix representation,

$$\boldsymbol{\psi}' = \mathbf{Q}\boldsymbol{\psi} \tag{11-65}$$

or, written in component form,

$$\psi'_q = \int Q_{qq'}\psi_{q'}\, dq' \equiv \int Q(q, q')\psi(q')\, dq'. \tag{11-66}$$

It is also sometimes helpful to consider the operator Q in this representation to be the integral operator $\int Q(q, q')\, dq'$. It operates on the function $\psi(q')$ to give

$$\psi'_q = \int Q(q, q')\, dq'\, \psi(q'). \tag{11–67}$$

It is interesting to note that a differential operator Q can be written as an integral operator by using as base vectors the functions $\delta(r - r')$, as in Eq. (11–59); from Eq. (11–61),

$$Q(r, r') = \int \delta(r - r'')Q''\, \delta(r' - r'')\, dr''. \tag{11–68}$$

The double prime on Q under the integral signifies that it operates on the variable r''. Q can be made to operate on the variable r'. The sign of the integral is changed if Q is an odd operator:

$$\begin{aligned} Q(r, r') &= \pm\int \delta(r - r'')Q'\, \delta(r' - r'')\, dr'' \\ &= \pm Q'\, \delta(r - r') \\ &= Q\, \delta(r - r'). \end{aligned} \tag{11–69}$$

The integral operator equivalent to the differential operator Q is thus $\int Q\, \delta(r - r')\, dr'$. If this operator operates on $f(r)$ the result is

$$Qf(r) = \int Q\, \delta(r - r')\, dr' f(r'). \tag{11–70}$$

Since the eigenfunctions of the position operator r are $\delta(r - r')$ [see Eqs. (4–38) *et seq.*], we can apply Eq. (11–62) to get the elements of the matrix $\mathbf{r}$ with the base functions $\delta(r - r')$:

$$r_{rr'} = r(r, r') = r\, \delta(r - r'). \tag{11–71}$$

This is clearly a diagonal matrix: this representation is, as expected, position-diagonal.

11–5 Summary. In this chapter, an equivalent formulation of quantum mechanics known as matrix mechanics has been introduced. It has been seen that both wave functions and operators can be written in matrix form and that these matrices then obey a set of rules of matrix algebra which include associative and distributive multiplication, addition, existence of a unit matrix, possible existence of inverses, and general noncommutativity. Commuting operators were seen to have commuting matrix representations, however.

Three general types of representations were discussed: Schrödinger, Heisenberg, and interaction representations. In a Schrödinger representation the base functions are time-independent, leading to time-dependent representations for wave functions. Heisenberg representations, on the other hand, have time-independent wave function representations, since the base functions are chosen to satisfy the time-dependent Schrödinger equation. In the interaction representation, the Hamiltonian is separated into two parts, one generally describing two independent systems and the other being a weak coupling term. The base functions are then chosen to be solutions of the Schrödinger equation, omitting the coupling term.

The case of infinite-dimensional spaces was discussed and, in particular, representations involving a continuous distribution of eigenfunctions. It was seen that essentially all the results of the discrete case could be taken over with only minor modification. Integral operators were introduced as a sometimes convenient alternative formulation.

Problems

11–1. (a) In a momentum representation, the wave function is a function of which variables? (b) What physical significance can be attached to the absolute value of this wave function? Assume that the system is composed of a single particle (without spin).

11–2. Consider a one-dimensional simple harmonic oscillator. At time $t = 0$ the position is measured and determined to be x_0. Show that a measurement of momentum one-quarter cycle later ($t = \pi/2\omega$) is certain to give the result

$$p = -\sqrt{km}\, x_0.$$

11–3. What can be said about the eigenvalues of a singular matrix?

11–4. In position representation, the Hamiltonian matrix for a single particle may be written as

$$H_{rr'} = \mathrm{H}\, \delta(r - r'),$$

where H is the Hamiltonian operator and acts on r. Show that the inverse of this matrix may be written as

$$H^{-1}_{rr'} = \sum_n E_n^{-1} \overline{\phi_n}(r') \phi_n(r),$$

where E_n and ϕ_n are energy eigenvalues and functions respectively. ϕ is assumed to form an orthonormal set. The above sum is to be interpreted as an integral over any continuous part of the energy distribution.

11–5. An *orthogonal matrix* is one for which $\tilde{\mathsf{T}} = \mathsf{T}^{-1}$. (a) Show that the matrix

$$\mathsf{T} = \begin{bmatrix} \cos\theta & -\sin\theta & 0 \\ \sin\theta & \cos\theta & 0 \\ 0 & 0 & 1 \end{bmatrix},$$

which produces a rotation through an angle θ about the z-axis, is orthogonal. (b) What is $\det \mathbf{T}$?

11–6. In a representation with $\mathbf{L}^2$ and $\mathbf{L}_z$ diagonal, obtain all the vectors which are simultaneously eigenvectors of $\mathbf{L}_x$ and $\mathbf{L}^2$ with the eigenvalue of $\mathbf{L}^2$ equal to $2\hbar^2$. (Use the matrix of Problem 11–5.)

11–7. A *projection operator* is an operator which projects a vector on a subspace. For example, the operator

$$\begin{bmatrix} 1 & 0 & 0 \\ 0 & 1 & 0 \\ 0 & 0 & 0 \end{bmatrix}$$

projects the vector

$$\begin{bmatrix} a \\ b \\ c \end{bmatrix}$$

on a two-dimensional subspace to give

$$\begin{bmatrix} a \\ b \\ 0 \end{bmatrix}.$$

(a) Show that any projection operator $\mathbf{P}$ satisfies the equation $\mathbf{P}^2 - \mathbf{P} = 0$ and has eigenvalues 1 and 0. (b) Show that the integral operator

$$\mathrm{P}_n(r) = \int u_n(r)\overline{u_n}(r')\, dr'$$

projects any vector $\psi(r)$ on the coordinate axis of Hilbert space defined by the normalized unit vector $u_n(r)$. (c) Show that a projection operator is Hermitian. (d) Show that

$$\mathrm{P} = \frac{1}{n}\sum_{q=1}^{n} \exp\left(2\pi \frac{i}{\hbar}\frac{q}{n}\mathrm{L}_z\right)$$

is a projection operator for the subspace for which the quantum number m_l takes on all values which are integral multiples of n.

11–8. If $\mathbf{A}$ is a Hermitian matrix, prove that $\exp(i\mathbf{A})$ is a unitary matrix.

11–9. (a) Show that in a Heisenberg representation, the operator

$$\mathrm{Q} \equiv \mathrm{P}\sin \omega t - m\omega \mathrm{X}\cos \omega t$$

for a simple harmonic oscillator is time-independent. (b) Is it a constant of the motion? (c) Can it be simultaneously diagonalized with the Hamiltonian?

CHAPTER 12

SPIN ANGULAR MOMENTUM

12–1 Matrix representation of angular-momentum operators. Some of the results of the last chapter will now be applied to the very important subject of angular momentum. First the matrix formalism for orbital angular-momentum operators will be developed. The set of functions which are spherical harmonics have been seen to form an orthonormal set of functions in the sense that

$$(Y_{lm}, Y_{l'm'}) = \int Y_{lm} Y_{l'm'} \, d\phi \sin\theta \, d\theta = \delta_{ll'} \, \delta_{mm'}. \tag{12–1}$$

Consequently, one can expand any wave function in terms of this set of spherical harmonics:

$$\psi = \sum_{l,m} a_{lm}(r, t) Y_{lm}(\theta, \phi). \tag{12–2}$$

The expansion coefficients are given by

$$(Y_{lm}, \psi) = a_{lm}, \tag{12–3}$$

where the integral is taken over angle variables only. The matrix elements for the z-component of the angular-momentum operator in this representation are

$$[\mathsf{L}_z]_{lm,l'm'} = (Y_{lm}, \mathrm{L}_z Y_{l'm'}) = m'\hbar \, \delta_{ll'} \, \delta_{mm'}. \tag{12–4}$$

In a similar manner, the matrix elements of the square of the angular momentum are

$$[\mathsf{L}^2]_{lm,l'm'} = (Y_{lm}, \mathrm{L}^2 Y_{l'm'}) = l(l+1)\hbar^2 \, \delta_{ll'} \, \delta_{mm'}. \tag{12–5}$$

Written out in matrix form, the matrices representing L_z and L^2 have the form:

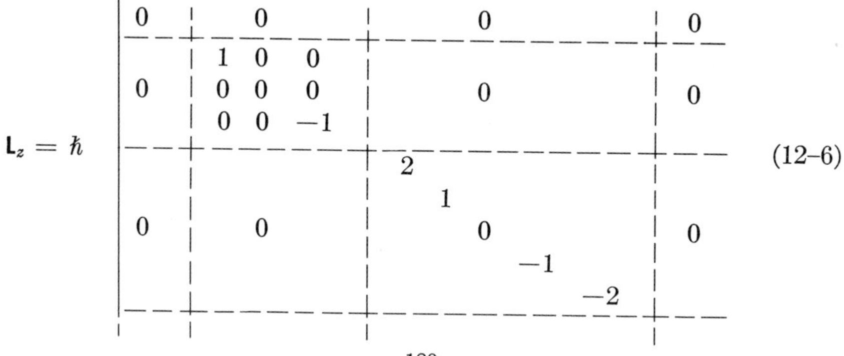

$$\mathsf{L}_z = \hbar \left[\begin{array}{c|ccc|ccccc|c} 0 & & 0 & & & & 0 & & & 0 \\ \hline & 1 & 0 & 0 & & & & & & \\ 0 & 0 & 0 & 0 & & & 0 & & & 0 \\ & 0 & 0 & -1 & & & & & & \\ \hline & & & & 2 & & & & & \\ & & & & & 1 & & & & \\ 0 & & 0 & & & & 0 & & & 0 \\ & & & & & & & -1 & & \\ & & & & & & & & -2 & \\ \hline & & & & & & & & & \end{array}\right. \tag{12–6}$$

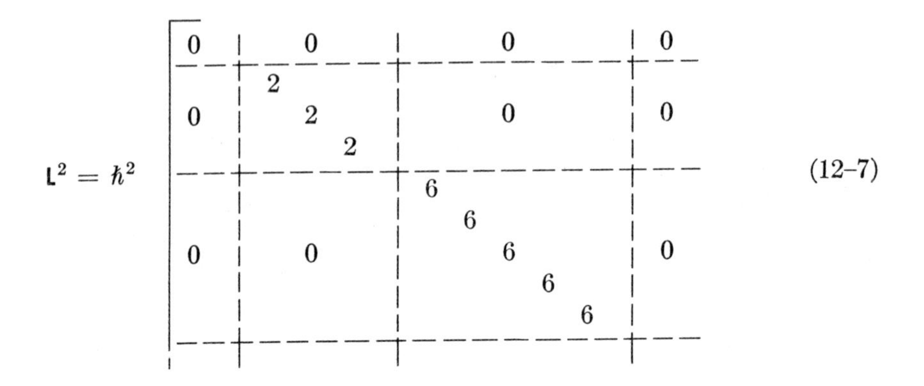

It should be noted that in these matrices all elements are zero except those on the diagonal and that on the diagonal are the eigenvalues of the corresponding operators. The rows and columns of the matrices have been so ordered that as one moves from the upper left-hand corner downward, the index l increases one unit every $2l + 1$ rows, while the index m decreases by one unit in going from row to row, starting with $m = l$ in the upper row of each l-submatrix.

The matrices $\mathbf{L}_z$ and $\mathbf{L}^2$ have thus been evaluated in the representation in which they are diagonal. The next problem is that of calculating the matrix elements for the operators L_x and L_y. To do this, use is made of the operators L_+ and L_- as defined earlier. From Eq. (9–59), we have directly

$$L_- Y_{lm} = \sqrt{(l + m)(l - m + 1)}\, \hbar Y_{l,m-1}. \tag{12–8}$$

From this, we can evaluate the matrix element of $\mathbf{L}_-$:

$$\begin{aligned} [\mathbf{L}_-]_{lm,l'm'} &= (Y_{lm}, L_- Y_{l'm'}) \\ &= \sqrt{(l' + m')(l' - m' + 1)}\, \hbar\, \delta_{ll'}\, \delta_{m,m'-1}. \end{aligned} \tag{12–9}$$

Since the operators L_+ and L_- are Hermitian adjoints,

$$\begin{aligned} [\mathbf{L}_-]_{lm,l'm'} &= (L_+ Y_{lm}, Y_{l'm'}) \\ &= \overline{(Y_{l'm'}, L_+ Y_{lm})}. \end{aligned} \tag{12–10}$$

Hence the matrix elements of $\mathbf{L}_+$ and $\mathbf{L}_-$ are related to each other by

$$[\mathbf{L}_-]_{lm,l'm'} = \overline{[\mathbf{L}_+]}_{l'm',lm}. \tag{12–11}$$

Writing these results in matrix form gives

$$\mathsf{L}_- = \hbar \left[\begin{array}{c|c|c} 0 & 0 & 0 \\ \hline 0 & \begin{matrix} 0 & 0 & 0 \\ \sqrt{2} & 0 & 0 \\ 0 & \sqrt{2} & 0 \end{matrix} & 0 \\ \hline 0 & 0 & \begin{matrix} 0 & 0 & 0 & 0 & 0 \\ 2 & 0 & 0 & 0 & 0 \\ 0 & \sqrt{6} & 0 & 0 & 0 \\ 0 & 0 & \sqrt{6} & 0 & 0 \\ 0 & 0 & 0 & 2 & 0 \end{matrix} \\ \hline \end{array}\right] \tag{12–12}$$

The matrix L_+ is, of course, obtained simply by reflecting the elements of L_- across the diagonal (and taking the complex conjugate). The matrix L_x then can be obtained from L_+ and L_- by making use of

$$\mathsf{L}_x = \tfrac{1}{2}(\mathsf{L}_+ + \mathsf{L}_-). \tag{12–13}$$

The L_y-matrix can be obtained in similar fashion:

$$\mathsf{L}_y = \frac{-i}{2}(\mathsf{L}_+ - \mathsf{L}_-). \tag{12–14}$$

Thus

$$\mathsf{L}_x = \frac{\hbar}{\sqrt{2}} \left[\begin{array}{c|c|c} 0 & 0 & 0 \\ \hline 0 & \begin{matrix} 0 & 1 & 0 \\ 1 & 0 & 1 \\ 0 & 1 & 0 \end{matrix} & 0 \\ \hline 0 & 0 & \end{array}\right. \tag{12–15}$$

and

$$\mathsf{L}_y = \frac{\hbar}{\sqrt{2}} \left[\begin{array}{c|c|c} 0 & 0 & 0 \\ \hline 0 & \begin{matrix} 0 & -i & 0 \\ i & 0 & -i \\ 0 & i & 0 \end{matrix} & 0 \\ \hline 0 & 0 & \end{array}\right. \tag{12–16}$$

The matrix formalism for the orbital angular-momentum operators having been developed, we now consider the spin angular momentum of the particle. If the independent variables which can be measured simultaneously include an internal variable for the particle describing the spin orientation, the wave function can be expanded in terms of the eigenfunctions of this variable:

$$\psi = \sum_{m_s=-s}^{+s} a_{m_s}(r, t)\phi_{m_s}. \tag{12–17}$$

The spin functions ϕ_{m_s} occurring in this equation may, in some future more complete theory, be a function of some internal variables of the particles, perhaps including the positions of subparticles out of which the "particle" is constructed. Fortunately, for problems not involving internal structure, it is not necessary to know these internal variables. As has been seen, it is possible to work with the coefficients a_{m_s}, which for the expansions in question are functions only of the position of the particle and time, and carry in the subscripts all reference to the spin angular momentum.

To illustrate the formalism, consider first a particle having a spin angular momentum of $\hbar$. In general, the spin of a particle is fixed and only its orientation can change. Consequently, the operator S^2 has a definite quantum number which is simply a constant. For the case of spin one under consideration, there are only three possible orientations for the spin, and the wave function can be written as a column matrix:

$$\psi = \begin{bmatrix} a_1(r, t) \\ a_0(r, t) \\ a_{-1}(r, t) \end{bmatrix} = \psi(r, t, \phi_{m_s}), \tag{12–18}$$

where m_s can take on only the values 0, ± 1. The matrix elements a_i are functions of the position of the particle and time. The matrices for the three components of the spin angular momentum are obtained directly from Eqs. (12–6), (12–15), and (12–16) simply by selecting the block in the matrix which refers to the $(l = 1)$-states:

$$\mathsf{S}_x = \frac{\hbar}{\sqrt{2}}\begin{bmatrix} 0 & 1 & 0 \\ 1 & 0 & 1 \\ 0 & 1 & 0 \end{bmatrix}, \qquad \mathsf{S}_y = \frac{\hbar}{\sqrt{2}}\begin{bmatrix} 0 & -i & 0 \\ i & 0 & -i \\ 0 & i & 0 \end{bmatrix},$$

$$\mathsf{S}_z = \hbar\begin{bmatrix} 1 & 0 & 0 \\ 0 & 0 & 0 \\ 0 & 0 & -1 \end{bmatrix}. \tag{12–19}$$

In similar fashion, S^2 can be written directly from Eq. (12–7):

$$\mathsf{S}^2 = 2\hbar^2 \begin{bmatrix} 1 & 0 & 0 \\ 0 & 1 & 0 \\ 0 & 0 & 1 \end{bmatrix} = 2\hbar^2\mathsf{I}. \tag{12–20}$$

This is seen to be essentially the identity matrix. The eigenvalue equation for S_z is

$$S_z\psi = m_s\psi \tag{12–21}$$

or, in matrix notation,

$$(\mathsf{S}_z - m_s\mathsf{I})\psi = 0. \tag{12–22}$$

This corresponds to a set of linear equations in the three unknown components of ψ that is homogeneous and has a nontrivial solution only when the determinant of the coefficients vanishes:

$$\det(\mathsf{S}_z - m_s\mathsf{I}) = 0. \tag{12–23}$$

If the determinant is expanded, one obtains

$$m_s(m_s^2 - \hbar^2) = 0, \tag{12–24}$$

which has roots

$$m_s = \hbar, 0, -\hbar. \tag{12–25}$$

This result is hardly new, but it was obtained to illustrate the algebraic techniques.

In this formalism, $|a_1|^2$ is interpreted as the probability that the z-component of $\mathbf{S}$ will have the value $+\hbar$ when the particle is located at a particular point $\mathbf{r}$. The expectation value of S_z can be written as

$$\langle S_z\rangle_r = \frac{\hbar|a_1|^2 + 0\cdot|a_0|^2 + (-\hbar)|a_{-1}|^2}{\sum_{m_s}|a_{m_s}|^2}. \tag{12–26}$$

In matrix notation this can be written as

$$\langle S_z\rangle_r = \frac{\psi^*\mathsf{S}_z\psi}{\psi^*\psi}. \tag{12–27}$$

If the column vector is normalized to unity, the denominator is unity. Here the star stands for the Hermitian adjoint matrix, which as defined before is formed by interchanging rows and columns and taking the complex conjugate of each element. As an example,

$$\begin{bmatrix} a_1 \\ a_0 \\ a_{-1} \end{bmatrix}^* = [\overline{a_1}, \overline{a_0}, \overline{a_{-1}}]. \tag{12–28}$$

It may be easily verified that the proper average value for the other two components of the matrix can also be written in this fashion, so that

$$\langle S \rangle_r = \frac{\psi^* \mathbf{S} \psi}{\psi^* \psi}. \tag{12–29}$$

If, instead of specifying that the particle be located at point r, we average over all possible positions of the particle, we find that the expectation value for the spin angular-momentum vector of the particle is

$$\langle S \rangle = (\psi, \mathbf{S}\psi) = \int \psi^* \mathbf{S} \psi \, dr, \tag{12–30}$$

where the ψ's are assumed to be normalized. Here the parentheses notation is meant to signify an integration over all position coordinates and a summation over all spin variables given by the matrix product.

12–2 Systems with spin one-half. Systems with spin one-half are of especial interest, since this is the spin encountered in the stable particles: electrons, positrons, protons, and neutrons. (The neutron is stable only in an atomic nucleus.) In this case, the wave function is of the form

$$\psi = \begin{bmatrix} a_{1/2}(r, t) \\ a_{-1/2}(r, t) \end{bmatrix}. \tag{12–31}$$

Making use of a procedure identical to that used above, one can obtain the spin angular-momentum component operators in matrix form:

$$\mathbf{S}_x = \frac{\hbar}{2}\begin{bmatrix} 0 & 1 \\ 1 & 0 \end{bmatrix}, \qquad \mathbf{S}_y = \frac{\hbar}{2}\begin{bmatrix} 0 & -i \\ i & 0 \end{bmatrix},$$
$$\mathbf{S}_z = \frac{\hbar}{2}\begin{bmatrix} 1 & 0 \\ 0 & -1 \end{bmatrix}. \tag{12–32}$$

The operators $\boldsymbol{\sigma} \equiv (2/\hbar)\mathbf{S}$ are known as the *Pauli spin operators.*

Note that for particles with spin one-half, there are only two possible orientations (eigenstates) of the spin with respect to some fixed direction in space, usually taken as the z-axis. These are commonly referred to as the orientations in which the spin is either *parallel* or *antiparallel* to z. However, the length of the spin vector is much greater than its projection in the z-direction. This situation can be represented by a vector model, as in Fig. 12–1. This is a way of visualizing the possible orientations of the spin vector in space. For example, when S_z is positive, the spin vector lies somewhere on the surface of a cone, although it is not possible to specify exactly the x- or y-components. In fact, the expectation values of S_x and S_y for the state characterized by $S_z = +\hbar/2$ are

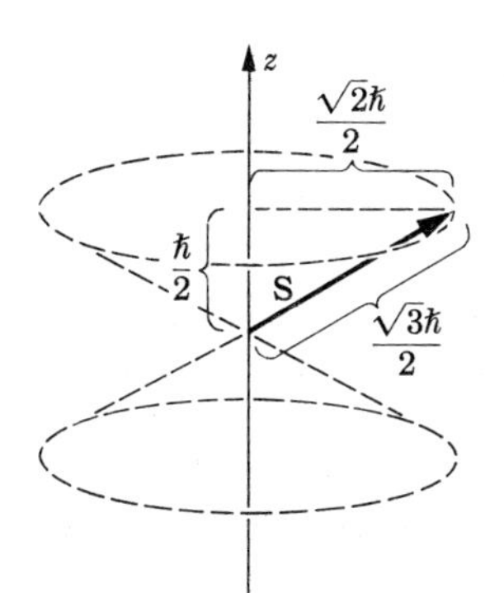

FIG. 12-1. A vector model of the angular momentum of a spin one-half particle.

zero. However, in this case the expectation value of both S_x^2 and S_y^2 are not zero but are equal to $\hbar^2/4$.

The component operators have the following simple algebraic properties:

$$\mathsf{S}_x\mathsf{S}_y + \mathsf{S}_y\mathsf{S}_x = 0 \tag{12-33}$$

(this is expressed by saying that S_x and S_y *anticommute*),

$$\mathsf{S}_x^2 = \mathsf{S}_y^2 = \mathsf{S}_z^2 = \frac{\hbar^2}{4}, \tag{12-34}$$

and

$$\mathsf{S}^2 = \mathsf{S}_x^2 + \mathsf{S}_y^2 + \mathsf{S}_z^2 = \frac{3\hbar^2}{4}. \tag{12-35}$$

12-3 Electron-spin precession. Before treating the quantum-mechanical case, it is worth considering what behavior we would expect classically from an electron whose spin angular momentum is taken to arise from rotation of the charged mass of the electron about an axis through its center, if it is placed in an externally applied uniform magnetic field. The effect of such a magnetic field is to produce a torque tending to line up the spin axis of the electron parallel to the magnetic field. This torque produces a precession of the spin axis about the direction of the magnetic field; in other words, the particle acts like a gyroscope because of its spin angular momentum. Any torque tending to line up the spin axis and the magnetic field results only in a precession of the spin about the field. The classical situation is shown in Fig. 12-2.

Now consider the quantum-mechanical treatment of an electron in a magnetic field. An electron has a magnetic moment parallel to its spin axis, and consequently we can associate with it a magnetic-moment operator

$$\boldsymbol{\mu} = -\frac{e}{mc}\,\mathbf{S}. \tag{12–36}$$

[Strictly speaking, the factor $-(e/mc)$ in this equation is only approximate. Careful measurements show that it should be roughly 0.1% larger. A detailed discussion of the reasons for the size of the moment is outside the scope of this text. The magnetic field is being treated as a classical entity. If the field as well as the electron is given a quantum treatment, it can be shown that the factor $-(e/mc)$ should be modified by so-called "radiative corrections," which introduce a change of about 0.1% in this proportionality factor.] If one neglects all other contributions to the energy of the electron (such as kinetic energy of translation) and considers only the interaction between the electron spin and a magnetic field, the expression for the energy, which can be taken as the Hamiltonian of the system, is

$$\mathbf{H} = -\boldsymbol{\mu}\cdot\boldsymbol{\mathcal{B}} = +\frac{e}{mc}\,\boldsymbol{\mathcal{B}}\cdot\mathbf{S}. \tag{12–37}$$

The magnetic field is given by the vector $\boldsymbol{\mathcal{B}}$. In the particular case of a

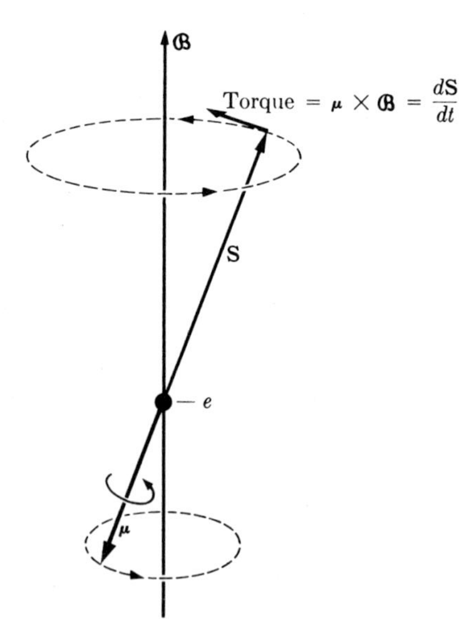

FIG. 12–2. Classical model of a particle with both angular momentum and a (parallel) magnetic dipole moment, when placed in a magnetic field. The torque acting on the magnetic dipole tends to make the angular momentum precess around the applied magnetic field.

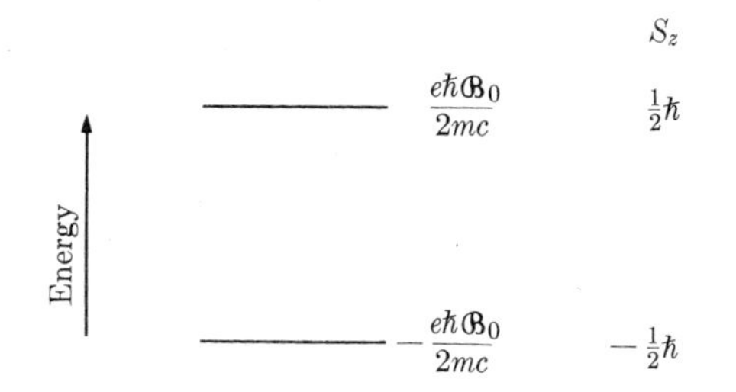

Fig. 12–3. The two possible energies of an electron spin when placed in a uniform magnetic field.

uniform static magnetic field $\mathcal{B}_0$ in the z-direction, this becomes

$$\mathsf{H} = +\frac{e}{mc}\,\mathcal{B}_0\mathsf{S}_z. \tag{12–38}$$

The values for the spin energy in this magnetic field are given by the eigenvalues of the time-independent Schrödinger equation

$$\mathsf{H}\psi = E\psi. \tag{12–39}$$

Since the eigenvalues of S_z are $\pm(\hbar/2)$, the two possible energies of the electron spin are as indicated in Fig. 12–3. The corresponding energy states are those for which the electron spin is either parallel or antiparallel to the magnetic field.

To investigate the quantum-mechanical analogue of the classical spin precession when the spin is initially not along the field (z-axis), assume that at time $t = 0$ the component of the spin angular momentum parallel to the x-axis is measured and that the value $\frac{1}{2}\hbar$ is obtained. This means that at this time the wave function is an eigenfunction of the operator S_x, with the eigenvalue $\frac{1}{2}\hbar$:

$$\psi(0) = \frac{1}{\sqrt{2}}\begin{bmatrix}1\\1\end{bmatrix}. \tag{12–40}$$

The Schrödinger time-dependent equation

$$\mathsf{H}\psi = i\hbar\,\frac{\partial}{\partial t}\,\psi \tag{12–41}$$

must be satisfied by the electron wave function. It is readily seen that the wave function

$$\psi(t) = \frac{1}{\sqrt{2}}\begin{bmatrix}\exp\left(\frac{-i\omega t}{2}\right)\\ \exp\left(\frac{i\omega t}{2}\right)\end{bmatrix}, \tag{12–42}$$

where ω has the value

$$\omega = \frac{e\mathcal{B}_0}{mc}, \tag{12-43}$$

satisfies the Schrödinger equation (12–41) and the initial condition of Eq. (12–40). With this state vector, at time $t = 0$

$$\mathsf{S}_x\psi(0) = \frac{\hbar}{2}\,\psi(0). \tag{12-44}$$

Thus, at time $t = 0$ the spin is lined up in the positive x-direction. On the other hand, at the later time $t = \pi/2\omega$, from Eqs. (12–32) and (12–42),

$$\mathsf{S}_y\psi\left(\frac{\pi}{2\omega}\right) = \frac{\hbar}{2}\,\psi\left(\frac{\pi}{2\omega}\right). \tag{12-45}$$

This says that at this later time, the spin points in the positive y-direction. In a similar manner,

$$\begin{aligned} \mathsf{S}_x\psi\left(\frac{\pi}{\omega}\right) &= -\frac{\hbar}{2}\,\psi\left(\frac{\pi}{\omega}\right), \\ \mathsf{S}_y\psi\left(\frac{3\pi}{2\omega}\right) &= -\frac{\hbar}{2}\,\psi\left(\frac{3\pi}{2\omega}\right) \end{aligned} \tag{12-46}$$

indicate that at a later time the spin can be found pointing in the negative x-direction and, at a still later time, in the negative y-direction. The precession of the spin about the field $\mathcal{B}_0$ occurs at a frequency ω, given by Eq. (12–43). This precession frequency is identical to that computed classically under these conditions. The closeness of this quantum-mechanical precession to the classical result is seen more readily by computing the expectation value for the spin in the x-direction:

$$\begin{aligned} \langle S_x\rangle = \psi^*(t)\mathsf{S}_x\psi(t) &= \frac{1}{2}\left[\exp\left(\frac{i\omega t}{2}\right), \exp\left(\frac{-i\omega t}{2}\right)\right]\mathsf{S}_x\begin{bmatrix}\exp\left(\frac{-i\omega t}{2}\right)\\ \exp\left(\frac{i\omega t}{2}\right)\end{bmatrix} \\ &= \frac{\hbar}{2}\cos\omega t, \end{aligned} \tag{12-47}$$

where it is seen that the average value of the x-component of the angular momentum oscillates with the angular frequency ω just as it does in the case of the classical motion of a gyroscope. The y-component can be shown in a similar way to oscillate at the same frequency:

$$\langle S_y \rangle = \frac{\hbar}{2} \sin \omega t. \tag{12-48}$$

This result can be seen in still another way. Consider the operator defined by

$$\mathsf{S}^\dagger \equiv \mathsf{S}_x \cos \omega t + \mathsf{S}_y \sin \omega t, \tag{12-49}$$

which represents the component of the spin in the xy-plane along a line rotating with circular frequency ω about the z-axis. Direct substitution shows that the wave function of Eq. (12-42) is an eigenfunction of this operator:

$$\mathsf{S}^\dagger \psi = \frac{\hbar}{2} \psi. \tag{12-50}$$

This equation states that the spin has a constant component $\hbar/2$ along this rotating line, which is a result identical to that obtained above by somewhat different considerations.

12-4 Paramagnetic resonance. Next, a somewhat more difficult but at the same time more interesting problem will be considered, namely, the situation of a system of electron spins in a uniform static magnetic field with an oscillating magnetic field perpendicular to the static field. The transitions between energy states caused by the oscillating field or, in other words, the probability that photon absorption and emission will lead to jumps from one energy state to another energy state, will be investigated.

First, however, we must consider how a system of spins, rather than one individual spin, should be treated. To do this, the static magnetization of a system containing N electrons per unit volume which are free to orient their spins with respect to the magnetic field will first be calculated. The electrons are assumed to be in thermal equilibrium with their surroundings at an absolute temperature T; for simplicity, we will make the additional assumption that the average thermal energy of each spin, kT, is large compared with the interaction energy of the spin with the magnetic field. In other words,

$$kT \gg \left| \frac{e\hbar\mathcal{B}_0}{mc} \right| \cdot \tag{12-51}$$

We shall assume that the probability that an energy state will be occupied is proportional to the Boltzmann factor, $\exp(-E/kT)$. This assumption will be justified in Chapter 18. Consequently, the magnetization of the medium is given by

$$M = -\mu_z N \left[\frac{\exp(-e\hbar\mathcal{B}_0/mckT) - 1}{\exp(-e\hbar\mathcal{B}_0/mckT) + 1}\right] \approx \frac{1}{2}\,\mu_z\,\frac{e\hbar\mathcal{B}_0}{mckT}\,N$$

$$= \frac{N}{2}\,\frac{e^2\hbar\mathcal{B}_0}{m^2c^2kT}\,m_s = \frac{N}{4}\,\frac{e^2\hbar^2}{m^2c^2kT}\,\mathcal{B}_0. \tag{12–52}$$

The corresponding magnetic susceptibility of the medium is

$$\chi \equiv \frac{M}{\mathcal{B}_0} = \frac{e^2\hbar^2 N}{4m^2c^2kT}\cdot \tag{12–53}$$

Making use of the connection between magnetic susceptibility and the permeability of the medium, we have for the permeability

$$\mu = 1 + 4\pi\chi = 1 + \frac{\pi e^2\hbar^2}{m^2c^2kT}\,N. \tag{12–54}$$

This formula correctly predicts the permeability of spin-paramagnetic materials such as certain organic free radicals and ammonia solutions of alkali metals.

To return to the dynamic problem of a spin in a large static magnetic field acted upon by a weak oscillating magnetic field perpendicular to the static field, let us assume that the driving field oscillates at a frequency approximately equal to the precession frequency of the electron spin in the static field. It is possible to replace the oscillating magnetic field by two rotating magnetic fields, rotating in opposite directions in such a way that the sum of the two rotating field vectors is a vector in the direction of the oscillating field. The rotating fields are taken to lie in the plane perpendicular to the static field. Only the component of the magnetic field rotating in the same direction as the precession of the electron spin plays a significant role in producing energy transitions from one energy level to the other; the other component produces only a small rapid nutation of the spin axis. Consequently, the development will be simplified if we assume that only this rotating magnetic field exists; the other rotating component will be ignored (see Fig. 12–4). The static magnetic field is taken to be in the direction of the positive z-axis, with the rotating field in the xy-plane. The interaction of the two magnetic fields with the electron spin gives a Hamiltonian of the form

$$\mathsf{H} = -\boldsymbol{\mu}\cdot\boldsymbol{\mathcal{B}} = \frac{e}{mc}\,(\mathcal{B}_0\mathsf{S}_z + \mathcal{B}_1\cos\omega t\,\mathsf{S}_x + \mathcal{B}_1\sin\omega t\,\mathsf{S}_y). \tag{12–55}$$

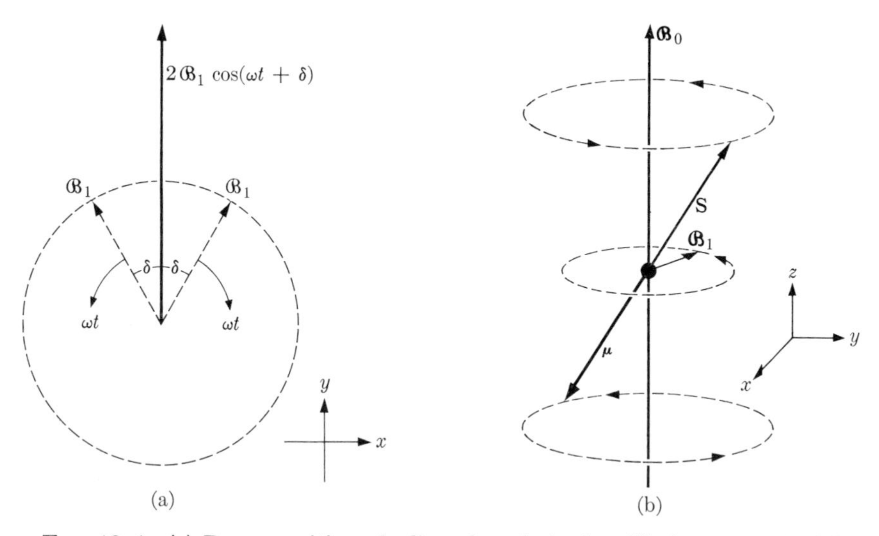

FIG. 12-4. (a) Decomposition of a linearly polarized oscillating magnetic field into two oppositely rotating magnetic fields. Only the component of the linear field rotating in the same direction as the precession of the electronic spin magnetic moment is effective in interacting with it, as shown in (b).

(The choice of $\mathcal{B}_1$ as the amplitude of the rotating field implies an oscillating field of amplitude $2\mathcal{B}_1$.) From Eq. (12-32), the Hamiltonian has in matrix notation the form

$$\mathsf{H} = \frac{e\hbar}{2mc}\begin{bmatrix} \mathcal{B}_0 & \mathcal{B}_1 \exp(-i\omega t) \\ \mathcal{B}_1 \exp(i\omega t) & -\mathcal{B}_0 \end{bmatrix}. \tag{12-56}$$

This is a Hamiltonian which depends explicitly on the time; energy is not conserved. The Schrödinger equation still has its original form under these circumstances, so that the wave function must still satisfy the equation

$$\mathsf{H}\psi = i\hbar \frac{\partial}{\partial t}\psi. \tag{12-57}$$

It is convenient to look for the so-called normal, or stationary, solutions to this equation, that is, solutions for which the probability that the electron will be found in each of the two energy states is constant in time. Such a normal solution has the form

$$\psi = \exp(i\lambda t)\begin{bmatrix} a_1 \exp\left(\frac{-i\omega t}{2}\right) \\ a_2 \exp\left(\frac{i\omega t}{2}\right) \end{bmatrix}. \tag{12-58}$$

It is clear that this is a stationary solution in the above sense, for the time appears only in phase factors of modulus 1. If a solution of this form is assumed and is substituted into Eq. (12–57), the result is

$$\frac{e\hbar}{2mc}\begin{bmatrix}(\mathcal{B}_0 a_1 + \mathcal{B}_1 a_2)\exp\left[i\left(\lambda - \frac{\omega}{2}\right)t\right] \\ (\mathcal{B}_1 a_1 - \mathcal{B}_0 a_2)\exp\left[i\left(\lambda + \frac{\omega}{2}\right)t\right]\end{bmatrix} = -\hbar\begin{bmatrix}a_1\left(\lambda - \frac{\omega}{2}\right)\exp\left[i\left(\lambda - \frac{\omega}{2}\right)t\right] \\ a_2\left(\lambda + \frac{\omega}{2}\right)\exp\left[i\left(\lambda + \frac{\omega}{2}\right)t\right]\end{bmatrix}. \tag{12–59}$$

This represents an equality between two column vectors; each element of one column vector can be set equal to the corresponding element of the other, giving the two equations

$$\begin{aligned}[\lambda + \tfrac{1}{2}(\omega_0 - \omega)]a_1 + \tfrac{1}{2}\omega_1 a_2 &= 0, \\ \tfrac{1}{2}\omega_1 a_1 + [\lambda - \tfrac{1}{2}(\omega_0 - \omega)]a_2 &= 0,\end{aligned} \tag{12–60}$$

where ω_1 and ω_0 are defined by

$$\omega_1 \equiv \frac{e\mathcal{B}_1}{mc}, \qquad \omega_0 \equiv \frac{e\mathcal{B}_0}{mc}. \tag{12–61}$$

Equations (12–60) are a set of two homogeneous equations in two unknowns that have a nontrivial solution only if the determinant of the coefficients vanishes:

$$\begin{vmatrix}\lambda + \frac{1}{2}(\omega_0 - \omega) & \frac{1}{2}\omega_1 \\ \frac{1}{2}\omega_1 & \lambda - \frac{1}{2}(\omega_0 - \omega)\end{vmatrix} = 0. \tag{12–62}$$

Multiplying out the determinant leads to the characteristic polynomial

$$\lambda^2 - \tfrac{1}{4}(\omega_0 - \omega)^2 - \tfrac{1}{4}\omega_1^2 = 0. \tag{12–63}$$

This has the two roots for λ,

$$\lambda = \pm\tfrac{1}{2}\sqrt{(\omega_0 - \omega)^2 + \omega_1^2}. \tag{12–64}$$

Either of the equations (12–60) can be solved to give

$$\begin{aligned}a_2 &= -\frac{2}{\omega_1}[\lambda + \tfrac{1}{2}(\omega_0 - \omega)]a_1 \\ &= -\frac{1}{\omega_1}[\pm\sqrt{(\omega_0 - \omega)^2 + \omega_1^2} + (\omega_0 - \omega)]a_1.\end{aligned} \tag{12–65}$$

These represent the stationary-state wave functions associated with the two roots λ. The remaining discussion will be simplified slightly by assuming that the rotating field is exactly at resonance: its frequency is exactly equal to the normal precession frequency of the spin. Then

$$\omega = \omega_0, \tag{12-66}$$

and Eq. (12–64) becomes

$$\lambda = \pm \frac{\omega_1}{2}. \tag{12-67}$$

Equation (12–65) becomes in this case

$$a_2 = \mp a_1. \tag{12-68}$$

From these relations, the normal solutions to the eigenvalue problem are found to be

$$\psi_\pm(t) = \frac{1}{\sqrt{2}} \exp(\pm i\omega_1 t) \begin{bmatrix} \exp\left(\dfrac{-i\omega_0 t}{2}\right) \\ \mp \exp\left(\dfrac{i\omega_0 t}{2}\right) \end{bmatrix}, \tag{12-69}$$

where a_1 has been chosen so as to normalize ψ.

An energy transition from one energy state to the other will now be investigated. (Such an energy transition is called a *spin flop* by workers in the fields of nuclear and paramagnetic resonance.) Assume that at time $t = 0$, the spin of the electron has been measured and has been determined to be exactly in the positive z-direction. In this case, the wave function has the form

$$\psi(t = 0) = \begin{bmatrix} 1 \\ 0 \end{bmatrix}. \tag{12-70}$$

Choose a linear combination of the two stationary states given by Eq. (12–69) such that the resulting function has this form when $t = 0$ (but only then). The required linear combination is

$$\psi(t) = \frac{1}{\sqrt{2}} [\psi_+(t) + \psi_-(t)]. \tag{12-71}$$

Written out completely in column-vector form, this is

$$\psi(t) = \begin{bmatrix} \cos\left(\dfrac{\omega_1 t}{2}\right) \exp\left(\dfrac{-i\omega_0 t}{2}\right) \\ -i \sin\left(\dfrac{\omega_1 t}{2}\right) \exp\left(\dfrac{i\omega_0 t}{2}\right) \end{bmatrix}. \tag{12-72}$$

It is apparent upon inspection that at time $t = 0$ this wave function is such that the spin is pointing in the positive z-direction. On the other hand, at the later time $\omega_1 t = \pi$, the wave function is such that the z-component of the spin angular momentum is equal to $-\frac{1}{2}\hbar$; in other words, the electron spin has "turned over" from pointing in the positive z-direction to pointing in the negative z-direction. At the still later time $\omega_1 t = 2\pi$ the electron spin is again pointing in the positive z-direction, so that the electron spin has again flopped over. Thus it can be seen that the electron spin flops back and forth between the positive and negative z-directions. There are times in between at which one cannot say with certainty whether the electron is pointing in a positive z-direction or a negative z-direction; there is a nonzero probability that a measurement of the component may lead to either value.

It is worth discussing briefly the validity of the type of calculation which has just been made. The electron spin has been treated quantum-mechanically, while the radiation field was treated, not as a dynamical system, but as an externally given force field acting on the particle. In other words, no quantum-mechanical effects associated with the radiation field itself were considered. It is clear that this procedure cannot lead to the concept of photons. This classical type of treatment of the field is valid if there are so many photons present in the electromagnetic field that one is dealing with very large quantum numbers for the field. Such a treatment can correctly describe the stimulated emission of radiation by an atomic system or the rate of absorption of energy by an atomic system, but it cannot give the spontaneous radiation rate of an atomic system, for this is intimately associated with quantum effects in the electromagnetic field. A treatment in which the rotating field is properly quantized shows that during a spin flop one photon is either absorbed from or emitted into the rotating field.

Finally, the results just obtained for an isolated spin must be related to the case of a system of many electrons. As seen at the beginning of this section, a system of electrons that comes into thermal equilibrium with its surroundings while in a static magnetic field of strength $\mathcal{B}_0$ has a resultant macroscopic magnetization given by Eq. (12–52). This can be considered to arise from the assemblage of N electrons, with

$$N \exp\left(\frac{-e\hbar\mathcal{B}_0}{mckT}\right)\left[\exp\left(\frac{-e\hbar\mathcal{B}_0}{mckT}\right) + 1\right]^{-1}$$

initially in the high-energy orientation with spin antiparallel to the field $\boldsymbol{\mathcal{B}}_0$, and with

$$N\left[\exp\left(\frac{-e\hbar\mathcal{B}_0}{mckT}\right) + 1\right]^{-1}$$

initially in the low-energy orientation with spin parallel to $\mathcal{B}_0$. A similar analysis to that given above for a spin originally in the negative z-direction shows that such a spin, originally opposite in orientation to the positively directed spin, remains so throughout the spin-flop process. The original cancellation of the magnetic moments of the spins is retained under the action of the oscillating field, and two such spins may be said to be "paired off." Only the excess spins in the more heavily populated state produce the net magnetism. This net magnetic moment arising from the "excess" spins originally in the positive z-orientation has the dynamical behavior of the isolated spin treated above; the entire macroscopic magnetization thus undergoes the indicated succession of flops.

12–5 Summary. In this chapter, the matrix representations of angular-momentum operators were developed, starting with an L_z- and L^2-diagonal representation of orbital angular-momentum operators. The algebraic properties of these operators developed earlier were used in the treatment. The important case of systems with spin one-half was next treated in some detail, and a classical vector model of such a system was given. Electrons were seen to have a quantum analogue to their classical gyroscopic precession about a static magnetic field. The quantum-mechanical description of the effect of a weak oscillating field perpendicular to the static field was seen to be the same as the classical description: the electron undergoes a succession of "spin flops" as its spin turns over with respect to the static field in response to the driving torque of the oscillating field. Finally, the macroscopic magnetization of a collection of spins was shown to behave quite like an isolated spin.

PROBLEMS

12–1. (a) Show that the (3×3)-submatrix of L_x corresponding to $l = 1$ satisfies the equation

$$\mathsf{L}_x(\mathsf{L}_x + \hbar)(\mathsf{L}_x - \hbar) = 0.$$

(b) Is this equation valid for $l = 2$? (c) Do the corresponding equations hold for L_y and L_z? (d) Show that for the $(l = 1)$-submatrix only,

$$\exp\left(\frac{i\theta\mathsf{L}_x}{\hbar}\right) = (\cos\theta - 1)\frac{\mathsf{L}_x^2}{\hbar^2} + i\sin\theta \cdot \frac{\mathsf{L}_x}{\hbar} + 1.$$

12–2. (a) Show directly from Eq. (12–32) that the operators S_x, S_y, and S_z for spin one-half particles satisfy the correct commutation rules. (b) Show that they anticommute and that

$$\mathsf{S}_x^2 = \mathsf{S}_y^2 = \mathsf{S}_z^2 = \frac{\hbar^2}{4}\,\mathsf{I}.$$

(c) What are the eigenvalues and eigenvectors of S_x and S_y? (d) Show that

$$\mathsf{S}_x\mathsf{S}_y = i\,\frac{\hbar}{2}\,\mathsf{S}_z.$$

(e) What is S^2?

12–3. The matrices σ_x and σ_y are each Hermitian, unitary, and nonsingular, and they anticommute. Discuss the corresponding properties of the matrices $\sigma_+ = \sigma_x + i\sigma_y$ and $\sigma_- = \sigma_x - i\sigma_y$.

12–4. A particle has a spin of $\hbar/2$. A measurement is made of the sum of its x- and z-components of spin angular momentum. (a) What are the possible results of this measurement?

After this measurement is made, the y-component of the spin is measured. (b) Calculate the probabilities of obtaining the results $\pm(\hbar/2)$.

12–5. A beam of particles of spin $\hbar/2$ is sent through a Stern-Gerlach apparatus, which divides the incident beam into two spatially separated components depending on the quantum numbers m_s of the particles. One of the resulting beams is removed and the other beam is sent through another similar apparatus, the magnetic field of which has an inclination α with respect to that of the first apparatus. What are the relative numbers of particles that appear in the two beams leaving the second apparatus? Derive the result using the Pauli spin formalism.

12–6. Show that the unitary operator $\exp\left[(i/\hbar)\theta\boldsymbol{n}\cdot\mathsf{S}\right]$ satisfies

$$\exp\left(\frac{i}{\hbar}\,\theta\boldsymbol{n}\cdot\mathsf{S}\right) = \cos\frac{\theta}{2} + i\,\frac{2\boldsymbol{n}\cdot\mathsf{S}}{\hbar}\sin\frac{\theta}{2},$$

where $\boldsymbol{n}$ is a constant unit vector and $s = \frac{1}{2}$. [*Hint:* First show it for $\boldsymbol{n} = \boldsymbol{i}$, $\boldsymbol{j}$, $\boldsymbol{k}$, where $\boldsymbol{i}$, $\boldsymbol{j}$, and $\boldsymbol{k}$ are unit vectors along the x-, y-, and z-axes respectively.]

12–7. A particle of spin one and magnetic moment μ is in a magnetic field of strength $\mathcal{B}$. At $t = 0$ the component of the spin along an axis at an angle θ with respect to the field is measured and found to be $m\hbar$. What is the probability as a function of time that a remeasurement will yield the eigenvalue $m'\hbar$? First use a Schrödinger representation. Then use a Heisenberg representation by calculating the expectation value of the appropriate projection operator, $\langle P_{m'} \rangle$. (See Problem 11–7.)

12–8. (a) Discuss the behavior of a spin one-half particle subjected to a weak oscillating magnetic field perpendicular to a strong static magnetic field for the case in which the oscillating field is off resonance. (b) What is the wave function for a particle found to have its spin along $+z$ at $t = 0$? (c) What is the classical behavior of such a spin for $t > 0$?

12–9. (a) For a particle of mass m, define the operator

$$\mathsf{T}^{1/2} \equiv \frac{1}{\sqrt{2m}} \mathbf{P} \cdot \boldsymbol{\sigma},$$

where $\mathbf{P}$ is the momentum operator and $\boldsymbol{\sigma}$ is given by the Pauli operators. Note that $\mathsf{T}^{1/2}$ commutes with the kinetic energy $\mathsf{T} = (1/2m)p^2\mathsf{I}$ and with $\mathbf{P}$. (b) Show explicitly that $\mathsf{T} = (\mathsf{T}^{1/2})^2$. (c) Show that $\mathsf{T}^{1/2}$ has the eigenvalues $\pm E^{1/2}$, where E is the kinetic energy of the particle. (d) Find simultaneous eigenfunctions of $\mathsf{T}^{1/2}$, T, and $\mathbf{P}$ in the form

$$\begin{bmatrix} a \\ b \end{bmatrix} \exp{(i\boldsymbol{k} \cdot \boldsymbol{r})},$$

where a and b are constants. (e) Show that the parity operator converts an eigenstate of $\mathsf{T}^{1/2}$ into an eigenstate with the eigenvalue of opposite sign.

CHAPTER 13

TRANSFORMATIONS OF REPRESENTATIONS

13–1 Introduction. As was seen in Chapter 11, there can be an infinite number of representations of the quantum-mechanical formalism, depending on the choice of the (complete) set of base functions. The problem which will now be considered is how to express a representation in terms of one set of base functions when it is known in terms of another, that is, how to *transform* between the two representations.

Consider two different representations based upon the orthonormal function sets u_k and v_j. Since each set is assumed to be complete, the functions v_j can be expanded in terms of the u_k:

$$v_j = \sum_k \overline{T_{jk}} u_k. \tag{13–1}$$

Multiplying this equation on both sides by the corresponding expression for $\overline{v_i}$ and integrating over all space gives

$$(v_i, v_j) = \sum_{l,k} T_{il}\overline{T_{jk}}(u_l, u_k). \tag{13–2}$$

Since the sets are orthonormal, this becomes

$$\begin{aligned} \delta_{ij} &= \sum_{l,k} T_{il}\overline{T_{jk}}\, \delta_{lk} \\ &= \sum_k T_{ik}\overline{T_{jk}}. \end{aligned} \tag{13–3}$$

Using matrix notation, this can be written as

$$\mathsf{I} = \mathsf{TT}^*. \tag{13–4}$$

This implies that the Hermitian adjoint T^* of T is equal to its inverse T^{-1}, that is, that T must be unitary.

If the representation of a wave function ψ with the v_j as base functions is ψ' with elements

$$\psi'_j = (v_j, \psi), \tag{13–5}$$

a substitution from Eq. (13–1) gives

$$\psi'_j = \sum_k T_{jk}(u_k, \psi) = \sum_k T_{jk}\psi_k, \tag{13–6}$$

where ψ_k is an element of the representation based on the u_k. This equation can be written in matrix notation as

$$\psi' = \mathsf{T}\psi. \tag{13-7}$$

It is clearly the desired transformation equation for a wave function.

In a similar way, the v_j-based representation of the operator Q has elements

$$Q'_{ij} = (v_i, \mathrm{Q} v_j). \tag{13-8}$$

Again using Eq. (13-1), one obtains

$$\begin{aligned} Q'_{ij} &= \sum_{k,l} T_{ik}\overline{T_{jl}}(u_k, \mathrm{Q}\, u_l) \\ &= \sum_{k,l} T_{ik} Q_{kl} T^*_{lj}, \end{aligned} \tag{13-9}$$

or

$$\mathsf{Q}' = \mathsf{TQT}^*, \tag{13-10}$$

as the desired operator transformation. Since T is unitary, this can be written as

$$\mathsf{Q}' = \mathsf{TQT}^{-1}. \tag{13-11}$$

A transformation of a matrix in accordance with Eq. (13-11) is called a *similarity transformation*. If the matrix T is unitary, as above, the transformation is said to be *unitary*. Matrix equations are left invariant under a similarity transformation. For example, consider the equations

$$\begin{aligned} \mathsf{W} &= \mathsf{QR}, \\ \mathsf{TWT}^{-1} = \mathsf{TQRT}^{-1} &= \mathsf{TQT}^{-1}\mathsf{TRT}^{-1}, \\ \mathsf{W}' &= \mathsf{Q}'\mathsf{R}'. \end{aligned} \tag{13-12}$$

In a similar way, it is readily shown that matrices reciprocal to each other remain reciprocal after a similarity transformation.

The more restrictive unitary transformation has properties not shared by the general similarity transformation. For example, the Hermitian property is invariant under a unitary transformation but not necessarily under a general similarity transformation. To see this, form the Hermitian adjoint of Eq. (13-11):

$$\mathsf{Q}'^* = \mathsf{T}^{-1*}\mathsf{Q}^*\mathsf{T}^*. \tag{13-13}$$

Note that the order of the factors on the right is reversed when the Hermitian adjoint is formed [see Eq. (11-23)]. This can be seen by writing out Eq. (13-11) in component form and taking the Hermitian adjoint, using Eq. (11-22). With the assumption that T is unitary, we find that Eq.

(13–13) becomes

$$\mathsf{Q}'^* = \mathsf{TQ}^*\mathsf{T}^{-1}. \tag{13–14}$$

Thus the unitary transforms of matrices adjoint to each other are adjoint.

13–2 A geometrical analogue—Hilbert space. In this section a very important geometrical analogue to the quantum-mechanical formalism will be developed. An ordinary three-dimensional vector is conveniently expressed in terms of its cartesian components; these can be represented by a column vector:

$$\mathsf{a} \equiv \begin{bmatrix} a_1 \\ a_2 \\ a_3 \end{bmatrix}. \tag{13–15}$$

A linear mapping in three-dimensional space is a linear transformation which *maps* (transforms) a vector a into another vector a' in accordance with

$$\mathsf{a}' \equiv \mathsf{Ra}. \tag{13–16}$$

R is a square (3×3)-matrix. The correspondence between this mapping in three-dimensional space and the transformation of the representation of a wave vector given by Eq. (13–7) is obvious, and accordingly it is often profitable to consider the wave function of quantum mechanics as a state vector in a suitable vector space. This vector space, to be suitable for quantum formalism, must usually be of infinite dimensions and complex (that is, the components of vectors can be complex numbers). Such a space is called a *Hilbert* or *functional* space.

There is a correspondence of certain operators, as well as of vectors, between the three-dimensional geometrical space and Hilbert space. Corresponding to the scalar product of two ordinary vectors (see Fig. 13–1),

$$\boldsymbol{a} \cdot \boldsymbol{b} = ab\cos\theta = \tilde{\mathsf{a}}\mathsf{b} = (a_1b_1 + a_2b_2 + a_3b_3), \tag{13–17}$$

there is the scalar product of two complex functions ψ' and ψ. This scalar product, defined by (ψ', ψ), can be expressed in terms of a matrix representation by

$$(\psi', \psi) = \sum_{j,k} \overline{\psi'_j}\psi_k(u_j, u_k) = \sum_j \overline{\psi'_j}\psi_j$$
$$= \psi'^*\psi. \tag{13–18}$$

Two ordinary three-dimensional vectors are orthogonal when

$$\boldsymbol{a} \cdot \boldsymbol{b} = \tilde{\mathsf{a}}\mathsf{b} = \mathsf{a}^*\mathsf{b} = 0. \tag{13–19}$$

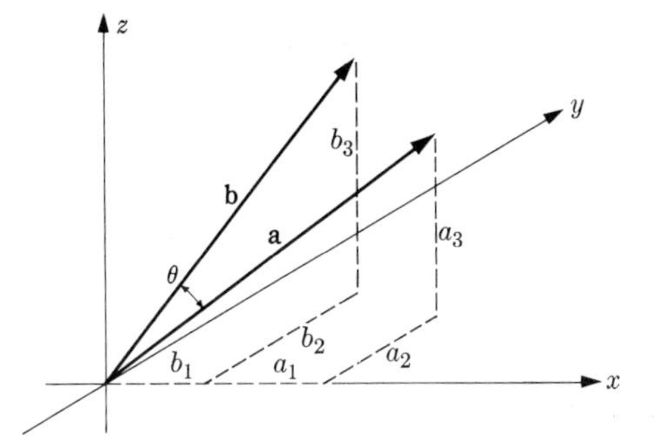

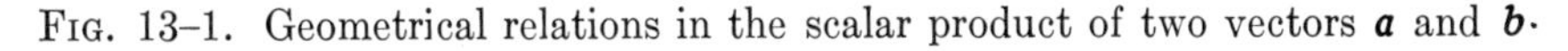
FIG. 13–1. Geometrical relations in the scalar product of two vectors $\boldsymbol{a}$ and $\boldsymbol{b}$.

The corresponding condition for state vectors in Hilbert space is the vanishing of Eq. (13–18):

$$\psi'^*\psi = 0. \tag{13–20}$$

An ordinary vector has unit length when

$$\boldsymbol{a} \cdot \boldsymbol{a} = \tilde{\mathsf{a}}\mathsf{a} = \mathsf{a}^*\mathsf{a} = 1. \tag{13–21}$$

The corresponding condition in Hilbert space is that the function ψ be normalized:

$$(\psi, \psi) = \psi^*\psi = 1. \tag{13–22}$$

A very important linear mapping of three-dimensional vectors is that which corresponds to a rigid rotation of the vector system relative to the coordinates or, equivalently, to a rotation of the coordinate axes with the system of vectors held fixed. Such a rigid rotation carries a system of orthogonal unit base vectors into another orthogonal system. Also, such a linear transformation can be characterized in part by the requirement that the scalar product of any two vectors be left unchanged. The corresponding mapping in Hilbert space is the transformation of the representation from one set of orthonormal base functions, u_j, to another, v_j. Here,

$$\psi = \sum_j \psi_j u_j, \tag{13–23}$$

where the ψ_j are the components of the complex vector ψ. The transformation to the different basis with base functions v_j is carried out by a unitary transformation, according to the earlier discussion [see Eq. (13–7)]:

$$\psi' = \mathsf{T}\psi. \tag{13–24}$$

The scalar product of two state vectors $\boldsymbol{a}'$ and $\boldsymbol{b}'$ is

$$(a', b') = \mathsf{a}'^*\mathsf{b}'. \tag{13–25}$$

Applying the transformation of Eq. (13–24),

$$\begin{aligned} \mathsf{a}' &= \mathsf{Ta}, \\ \mathsf{b}' &= \mathsf{Tb}, \end{aligned} \tag{13–26}$$

the scalar product becomes, since T is unitary,

$$\mathsf{a}'^*\mathsf{b}' = (\mathsf{Ta})^*\mathsf{Tb} = \mathsf{a}^*\mathsf{T}^*\mathsf{Tb} = \mathsf{a}^*\mathsf{b}. \tag{13–27}$$

Thus scalar products are left invariant under a unitary transformation, and such a transformation can accordingly be interpreted as a coordinate rotation in Hilbert space. This is vital to the consistency of the formalism, for the physically measurable expectation value $(\psi, Q\psi)$ of any operator Q is clearly a scalar product and must be an invariant with respect to choice of base functions if the postulated physical meaning is to be given to such an expression.

Note from Eq. (13–27) that a unitary transformation preserves the orthogonal character of vectors. An orthonormal set of vectors remains orthonormal after a unitary transformation.

There is an interesting and significant difference between rotations in an ordinary real vector space and in a Hilbert space. In a real vector space, coordinate rotations (more properly, orthogonal transformations) may be divided into two classes, ordinary or proper rotations, and improper "rotations." Improper rotations reflect the coordinate system from a right-handed system into a left-handed system. This distinction does not exist for a Hilbert space. All unitary transformations are simply "rotations."

13–3 Eigenvalue equations.

The eigenvalue equation

$$Q\psi_j = q_j\psi_j, \tag{13–28}$$

when expressed in a matrix representation, becomes

$$\mathsf{Q}\boldsymbol{\psi}_j = q_j\boldsymbol{\psi}_j. \tag{13–29}$$

This equation represents a homogeneous set of linear equations, which for a finite-dimensional space has a nontrivial solution for $\boldsymbol{\psi}_j$ if and only if the determinant of the coefficients vanishes:

$$\det[\mathsf{Q} - q\mathsf{I}] = 0 \tag{13–30}$$

(the subscript of q has been dropped for convenience). If the (finite) space is n-dimensional, this equation becomes, upon expansion of the determinant, an nth-order polynomial in q:

$$q^n + c_1 q^{n-1} + \cdots + c_n = 0. \tag{13–31}$$

This is known as the *characteristic polynomial.* If we write the n roots of this equation as q_j, we can factor the polynomial:

$$(q - q_1)(q - q_2) \cdots (q - q_n) = 0. \tag{13–32}$$

From this, it can be seen that

$$\begin{aligned} c_1 &\equiv -\sum_i q_i, \\ c_n &\equiv (-1)^n \prod_i q_i = (-1)^n q_1 q_2 q_3 \cdots q_n. \end{aligned} \tag{13–33}$$

It can also be seen directly from the expansion of the determinant of Eq. (13–30) that the *trace* (or *spur*) of the matrix $\mathbf{Q}$, which is defined as the sum of the diagonal elements of the matrix, is given by

$$\operatorname{tr} \mathbf{Q} \equiv \sum_i Q_{ii} = -c_1 = \sum_i q_i, \tag{13–34}$$

and is equal to the sum of the eigenvalues of $\mathbf{Q}$. Similarly, the determinant of the matrix $\mathbf{Q}$ is given by

$$\det \mathbf{Q} = (-1)^n c_n = q_1 q_2 \cdots q_n, \tag{13–35}$$

and is equal to the product of the eigenvalues of $\mathbf{Q}$.

The eigenvalue equation, Eq. (13–28), is unchanged in form under a similarity transformation, as can be shown by arguments similar to those leading to Eq. (13–12). From this, the eigenvalues are unchanged, implying that the characteristic polynomial is also unchanged and that the coefficients of this polynomial, including the trace, $-c_1$, are invariant under similarity transformations. The determinant of the matrix is also unchanged, from Eq. (13–30).

It is possible to write the matrix eigenvalue equation, Eq. (13–29), in the form

$$\mathbf{QT} = \mathbf{TQ}_d, \tag{13–36}$$

where $\mathbf{T}$ is an $n \times n$ matrix having the n columns ψ_j, and $\mathbf{Q}_d$ is an $n \times n$ diagonal matrix with elements

$$(\mathbf{Q}_d)_{ij} = q_i\, \delta_{ij}. \tag{13–37}$$

For a Hermitian matrix Q, the vectors ψ_j can always be chosen to be an orthonormal set. Assuming that this has been done, we find that

$$\mathsf{T}^*\mathsf{T} = \mathsf{I} \tag{13–38}$$

and

$$\mathsf{T}^*\mathsf{Q}\mathsf{T} = \mathsf{Q}_d. \tag{13–39}$$

Hence any Hermitian matrix Q can be diagonalized by this unitary transformation. The eigenvalues of Q appear on the diagonal of Q_d.

13–4 Group properties of unitary transformations. Two unitary transformations applied in sequence are equivalent to another single unitary transformation. This is defined as the *product transformation.* Such multiplication is associative. The unit transformation exists and transforms any unitary matrix (of equal dimension) into itself. In addition, for any transformation T there exists an inverse transformation such that $\mathsf{T}\mathsf{T}^* = \mathsf{I}$. These are the algebraic properties of a *group*, and the set of all unitary transformations on an n-dimensional space is said to form a group.

13–5 Continuous matrices. Thus far, the discussion of representation transformations has considered only discrete sets of base functions. This section will consider how continuous matrices act under transformations.

One representation of considerable interest is the *Fourier representation.* Certain simple aspects of this representation have already been discussed in Chapter 4. Here, instead of following the methods that were employed there, we will use geometrical ideas. First let us employ the position-diagonal representation (Eq. 11–69) and then use a unitary transformation (a rotation in Hilbert space) to transform the representation to one in which the momentum operator is diagonal. In the position-diagonal representation, the momentum operator

$$\mathbf{P} = -i\hbar\boldsymbol{\nabla} \tag{13–40}$$

can be considered to be a continuous matrix with elements

$$P(r, r') = \mathbf{P}\,\delta(r - r'). \tag{13–41}$$

From the discussion in connection with Eq. (13–36), the desired unitary matrix is U, whose columns consist of the normalized eigenfunctions of the operator $\mathbf{P}$. These were developed earlier (Eq. 6–50) for the one-dimensional case; the three-dimensional eigenfunctions are

$$U(r, p) = \left(\frac{1}{2\pi\hbar}\right)^{3/2} \exp\left(\frac{ip \cdot r}{\hbar}\right). \tag{13–42}$$

These define the infinite matrix $\mathbf{U}$, whose columns are specified by p and whose rows are specified by r. The Hermitian adjoint of $\mathbf{U}$ has elements which are the complex conjugate of Eq. (13–42), with p and r now specifying rows and columns respectively. By making use of Eq. (13–39), we can diagonalize $\mathbf{P}$ by this unitary transformation. The matrix $\mathbf{P}$ in this representation, denoted by a † superscript ($\mathbf{P}^\dagger$) has elements

$$\begin{aligned} P^\dagger(p, p') &= \int \overline{U}(r, p)[-i\hbar\nabla]\,\delta(r - r')U(r', p')\,dr\,dr' \\ &= \int \overline{U}(r, p)[-i\hbar\nabla]U(r, p')\,dr \\ &= p'\int \overline{U}(r, p)U(r, p')\,dr \\ &= p'\,\delta(p - p') \\ &= p\,\delta(p - p'). \end{aligned} \tag{13–43}$$

This is clearly diagonal.

In a similar manner, the position matrix in this momentum representation is $\mathbf{R}^\dagger$, with elements

$$\begin{aligned} R^\dagger(p, p') &= \int \overline{U}(r, p)r\,\delta(r - r')U(r', p')\,dr\,dr' \\ &= \int \overline{U}(r, p)rU(r, p')\,dr \\ &= \int i\hbar\nabla_p\overline{U}(r, p)U(\mathbf{r}, p')\,dr, \end{aligned} \tag{13–44}$$

where the gradient operator operates in p-space on p. This operator can therefore be taken outside the integral, which then becomes $\delta(p - p')$, giving

$$R^\dagger(p, p') = i\hbar\nabla_p\,\delta(p - p'). \tag{13–45}$$

The wave function in a momentum-diagonal representation is obtained from the same unitary transformation:

$$\psi^\dagger(p) = \int \overline{U}(r, p)\psi(r)\,dr. \tag{13–46}$$

This is equivalent to the matrix equation

$$\psi^\dagger = \mathbf{U}^*\psi. \tag{13–47}$$

Operating on the left by $\mathbf{U}$, we find

$$\mathbf{U}\psi^\dagger = \mathbf{U}\mathbf{U}^*\psi = \psi. \tag{13–48}$$

In component form, this equation can be written as

$$\psi(r) = \int U(r, p)\psi^\dagger(p)\, dp. \tag{13–49}$$

The product of the operator r and the wave function $\psi(r)$ is, in momentum representation, $\mathbf{R}^\dagger\psi^\dagger$, with components

$$\begin{aligned}[\mathbf{R}^\dagger\psi^\dagger](p) &= \int i\hbar\nabla_p\, \delta(p - p')\psi^\dagger(p')\, dp' \\ &= i\hbar\nabla_p\psi^\dagger(p).\end{aligned} \tag{13–50}$$

There is a simple rule of thumb for going from the position to the momentum representation: replace the wave function by its Fourier transform, replace the momentum operator by its value (p), and replace the position operator by $i\hbar\nabla_p$.

This section will be concluded by considering the interesting form of the Heisenberg representation which is position-diagonal at $t = 0$. Because of the time dependence of the operators (Chapter 11), the position operator does not remain diagonal. A unitary transformation will be used to go from the position-diagonal Schrödinger representation to a Heisenberg representation. It is assumed in the following that the Hamiltonian does not depend explicitly on the time.

Recall that a Heisenberg representation is characterized by time-independent wave functions. It is therefore necessary to find a unitary transformation that transforms $\psi(r, t)$, a solution of the Schrödinger equation

$$\mathrm{H}\psi = i\hbar\,\frac{\partial\psi}{\partial t}, \tag{13–51}$$

into a time-independent function of r. If the representation is to be position-diagonal at $t = 0$, the unitary transformation must reduce to the identity transformation I at $t = 0$. The operator $\exp(i\mathrm{H}t/\hbar)$, defined by the series

$$\exp\left(\frac{i\mathrm{H}t}{\hbar}\right) \equiv \mathrm{I} + \frac{i\mathrm{H}t}{\hbar} + \frac{1}{2!}\left(\frac{i\mathrm{H}t}{\hbar}\right)^2 + \cdots, \tag{13–52}$$

is seen to be a unitary operator: its Hermitian adjoint is $\exp(-i\mathrm{H}t/\hbar)$, which also is its reciprocal. Moreover, this transformation, which reduces to the identity transformation at $t = 0$, will produce the desired result. To see this, expand ψ in energy eigenfunctions:

$$\psi = \sum_j c_j \exp\left(-\frac{iE_jt}{\hbar}\right) u_j(r). \tag{13–53}$$

If the operator of Eq. (13–52) operates on $u_j(r)$, the result is

$$\exp\left(\frac{i\mathrm{H}t}{\hbar}\right)u_j = \exp\left(\frac{iE_jt}{\hbar}\right)u_j, \tag{13–54}$$

since the right side of Eq. (13–52) operating on u_j is the power-series expansion of the right side of Eq. (13–54).

Therefore, if the operator of Eq. (13–52) operates on the wave function of Eq. (13–53) the result is

$$\psi'(r) = \psi(r, 0) = \exp\left(\frac{i\mathrm{H}t}{\hbar}\right)\psi(r, t) \tag{13–55}$$

or, conversely,

$$\psi(r, t) = \exp\left(-\frac{i\mathrm{H}t}{\hbar}\right)\psi(r, 0). \tag{13–56}$$

The position-diagonal (differential) operator Q is transformed, from Eq. (13–10), into

$$\mathrm{Q}' = \exp\left(\frac{i\mathrm{H}t}{\hbar}\right)\mathrm{Q}\exp\left(-\frac{i\mathrm{H}t}{\hbar}\right). \tag{13–57}$$

From this, a representation diagonal in momentum at $t = 0$ can be obtained:

$$Q^{\dagger}(p, p') = \int \overline{U}(r, p)\mathrm{Q}'U(r, p')\,dr. \tag{13–58}$$

13–6 Canonical transformations. It has been seen that unitary transformations represent coordinate rotations in a (generally infinite-dimensional) complex space which contains the wave function as a vector. The physical significance of the wave function is unchanged by such a transformation; the wave function is merely expressed in terms of another coordinate system. In like manner, the physical significance of operators representing observables is unchanged by a unitary transformation.

The above, however, is not the only possible interpretation which can be given to a unitary transformation. If the wave function ψ is transformed by the unitary transformation T to ψ',

$$\psi' = \mathrm{T}\psi, \tag{13–59}$$

but the operators representing observables are *not* so transformed, then the transformation can be interpreted as producing a change in the state of the system. Similarly, if the unitary transformation T is applied to all the operators Q, but not to the wave function, the transformation can be interpreted as a replacement of the operators Q by other operators Q′

corresponding to different physical observables. Such a transformation is an example of a *canonical transformation.*

Consider, for example, the effect of the unitary transformation

$$\mathrm{T} = \exp\left(\frac{i}{\hbar}\,\mathbf{P}\cdot \boldsymbol{a}\right), \tag{13–60}$$

where $\boldsymbol{a}$ is a constant vector, on the operator $\boldsymbol{r}$. The transformed operator is

$$\boldsymbol{r}' = \exp\left(\frac{i}{\hbar}\,\mathbf{P}\cdot \boldsymbol{a}\right)\boldsymbol{r}\exp\left(-\frac{i}{\hbar}\,\mathbf{P}\cdot \boldsymbol{a}\right)\cdot \tag{13–61}$$

Since

$$\mathbf{P} = i\hbar\boldsymbol{\nabla}, \tag{13–62}$$

we see that

$$\exp\left(\frac{i}{\hbar}\,\mathbf{P}\cdot \boldsymbol{a}\right) = \exp\,(\boldsymbol{a}\cdot\boldsymbol{\nabla}). \tag{13–63}$$

Expanding this operator as in Eq. (13–52) and letting it operate on an arbitrary function $f(\boldsymbol{r})$, we obtain

$$\exp\,(\boldsymbol{a}\cdot\boldsymbol{\nabla})f(\boldsymbol{r}) = \sum_{n=0}^{\infty}\frac{(\boldsymbol{a}\cdot\boldsymbol{\nabla})^n}{n!}f(\boldsymbol{r}). \tag{13–64}$$

The right side of this equation can be recognized as the Taylor-series expansion of $f(\boldsymbol{r}+\boldsymbol{a})$ about the point $\boldsymbol{r}$:

$$f(\boldsymbol{r}+\boldsymbol{a}) = \sum_{n=0}^{\infty}\frac{(\boldsymbol{a}\cdot\boldsymbol{\nabla})^n}{n!}f(\boldsymbol{r}). \tag{13–65}$$

From this, the transformed position operator $\boldsymbol{r}'$ of Eq. (13–61) is given by

$$\begin{aligned} \boldsymbol{r}'f(\boldsymbol{r}) &= \exp\,(\boldsymbol{a}\cdot\boldsymbol{\nabla})\boldsymbol{r}\exp\,(-\boldsymbol{a}\cdot\boldsymbol{\nabla})f(\mathbf{r}) \\ &= \exp\,(\boldsymbol{a}\cdot\boldsymbol{\nabla})[\boldsymbol{r}f(\boldsymbol{r}-\boldsymbol{a})] \\ &= (\boldsymbol{r}+\boldsymbol{a})f(\boldsymbol{r}-\boldsymbol{a}+\boldsymbol{a}) \\ &= (\boldsymbol{r}+\boldsymbol{a})f(\boldsymbol{r}), \end{aligned} \tag{13–66}$$

or

$$\boldsymbol{r}' = \boldsymbol{r}+\boldsymbol{a}. \tag{13–67}$$

A position operator of the form $g(\boldsymbol{r})$ becomes

$$g'(\boldsymbol{r}) = g(\boldsymbol{r}+\boldsymbol{a}), \tag{13–68}$$

by identical arguments.

The momentum operator $\mathbf{P}$, on the other hand, is left unchanged by this transformation:

$$\begin{aligned}\mathbf{P}' &= \exp\left(\frac{i}{\hbar}\,\mathbf{P}\cdot\boldsymbol{a}\right)\mathbf{P}\exp\left(-\frac{i}{\hbar}\,\mathbf{P}\cdot\boldsymbol{a}\right)\\ &= \exp\left(\frac{i}{\hbar}\,\mathbf{P}\cdot\boldsymbol{a}\right)\exp\left(-\frac{i}{\hbar}\,\mathbf{P}\cdot\boldsymbol{a}\right)\mathbf{P}\\ &= \mathbf{P}.\end{aligned} \tag{13–69}$$

It is clear that this transformation has merely translated the operators in ordinary position space; it can therefore be interpreted as a translation in ordinary position space, rather than as a rotation in Hilbert space. If the transformation is applied to the wave function as well as to the operators, it can be interpreted as a simultaneous translation of both operators and wave function.

Infinitesimal canonical transformations can be used to show an important property of Poisson brackets in classical mechanics that has its quantum-mechanical analogue. As shown in Chapter 5, the Poisson bracket of a constant of the motion of a system and its Hamiltonian, $\{G, H\}$, vanishes. The vanishing of the Poisson bracket $\{G, H\}$ thus provides a way of finding constants of the motion and hence a solution to the dynamical problem. Moreover, as will be shown below, if $G(q_i, p_i)$ is the generating function of an infinitesimal canonical transformation, the vanishing of $\{G, H\}$ implies that the Hamiltonian is invariant under the infinitesimal transformation. Since the symmetry properties of the physical system often determine which transformations leave the Hamiltonian invariant (if the system is symmetrical under a given operation, it is clear that the Hamiltonian must be unaffected by this operation), one can often immediately obtain constants of the motion from the symmetries.

It was seen in Chapter 5 that infinitesimal changes in canonically conjugate variables can be generated classically by a generating function $G(q_i, p_i)$ such that the new variables $q_i + \delta q_i$ and $p_i + \delta p_i$ are still canonical variables. From this earlier development, the changes are

$$\delta q_i = \epsilon\,\frac{\partial G}{\partial p_i}, \qquad \delta p_i = -\epsilon\,\frac{\partial G}{\partial q_i}, \tag{13–70}$$

where ϵ is a constant infinitesimal and $G(q_i, p_i)$ is any differentiable function. Any function W is changed an amount δW by this transformation, where

$$\delta W = \epsilon\{W, G\}. \tag{13–71}$$

Taking W as the Hamiltonian H, one has the result given above, namely,

$$\delta H = \epsilon\{H, G\}, \tag{13–72}$$

showing that, since $\{H, G\}$ vanishes for a constant of the motion (see Chapter 5), a constant of the motion acting as a generating function for an infinitesimal canonical transformation leaves the Hamiltonian invariant.

The above result can be translated into quantum-mechanical formalism by use of the connection between the classical Poisson bracket and the quantum commutator (Postulate 7, Chapter 6):

$$\delta \mathrm{W} = \frac{i\epsilon}{\hbar}[\mathrm{G}, \mathrm{W}] \equiv \frac{i\epsilon}{\hbar}(\mathrm{GW} - \mathrm{WG}). \tag{13–73}$$

The physical significance is clearly the same in quantum and classical mechanics.

Now a few simple examples of infinitesimal contact transformations will be given. If the generating function is

$$G = p_j, \tag{13–74}$$

the transformation is an infinitesimal generalized displacement:

$$\delta q_i = \epsilon\delta_{ij}, \qquad \delta p_i = 0. \tag{13–75}$$

Similarly, if

$$G = -q_j, \tag{13–76}$$

then

$$\delta q_i = 0, \qquad \delta p_i = \epsilon\delta_{ij}. \tag{13–77}$$

These are examples of an important class of transformations. Under such a transformation, the Hamiltonian changes by

$$\delta \mathrm{H} = \frac{i\epsilon}{\hbar}[\mathrm{G}, \mathrm{H}]. \tag{13–78}$$

If it happens from symmetries in the physical system that the energy is unchanged by the transformation, $\delta\mathrm{H}$ must vanish. On the other hand, from the equation of motion, Eq. (8–14),

$$\frac{d}{dt}\langle \mathrm{G}\rangle = \frac{i}{\hbar}\langle[\mathrm{H}, \mathrm{G}]\rangle \tag{13–79}$$

(assuming that G is not an explicit function of time). Thus, if $\delta\mathrm{H}$ vanishes, so must $(d/dt)\langle \mathrm{G}\rangle$, and from considerations of symmetry alone, it may be possible to choose a set of constants of the motion, as mentioned above.

Another elementary example of a displacement generator is the Hamiltonian. From Eq. (13–70) and Hamilton's equations,

$$\delta q_i = \epsilon \frac{\partial H}{\partial p_i} = \epsilon \dot{q}_i,$$

$$\delta p_i = -\epsilon \frac{\partial H}{\partial q_i} = \epsilon \dot{p}_i, \tag{13–80}$$

and therefore the infinitesimal ϵ must be taken to be

$$\epsilon = \delta t. \tag{13–81}$$

Then Eq. (13–73) gives

$$\delta \mathrm{W} = \frac{i}{\hbar}\, \delta t[\mathrm{H}, \mathrm{W}], \tag{13–82}$$

and the change $\delta\mathrm{W}$ (assuming that W is not an explicit function of time) can be interpreted as the effect of a displacement in time by an amount δt.

As a final example, consider the infinitesimal rotation generated by

$$\mathrm{G} = \mathrm{J}_z, \tag{13–83}$$

where J_z is the total z-component of the angular momentum of the system. This transformation generates the following changes in the cartesian coordinates of the position of any particle [see Eqs. (9–2) and (13–73)]:

$$\delta x = \delta\phi \frac{i}{\hbar} [\mathrm{J}_z, x] = -\delta\phi\, y,$$

$$\delta y = \delta\phi \frac{i}{\hbar} [\mathrm{J}_z, y] = \delta\phi\, x, \tag{13–84}$$

$$\delta z = \delta\phi \frac{i}{\hbar} [\mathrm{J}_z, z] = 0.$$

It is clear that J_z generates a rotation of the whole system about the z-axis by the angle $\delta\phi$. Consider any vector **T** which transforms under a coordinate rotation as $\boldsymbol{r}$ does. It must then satisfy

$$\delta \mathrm{T}_x = \delta\phi \frac{i}{\hbar} [\mathrm{J}_z, \mathrm{T}_x]$$

$$= -\delta\phi \mathrm{T}_y, \qquad \text{etc.} \tag{13–85}$$

It is not necessary to compute the commutators, since they follow from the geometrical significance of the infinitesimal rotation. These results are, of course, in agreement with those of Eq. (9–81), as **T** is clearly of class **T**.

Return now to Eq. (13–73); this can be written, if we neglect higher-order infinitesimals, as

$$\mathrm{W}' = \mathrm{W} + \delta\mathrm{W} = \left(1 + \frac{i\epsilon}{\hbar}\,\mathrm{G}\right)\mathrm{W}\left(1 - \frac{i\epsilon}{\hbar}\,\mathrm{G}\right). \tag{13–86}$$

The operator $1 + (i\epsilon/\hbar)\,\mathrm{G}$ will be recognized as unitary to the first order in ϵ, provided G is Hermitian (this is assumed). This equation thus represents an infinitesimal unitary transformation on W. If this transformation is iterated n times,

$$\mathrm{W}'' = \left(1 + \frac{i\epsilon}{\hbar}\,\mathrm{G}\right)^n \mathrm{W}\left(1 - \frac{i\epsilon}{\hbar}\,\mathrm{G}\right)^n. \tag{13–87}$$

Going to the limits $n \to \infty$ and $n\epsilon \to a$, we find that

$$\left(1 + \frac{i\epsilon}{\hbar}\,\mathrm{G}\right)^n \to \exp\left(\frac{ia}{\hbar}\,\mathrm{G}\right). \tag{13–88}$$

This is a unitary operator which generates a finite transformation. Examples of such iterated infinitesimal transformations are $\exp\,(i\mathrm{H}t/\hbar)$, which generates a translation in time by an amount t; $\exp\,(i\mathrm{P}_x a/\hbar)$, which generates a translation in x by an amount a (P_x is the x-component of the total momentum of the system); and $\exp\,[(i\phi/\hbar)\mathrm{J}_z]$, which generates a rotation about the z-axis of the system by an amount ϕ. If the Hamiltonian is invariant under such a rotation, then

$$\delta\mathrm{H} = 0 = \frac{i\phi}{\hbar}\,[\mathrm{J}_z, \mathrm{H}], \tag{13–89}$$

and H and the z-component of the total angular momentum J_z commute. This is an example of the statement made earlier that the system symmetries can make it possible at times to decide a question of operator commutation on the basis of simple geometrical properties.

13–7 Summary. In this chapter, we have shown how unitary matrices transform matrices from one representation basis to another, and we have shown the invariance of matrix equations under such transformations. Hermitian matrices were seen to remain Hermitian after a unitary transformation. The close analogy between rotations in three-dimensional space and unitary rotations in Hilbert space was pointed out. Then the solution of eigenvalue equations by diagonalization of the corresponding matrices was considered, and the group properties of unitary transformations were mentioned briefly. These ideas were presented in relation to discrete matrices; the extension to continuous infinite matrices was then discussed. Finally, canonical transformations, and especially infinitesimal canonical transformations, were discussed in their relation to classical infinitesimal canonical transformations, and the iteration of several infinitesimal transformations was considered. It was shown that simple geometrical properties of a physical system can sometimes be used to decide a question concerning operator commutation.

Problems

13–1. Given

$$\mathbf{R} = \begin{bmatrix} 0 & 1 & 0 \\ 1 & 0 & 0 \\ 0 & 0 & 1 \end{bmatrix}.$$

(a) What are the eigenvalues and column eigenvectors of $\mathbf{R}$? (b) By evaluating $\mathbf{R}_d = \mathbf{T}^{-1}\mathbf{R}\mathbf{T}$, show explicitly that the similarity transformation produced by the matrix $\mathbf{T}$ having normalized eigenvectors of $\mathbf{R}$ as columns will diagonalize $\mathbf{R}$. (c) Show that the eigenvalues of the matrix $\mathbf{R}_d = \mathbf{T}^{-1}\mathbf{R}\mathbf{T}$ are the same as those of $\mathbf{R}$.

13–2. (a) Construct a matrix $\mathbf{T}$ having as columns the normalized eigenvectors of the matrix $\mathbf{S}_x$ [see Eq. (12–32)]. Do this in such a way that the diagonal elements are positive-real. (b) Show that $\mathbf{T}$ is unitary and that it transforms $\mathbf{S}_x$ into diagonal form. (c) Show that $\mathbf{T}$ can also be constructed as one of the rotation operators

$$\mathbf{T} = \exp\left(\pm \frac{i\pi}{2\hbar}\,\mathbf{S}_y\right).$$

(d) From the point of view of a rotation in real three-dimensional space, what is the significance of this transformation? (e) Considered as a rotation in two-dimensional complex function space, what is the significance?

13–3. Show that in a momentum representation, the energy eigenfunctions of the one-dimensional harmonic oscillator can be written as

$$\Psi_n(p) = u_n\left(\frac{1}{\sqrt{km}}\,p\right),$$

where $u_n(x)$ is the energy eigenfunction in a position representation.

13–4. For an electron whose spin precesses about a magnetic field due to its magnetic moment, the Hamiltonian corresponding to the spin energy can be written as

$$\mathrm{H} = -\omega \mathrm{S}_z,$$

where $\omega = e\mathcal{B}/mc$ is the precessional frequency. Use the unitary operator $\mathrm{T} = \exp(i\mathrm{H}t/\hbar)$ to transform the operators S_x and S_y to a Heisenberg representation and show that the transformed operators obey the equations of motion

$$\dot{S}_x^\dagger = \omega S_y^\dagger, \qquad \dot{S}_y^\dagger = -\omega S_x^\dagger,$$

where $S_x^\dagger = TS_xT^*$, etc. Note that these equations of motion are just what would be expected for the classical equations of motion of a top with angular momentum $\hbar/2$ and magnetic moment $e\hbar/2mc$ in a magnetic field of strength $\mathcal{B}$.

13–5. (a) Show that the transformation of spin operators induced by the unitary transformation operator T (Problem 13–4) can be interpreted as a canonical transformation, namely, a coordinate rotation in position space about the z-axis by the angle $\theta = -\omega t$.

Given this interpretation, $S_x^\dagger$ and $S_y^\dagger$ are spin angular-momentum components along the new steadily rotating coordinate axes, and only the operators are transformed by the unitary transformation, not the wave function. (b) Show that T^* induces a rotation about the z-axis in the opposite direction. (c) Show that $\mathbf{S}^{\dagger\dagger}$ derived from $\mathbf{S}$ with a canonical transformation induced by T^* has a time-independent expectation value for all three components. (d) Explain this result.

13–6. A one-electron atom has compatible measurements made on it, yielding the results that $l = 3, j = \frac{7}{2}$, and $m_j = \frac{1}{2}$. (a) What is the probability that a succeeding measurement of S_x will yield $\frac{1}{2}$? (b) If a later set of measurements yields $l = 1$, $m_l = 0$, and $m_s = \frac{1}{2}$, what is the probability that a further measurement will yield $j = \frac{3}{2}$?

13–7. The unitary operator $\exp(-iHt/\hbar)$ transforms the position and momentum operators x and P_x into (Heisenberg representation)

$$X^\dagger = \exp\left(\frac{iHt}{\hbar}\right) x \exp\left(-\frac{iHt}{\hbar}\right),$$

$$P_x^\dagger = \exp\left(\frac{iHt}{\hbar}\right) P_x \exp\left(-\frac{iHt}{\hbar}\right).$$

(a) Show that these transformed operators obey classical equations of motion. (b) Show that for a simple harmonic oscillator and x and P_x of the usual differential-operator form, the transformed operators are

$$X^\dagger = x \cos \omega t - \frac{1}{\sqrt{km}} i\hbar \sin \omega t \frac{\partial}{\partial x},$$

$$P_x^\dagger = -i\hbar \cos \omega t \frac{\partial}{\partial x} - \sqrt{km}\, x \sin \omega t.$$

13–8. The transformation induced by the unitary operator $\exp(iHt/\hbar)$, interpreted as a canonical transformation, transforms x and P_x into

$$X^{\dagger\dagger} = \exp\left(-\frac{iHt}{\hbar}\right) x \exp\left(\frac{iHt}{\hbar}\right)$$

$$P_x^{\dagger\dagger} = \exp\left(-\frac{iHt}{\hbar}\right) P_x \exp\left(\frac{iHt}{\hbar}\right).$$

(a) Show that although these operators are explicit functions of the time, they represent observables that are constants of the motion. [*Hint:* Transform to a Heisenberg representation and make use of Eq. (11–46).] (b) Show that these operators may be interpreted as representing the corresponding quantities but observed at $t = 0$.

13–9. The spin angular-momentum operator can be considered as the generator of an infinitesimal rotation of spin angular-momentum vectors in space. Consequently, a canonical transformation produced by the unitary matrix $\mathsf{V} = \exp(i\theta \mathsf{S}_z/\hbar)$ should produce a rotation of the spin coordinate system about the z-axis by an angle θ. (a) For the case of spin one-half for which $\mathbf{S} = \frac{1}{2}\hbar\boldsymbol{\sigma}$, show that

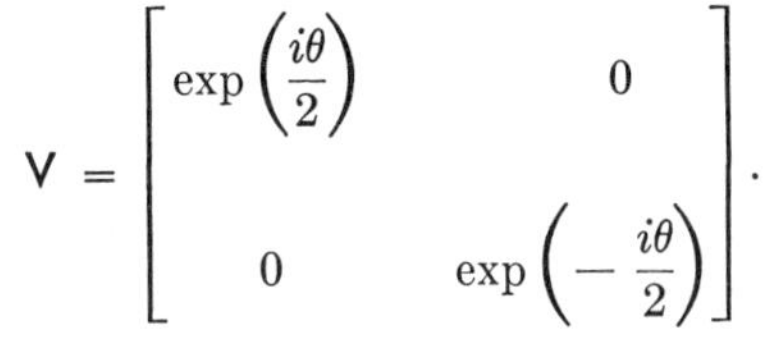

$$\mathsf{V} = \begin{bmatrix} \exp\left(\dfrac{i\theta}{2}\right) & 0 \\ 0 & \exp\left(-\dfrac{i\theta}{2}\right) \end{bmatrix}.$$

(b) Evaluate $\mathsf{V}^{-1}\boldsymbol{\sigma}\mathsf{V}$. (c) Show that this can be interpreted as $\boldsymbol{\sigma}$ in a rotated coordinate system. (d) In the case of a rotation through 90°, show that V transforms an eigenvector of σ_x into one of σ_y, etc. (e) By using commutation relations and without making use of the explicit form of $\boldsymbol{\sigma}$, show that a transformation induced by the unitary matrix $\mathsf{W} = \exp(i\theta\boldsymbol{n}\cdot\boldsymbol{\sigma}/2)$, where $\boldsymbol{n}$ is a constant unit vector, induces a rotation through an angle θ about the axis $\boldsymbol{n}$ when applied to $\boldsymbol{\sigma}$.

13–10. An electron is in a state characterized by the quantum numbers j, l, and m_j. The z-component of the spin angular momentum is measured. Calculate the probability of obtaining the result $+\hbar/2$.

13–11. Show that the characteristic polynomial, Eq. (13–31), is satisfied with q replaced by the matrix Q (Cayley-Hamilton theorem). [*Hint:* Let the resulting matrix operate on an arbitrary column vector expanded in appropriate base functions.]

CHAPTER 14

APPROXIMATION METHODS

14–1 The need for approximation methods. Thus far in the development of quantum mechanics, only very simple physical situations for which it is possible to obtain exact solutions to the Schrödinger equation have been treated. However, this happy situation has prevailed only because of the relative simplicity of the Hamiltonians considered. For the large majority of systems of physical interest, the exact solution of the Schrödinger equation presents great mathematical difficulties.

Despite the complexity commonly met, however, much valuable knowledge about the behavior of a system of interest can frequently be obtained. There are two ways in which this can be done. One way is to ask for less knowledge about the system than is provided by the wave function. The energy of the system might be required, for example, without the necessity of the additional details provided by the wave function.

The other way in which information about a complex system can be obtained is by its comparison with a similar but simpler system. Thus, if the Hamiltonian consists of two parts, a simple part that if present alone would permit solution of Schrödinger's equation, and a second part consisting of one or more relatively small additional terms, then the approximate system behavior can be obtained by considering the solvable simple part as giving the dominant behavior and treating the actual behavior as a relatively minor variation, or perturbation, from this calculable behavior. The small perturbation can be estimated by a study of the small complicating terms previously ignored.

Techniques based on each of these approaches will be developed and illustrated in this chapter, thereby immensely widening the range of problems that can be handled quantum-mechanically with some degree of assurance.

14–2 Time-independent perturbation theory. The first approximation method to be considered is known as *perturbation theory*. It is an example of the second approach outlined above. Consider the case in which the Hamiltonian can be written in the form

$$\mathrm{H} = \mathrm{H}_0 + \mathrm{H}_1, \tag{14–1}$$

where H_0 is large compared with H_1; i.e., the energy associated with H_0

is large compared with that associated with H_1. Two additional assumptions are made, that H does not depend on the time explicitly and that H_0 leads to a solved energy-eigenvalue equation:

$$H_0 u_k = E_k u_k. \tag{14–2}$$

Here the u_k are (known) eigenfunctions corresponding to the (known) eigenvalues E_k of the Hamiltonian H_0.

It is always possible to write Eq. (14–1) as a special case of the Hamiltonian

$$H = H_0 + \lambda H_1, \tag{14–3}$$

where λ is an arbitrary parameter which can later be taken equal to unity to obtain the desired solution to the eigenvalue problem with the Hamiltonian of Eq. (14–1). It is assumed that it is possible to expand the eigenfunctions and eigenenergies of the total Hamiltonian H of Eq. (14–3) in a power series in λ:

$$\begin{aligned} \psi &= \psi_0 + \lambda\psi_1 + \lambda^2\psi_2 + \lambda^3\psi_3 + \cdots, \\ E &= E_0 + \lambda E_1 + \lambda^2 E_2 + \lambda^3 E_3 + \cdots \end{aligned} \tag{14–4}$$

In the limit as $\lambda \to 0$, the energy-eigenvalue equation becomes

$$H_0\psi_0 = E_0\psi_0. \tag{14–5}$$

Equation (14–2) shows that the identifications

$$\psi_0 \equiv u_k \tag{14–6}$$

and

$$E_0 \equiv E_k \tag{14–7}$$

must be made; u_k is one of the eigenfunctions of the unperturbed system, and E_k is the corresponding eigenenergy.

Writing the energy-eigenvalue equation with the use of Eqs. (14–3) and (14–4) gives

$$\begin{aligned} &(H_0 + \lambda H_1)(\psi_0 + \lambda\psi_1 + \lambda^2\psi_2 + \cdots) \\ &\quad = (E_0 + \lambda E_1 + \lambda^2 E_2 + \cdots)(\psi_0 + \lambda\psi_1 + \lambda^2\psi_2 + \cdots), \\ &H_0\psi_0 + \lambda(H_1\psi_0 + H_0\psi_1) + \lambda^2(H_0\psi_2 + H_1\psi_1) + \cdots \\ &\quad = E_0\psi_0 + \lambda(E_1\psi_0 + E_0\psi_1) + \lambda^2(E_2\psi_0 + E_1\psi_1 + E_0\psi_2) + \cdots \end{aligned} \tag{14–8}$$

Since λ is an arbitrary parameter, one can equate coefficients of like powers of λ on each side of this equation. This gives the set of equations

$$\begin{aligned} \mathrm{H}_0\psi_0 &= E_0\psi_0, \\ \mathrm{H}_1\psi_0 + \mathrm{H}_0\psi_1 &= E_1\psi_0 + E_0\psi_1, \\ \mathrm{H}_0\psi_2 + \mathrm{H}_1\psi_1 &= E_2\psi_0 + E_1\psi_1 + E_0\psi_2, \\ &\vdots \end{aligned} \tag{14–9}$$

The first of these equations has already been discussed. If we expand ψ_1 in terms of the unperturbed functions u_k,

$$\psi_1 = \sum_n c_n u_n, \tag{14–10}$$

and if we use Eqs. (14–6) and (14–7), we obtain from the second of equations (14–9)

$$\begin{aligned} \mathrm{H}_1 u_k + \mathrm{H}_0 \sum_n c_n u_n &= E_1 u_k + E_k \sum_n c_n u_n, \\ \mathrm{H}_1 u_k + \sum_n c_n E_n u_n &= E_1 u_k + \sum_n c_n E_k u_n. \end{aligned} \tag{14–11}$$

Multiplying on the left by $\overline{u_j}$ and integrating over all space gives

$$\begin{aligned} (u_j, \mathrm{H}_1 u_k) + \sum_n c_n E_n (u_j, u_n) &= E_1 (u_j, u_k) + \sum_n c_n E_k (u_j, u_n), \\ (u_j, \mathrm{H}_1 u_k) + c_j E_j &= E_1\, \delta_{jk} + c_j E_k. \end{aligned} \tag{14–12}$$

For the case $j = k$, this becomes

$$E_1 = (u_k, \mathrm{H}_1 u_k) = (\mathsf{H}_1)_{kk}. \tag{14–13}$$

Thus the first-order perturbation to the energy of the state corresponding to the unperturbed state of energy E_k is given by the matrix element $(\mathsf{H}_1)_{kk}$. Equation (14–12), for the case $j \neq k$, gives an expression for c_j and hence for the first-order perturbation ψ_1 to the corresponding eigenfunction u_k:

$$c_j = \frac{(\mathsf{H}_1)_{jk}}{E_k - E_j}. \tag{14–14}$$

The value of c_k is not determined by this process. Since the wave function is assumed normalized,

$$\begin{aligned}
1 &= (\psi, \psi) \\
&= (\psi_0 + \lambda\psi_1 + \cdots, \psi_0 + \lambda\psi_1 + \cdots) \\
&= (\psi_0, \psi_0) + \lambda[(\psi_1, \psi_0) + (\psi_0, \psi_1)] \\
&\qquad\qquad + \lambda^2[(\psi_0, \psi_2) + (\psi_1, \psi_1) + (\psi_2, \psi_0)] + \cdots \\
&= 1 + \lambda[(\psi_1, \psi_0) + (\psi_0, \psi_1)] + \lambda^2[(\psi_0, \psi_2) + (\psi_1, \psi_1) + (\psi_2, \psi_0)] + \cdots
\end{aligned} \tag{14–15}$$

Since λ is arbitrary and nonzero, each term in brackets must separately vanish. In particular,

$$(\psi_1, \psi_0) + (\psi_0, \psi_1) = 0. \tag{14–16}$$

From Eq. (14–10), this can be written as

$$\begin{aligned}
\left(\sum_n c_n u_n, u_k\right) + \left(u_k, \sum_n c_n u_n\right) &= 0, \\
\overline{c_k} + c_k &= 0.
\end{aligned} \tag{14–17}$$

Thus the real part of c_k must vanish:

$$c_k = i\gamma. \tag{14–18}$$

To first order, then, the wave function ψ can be written as

$$\begin{aligned}
\psi &= \psi_0 + \lambda\psi_1 \\
&= u_k + i\gamma\lambda u_k + \lambda \sum_{n \neq k} \frac{(\mathsf{H}_1)_{nk}}{E_k - E_n} u_n \\
&= (1 + i\gamma\lambda)u_k + \lambda \sum_{n \neq k} \frac{(\mathsf{H}_1)_{nk}}{E_k - E_n} u_n.
\end{aligned} \tag{14–19}$$

Since normalization only to the first order in λ is of interest at present, $1 + i\gamma\lambda$ can be replaced by

$$1 + i\gamma\lambda \approx \exp(i\gamma\lambda). \tag{14–20}$$

From this it is seen that the coefficient c_k in Eq. (14–10) has the effect of changing the phase of the original unperturbed wave function u_k relative to the phase of the perturbation terms. To maintain the orthogonality of the perturbed wave functions, this phase must be taken equal to zero:

$$c_k = 0. \tag{14–21}$$

The effect of the perturbation term H_1 in the Hamiltonian on both the wave function and eigenenergy has been obtained to the first order. Second-order terms can be obtained in a similar way by using the first-order solutions and the terms of order λ^2 in the power-series developments. Only the results of such a treatment will be given here. To the second order, the wave function is

$$\psi = u_k + \sum_{n \neq k} \frac{(\mathsf{H}_1)_{nk}}{E_k - E_n} u_n$$
$$+\sum_{n \neq k}\left\{\left[\sum_{m \neq k} \frac{(\mathsf{H}_1)_{nm}(\mathsf{H}_1)_{mk}}{(E_k - E_n)(E_k - E_m)} - \frac{(\mathsf{H}_1)_{nk}(\mathsf{H}_1)_{kk}}{(E_k - E_n)^2}\right] u_n - \frac{1}{2}\frac{|(\mathsf{H}_1)_{nk}|^2}{(E_k - E_n)^2} u_k\right\}, \tag{14–22}$$

and the energy is

$$E = E_k + (\mathsf{H}_1)_{kk} + \sum_{n \neq k} \frac{|(\mathsf{H}_1)_{nk}|^2}{E_k - E_n}. \tag{14–23}$$

As an example of perturbation theory, consider the anharmonic one-dimensional oscillator whose Hamiltonian is

$$\mathrm{H} = \frac{\mathrm{P}^2}{2m} + \tfrac{1}{2}kx^2 + ax^4. \tag{14–24}$$

Here the unperturbed Hamiltonian consists of the first two terms, and the perturbation, assumed to be small, is given by

$$\mathrm{H}_1 \equiv ax^4. \tag{14–25}$$

For the ground state whose wave function ψ_0 is given by Eq. (4–60), the first-order correction to the energy is

$$\begin{aligned} E_1 &= (\psi_0, \mathrm{H}_1\psi_0) \\ &= \left(\frac{k}{\pi\hbar\omega}\right)^{1/2} \int_{-\infty}^{\infty} \exp\left(-\frac{kx^2}{2\hbar\omega}\right) ax^4 \exp\left(-\frac{kx^2}{2\hbar\omega}\right) dx \\ &= \left(\frac{k}{\pi\hbar\omega}\right)^{1/2} a\int_{-\infty}^{\infty} x^4 \exp\left(-\frac{kx^2}{\hbar\omega}\right) dx \\ &= \frac{3a}{4}\left(\frac{\hbar\omega}{k}\right)^2. \end{aligned} \tag{14–26}$$

Therefore, the ground-state energy of the anharmonic oscillator is approximately

$$E \approx \frac{\hbar\omega}{2}\left[1 + \frac{3a}{2}\left(\frac{\hbar\omega}{k^2}\right)\right]. \tag{14–27}$$

This development has assumed that the state under consideration is nondegenerate. If, on the contrary, the state is degenerate, the treatment must be altered. The difficulty arises because the energy denominator of Eq. (14–14) vanishes when the state k under consideration (with unperturbed energy E_k) is degenerate with state j and when nonvanishing matrix elements $(\mathsf{H}_1)_{jk}$ couple the states. The difficulty is resolved when all matrix elements of the perturbing term in the Hamiltonian vanish between all pairs of degenerate states. This means that the Hamiltonian matrix

$$H_{jk} = (\mathsf{H}_0)_{jk} + (\mathsf{H}_1)_{jk} \tag{14–28}$$

must be diagonal so far as each submatrix referring to a group of degenerate states is concerned. Thus the difficulty of applying the perturbation approach to degenerate states is removed by an exact diagonalization of the appropriate submatrix of the total Hamiltonian.

This can always be done. It amounts to finding the proper orthonormal linear combinations v_j of the degenerate states u_k such that H_1 has vanishing off-diagonal matrix elements between the states v_j:

$$(v_i, \mathrm{H}_1 v_j) = 0, \qquad i \neq j, \tag{14–29}$$

where

$$v_j = \sum_{k=1}^{m} a_{jk}^{(s)} u_k. \tag{14–30}$$

Here the u_k are the original set of degenerate wave functions of energy E_s. It is assumed here that the degeneracy is m-fold.

Referring to the earlier generalization wherein the perturbing term is $\lambda \mathrm{H}_1$, it is clear that as λ approaches zero, the wave functions must approach those of the unperturbed Hamiltonian H_0. However, in the case of degeneracy, the appropriate function will not in general be one of the original u_k of Eq. (14–2), but instead will be a linear combination of these, as in Eq. (14–30). The diagonalization procedure indicated above merely ensures that the perturbed wave functions approach the proper functions v_j as $\lambda \rightarrow 0$.

An example of the problem raised by degeneracy and its resolution is afforded by a paramagnetic ion in a suitable location in a crystal lattice. The Hamiltonian for such an ion is usually extremely complex. It contains terms corresponding to the kinetic energies of the electrons, the coulombic interactions between the electrons and between them and the ionic nucleus, interactions between the ionic electrons and the crystal fields set up by neighboring atoms, spin-orbit interactions, and possibly many others, such as Zeeman energies, hyperfine interactions, quadrupole interactions, etc.

However, for many problems of interest, perturbation theory can be successfully applied to such a system. An exceptionally simple case will be considered, that of the lowest group of electronic states associated with an ion with an effective spin $S = 1$ located at a crystallographic lattice point where the effective potential seen by the ion has rhombic symmetry. The lowest energy levels are describable in terms of a so-called *spin Hamiltonian,** whose parameters are directly related to the ionic crystal properties. In the absence of an applied magnetic field, the spin Hamiltonian can be written in the form

$$\mathrm{H} = D\mathrm{S}_z^2 + E(\mathrm{S}_x^2 - \mathrm{S}_y^2). \tag{14-31}$$

The term $D\mathrm{S}_z^2$ arises when the (dominant) octahedral symmetry seen by the paramagnetic ion in many cases is distorted to tetragonal (or trigonal) symmetry. A further distortion to (the lower) rhombic symmetry gives rise to the term $E(\mathrm{S}_x^2 - \mathrm{S}_y^2)$. The spin Hamiltonian of Eq. (14-31) applies to many crystals, among them the nickel Tutton salt $K_2Ni(SO_4)_2 \cdot 6H_2O$.

In the following treatment, the rhombic term $E(\mathrm{S}_x^2 - \mathrm{S}_y^2)$ will be considered as a perturbation on the system. This is reasonable, since E is usually considerably smaller than D, and the energies associated with both terms are small compared with the much larger kinetic energy and coulombic terms. The appropriate eigenfunctions for the term $D\mathrm{S}_z^2$ are those for S_z; in matrix notation,

$$\psi_1 = \begin{bmatrix} 1 \\ 0 \\ 0 \end{bmatrix}, \qquad \psi_2 = \begin{bmatrix} 0 \\ 1 \\ 0 \end{bmatrix}, \qquad \psi_3 = \begin{bmatrix} 0 \\ 0 \\ 1 \end{bmatrix}. \tag{14-32}$$

The corresponding (unperturbed) energies are

$$E_1^0 = \frac{D\hbar^2}{4}, \qquad E_2^0 = 0, \qquad E_3^0 = \frac{D\hbar^2}{4}. \tag{14-33}$$

It is seen that E_1^0 and E_3^0 are degenerate. If the first-order corrections to the energies are computed for the term $E(\mathrm{S}_x^2 - \mathrm{S}_y^2)$, it is found that they all vanish, since

$$\begin{aligned} E(\mathsf{S}_x^2 - \mathsf{S}_y^2)\psi_1 &= \hbar^2 E\psi_3, \\ E(\mathsf{S}_x^2 - \mathsf{S}_y^2)\psi_2 &= 0, \\ E(\mathsf{S}_x^2 - \mathsf{S}_y^2)\psi_3 &= \hbar^2 E\psi_1, \end{aligned} \tag{14-34}$$

---

* B. Bleaney and K. W. H. Stevens, "Paramagnetic Resonance," *Rpts. Progr. Phys.* **16,** 108 (1953). K. D. Bowers and J. Owen, "Paramagnetic Resonance II," *Rpts. Progr. Phys.* **18,** 304 (1955).

and thus

$$\begin{aligned} (1|E(\mathsf{S}_x^2 - \mathsf{S}_y^2)|1) &= \hbar^2 E(1|3) = 0, \\ (2|E(\mathsf{S}_x^2 - \mathsf{S}_y^2)|2) &= 0, \\ (3|E(\mathsf{S}_x^2 - \mathsf{S}_y^2)|3) &= \hbar^2 E(3|1) = 0. \end{aligned} \tag{14–35}$$

This result is in agreement with that of Eq. (9–35), which showed that the average values of the squares of the x and y angular-momentum components are equal when the z-component is known. A convenient notation for matrix elements, introduced by Dirac, is used in Eq. (14–35): the first and second subscripts are written before and after the Hamiltonian, respectively. This allows ample room for writing multiple subscripts should they be needed. Equations (14–34) can readily be obtained from equations (14–32) and the matrix form of the perturbation:

$$E(\mathsf{S}_x^2 - \mathsf{S}_y^2) = \hbar^2 E \begin{bmatrix} 0 & 0 & 1 \\ 0 & 0 & 0 \\ 1 & 0 & 0 \end{bmatrix}. \tag{14–36}$$

It can be seen from Eqs. (14–33) and (14–35) that the second-order perturbation energy cannot be obtained from the direct application of Eq. (14–23), for the unperturbed states ψ_1 and ψ_3 are degenerate. We must therefore take linear combinations of these states as the unperturbed functions such that the perturbation has no cross matrix elements between the new state functions. Let

$$\psi_\pm \equiv \begin{bmatrix} a_\pm \\ 0 \\ b_\pm \end{bmatrix} \tag{14–37}$$

be the required linear combinations of ψ_1 and ψ_3. To avoid cross terms, the submatrix of the perturbation for these states must be diagonal:

$$E(\mathsf{S}_x^2 - \mathsf{S}_y^2)\psi_\pm = \gamma_\pm \psi_\pm, \tag{14–38}$$

or

$$\hbar^2 E \begin{bmatrix} 0 & 0 & 1 \\ 0 & 0 & 0 \\ 1 & 0 & 0 \end{bmatrix} \begin{bmatrix} a_\pm \\ 0 \\ b_\pm \end{bmatrix} = \gamma_\pm \begin{bmatrix} a_\pm \\ 0 \\ b_\pm \end{bmatrix}. \tag{14–39}$$

Solving this set of linear equations gives as normalized wave functions

$$\psi_\pm = \frac{1}{\sqrt{2}} \begin{bmatrix} 1 \\ 0 \\ \pm 1 \end{bmatrix}. \tag{14–40}$$

It is readily seen that these states are orthogonal to ψ_2. With these new states, the following relations are easily obtained:

$$E(\mathsf{S}_x^2 - \mathsf{S}_y^2)\psi_+ = \hbar^2 E\psi_+,$$
$$E(\mathsf{S}_x^2 - \mathsf{S}_y^2)\psi_- = -\hbar^2 E\psi_-. \tag{14–41}$$

Therefore

$$(+|E(\mathsf{S}_x^2 - \mathsf{S}_y^2)|+) = \hbar^2 E,$$
$$(-|E(\mathsf{S}_x^2 - \mathsf{S}_y^2)|-) = -\hbar^2 E, \tag{14–42}$$
$$(+|E(\mathsf{S}_x^2 - \mathsf{S}_y^2)|-) = (-|E(\mathsf{S}_x^2 - \mathsf{S}_y^2)|+) = 0.$$

Thus the second-order energy perturbation now vanishes, and the energies of the three states are given by

$$E_+ = \frac{D\hbar^2}{4} + \hbar^2 E,$$
$$E_2 = 0, \tag{14–43}$$
$$E_- = \frac{D\hbar^2}{4} - \hbar^2 E$$

(see Fig. 14–1).

Note that in this simple case, the diagonalization of the submatrix for the subspace (1, 3) diagonalizes the entire Hamiltonian of Eq. (14–31) and thus solves the energy-eigenvalue problem exactly, rather than only to the second order in the perturbing term.

As a final illustration of the use of perturbation theory, consider a term found in the Hamiltonian of isolated atoms, the *spin-orbit interaction*

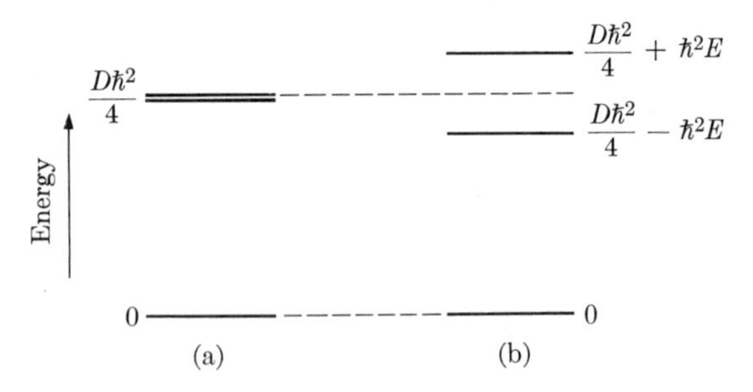

FIG. 14–1. An energy-level diagram for an ion with an effective spin $S = 1$ in a crystal lattice, in zero magnetic field. (a) Energy levels due to a tetragonal crystal symmetry. (b) Further splitting of the degenerate pair of states by an additional small rhombic distortion.

term. This is another type of interaction of the magnetic moment of an electron with its surroundings. To simplify the discussion, consider the effect of this term on the energy levels of alkali metal atoms (and hydrogen) associated with the excitation of the outermost (valence) electron. The inner (core) electrons contribute only slightly in a dynamical way to the motion of the valence electron. Their effect on the valence electron will be considered expressible by an effective radial potential which, combined with the nuclear coulomb potential, can be written as $V(r)$.

To treat the problem, it must be remembered that although in a frame of reference for which the atom is at rest one sees only an electric field produced by the nucleus and the surrounding cloud of core electrons, in a coordinate system which is moving with the valence electron one sees a magnetic field as a result of the relativistic transformation that occurs between electric and magnetic fields. The magnitude of this field is given by

$$\boldsymbol{\mathcal{B}} = -\frac{\boldsymbol{v}}{c} \times \boldsymbol{\mathcal{E}}, \tag{14–44}$$

where the velocity $\boldsymbol{v}$ is that at which the electron is moving through the atom, the vector $\boldsymbol{\mathcal{E}}$ refers to the strength of the electric field through which the electron is moving, and $\boldsymbol{\mathcal{B}}$ is the resultant magnetic field seen by the moving electron.

The magnetic field interacts with the magnetic moment of the electron, producing a torque which tends to twist the spin axis and resulting in a precession of the electron spin. To obtain the interaction energy between the electron spin and this motional magnetic field, we take the (negative of the) scalar product of the magnetic field strength, as given by Eq. (14–44), and the magnetic moment of the electron, as given by Eq. (12–36). However, a further relativistic effect must now be included in addition to the transformation of the electromagnetic field. This purely kinematical effect, caused by the acceleration of the electron, results in a multiplicative factor of one-half in the interaction energy. This factor, known as the *Thomas factor*,* permits us to write the interaction energy between the spin of the electron and the motional magnetic field as

$$\begin{aligned} \mathrm{H}_{so} &= \frac{1}{2}\boldsymbol{\mu}\cdot\left(\frac{\boldsymbol{v}}{c}\times\boldsymbol{\mathcal{E}}\right) = -\frac{1}{2}\frac{\boldsymbol{\mu}}{mc}\cdot(\boldsymbol{\mathcal{E}}\times\mathbf{P}) = \frac{1}{2}\frac{1}{mc}\frac{1}{r}\frac{d\phi}{dr}(r\times\mathbf{P})\cdot\boldsymbol{\mu} \\ &= \frac{e}{2m^2c^2}\frac{1}{r}\frac{d\phi}{dr}\mathbf{L}\cdot\mathbf{S} = \frac{1}{2m^2c^2}\frac{1}{r^2}\frac{dV}{dr}\mathbf{L}\cdot\mathbf{S}, \end{aligned} \tag{14–45}$$

---

* L. H. Thomas, "The Motion of the Spinning Electron," *Nature* **117,** 514 (1926).

where ϕ represents the electrostatic potential function (the negative gradient of which gives the electric field), and V is the total effective potential energy of the electron in the electric field. Here it has been assumed that the electric field is purely radial (in other words, that so far as the valence electron is concerned, we are dealing with a central-force problem). It is seen that the interaction energy is proportional to the scalar product of the orbital angular momentum of the electron and its spin angular momentum. Adding this interaction energy to the Hamiltonian for the valence electron gives

$$\mathrm{H} = \frac{1}{2m}\,\mathrm{P}^2 + V(r) + \frac{1}{2m^2c^2}\,\frac{1}{r}\,\frac{dV}{dr}\,\mathbf{L}\cdot\mathbf{S}. \tag{14–46}$$

The first-order perturbation in the energy levels depends on the radial-wave function and on the angular momentum associated with the state through the scalar product $\mathbf{L}\cdot\mathbf{S}$. In Chapter 9, it was seen that the operators J^2, L^2, and S^2 commute with one another, and now we see that the Hamiltonian of Eq. (14–46) commutes with these operators. We can therefore characterize an atomic state by the quantum numbers n, j, l, and s, where n, the *principal quantum number*, is associated with the radial part of the wave function (see Chapter 10). From Eq. (9–71), the Hamiltonian can be rewritten in the form

$$\mathrm{H} = \frac{1}{2m}\,\mathrm{P}^2 + V(r) + \frac{1}{4m^2c^2}\,\frac{1}{r}\,\frac{dV}{dr}\,(\mathrm{J}^2 - \mathrm{L}^2 - \mathrm{S}^2). \tag{14–47}$$

Inasmuch as the operator in parentheses in the third term of this equation will, for each of the stationary energy states, be operating on an eigenfunction of each of the operators in parentheses, the parenthetical term becomes simply a number, resulting in a modified effective potential energy V' for a particular state given by

$$V'(r) = V(r) + \frac{1}{4m^2c^2}\,\frac{1}{r}\,\frac{dV}{dr}\,[j(j+1) - l(l+1) - \tfrac{3}{4}]\hbar^2 \tag{14–48}$$

(where $s = \frac{1}{2}$ for the valence electron has been explicitly used).

The spin-orbit correction to the energy of an electron is small compared with the remainder of the energy and can be written as

$$E_{nlj} = \frac{1}{4m^2c^2}\left\langle\frac{1}{r}\,\frac{dV}{dr}\right\rangle_{nl}[j(j+1) - l(l+1) - \tfrac{3}{4}]\hbar^2. \tag{14–49}$$

This has the effect of splitting the degeneracy of energy levels of equal n and l but different relative orientations of $\boldsymbol{L}$ and $\mathbf{S}$, that is, different j. In particular, for all states other than S-states ($l = 0$), each level becomes a doublet, corresponding to $j = l \pm \frac{1}{2}$. From Eq. (14–49), the doublet separation is given by

$$\Delta E_{\text{doublet}} = \frac{\hbar^2}{4m^2c^2}(2l+1)\left\langle \frac{1}{r}\frac{dV}{dr}\right\rangle_{nl}. \tag{14–50}$$

Thus, the $P_{3/2}$-state ($l = 1, j = 3/2$) differs in energy from the $P_{1/2}$-level by

$$\Delta E_{P_{3/2}-P_{1/2}} = \frac{3\hbar^2}{4m^2c^2}\left\langle \frac{1}{r}\frac{dV}{dr}\right\rangle_{nl}. \tag{14–51}$$

The familiar sodium D-lines are produced by transitions from the lowest $P_{3/2}$- and $P_{1/2}$-states to the ground $S_{1/2}$-state; it is because of the spin-orbit interaction that these two lines appear separated. In potassium, the corresponding lines lie in the near infrared (see Fig. 14–2).

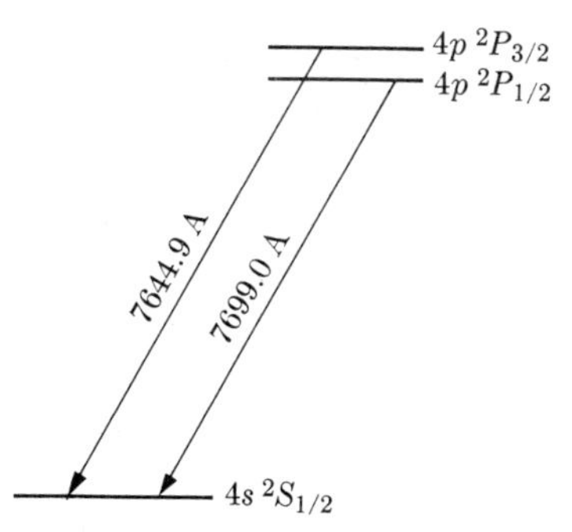

FIG. 14–2. A (partial) energy-level diagram for potassium, showing the optical transitions from the lowest-lying P-states to the ground S-state.

Note that the calculation of spin-orbit interaction energy again involves degenerate perturbation theory because, in the absence of this term, the levels for $j = l \pm \frac{1}{2}$ are degenerate. However, by the choice of the wave functions as eigenfunctions of H, J^2, L^2, and S^2, the original functions were such as to diagonalize the perturbation matrix, and the degeneracy never became explicit.

14–3 Time-dependent perturbation theory. Now consider the case in which the Hamiltonian can again be separated into two parts H_0 and H_1, as in Eq. (14–1), but in which the small perturbing term H_1 depends explicitly upon the time. The Schrödinger equation is then

$$(H_0 + H_1)\psi = i\hbar\frac{\partial\psi}{\partial t}. \tag{14–52}$$

The time-independent energy eigenfunctions u_k of the unperturbed time-independent Hamiltonian H_0 again satisfy

$$\mathrm{H}_0 u_k = E_k u_k \tag{14–53}$$

and once more form an orthonormal set for the expansion of any arbitrary function. Consequently, the wave function in Eq. (14–52) can be expanded:

$$\psi = \sum_k c_k(t) \exp(-i\omega_k t) u_k, \qquad \omega_k \equiv \frac{E_k}{\hbar}. \tag{14–54}$$

The matrix elements of the terms $\mathbf{H}_0$ and $\mathbf{H}_1$ are

$$\begin{aligned} (j|\mathbf{H}_0|k) &\equiv E_k\, \delta_{jk}, \\ (j|\mathbf{H}_1|k) &\equiv (u_j, \mathrm{H}_1 u_k). \end{aligned} \tag{14–55}$$

Note that the matrix of H_0 is diagonal, as it should be, since the base functions are eigenfunctions of H_0. If the Schrödinger equation, Eq. (14–52), is multiplied by (the complex-conjugate of) one of the eigenfunctions and integrated over all coordinates, the result is

$$(u_j, \mathrm{H}\psi) = \left(u_j, i\hbar \frac{\partial \psi}{\partial t}\right). \tag{14–56}$$

By making use of Eqs. (14–54) and (14–55), we can reduce this to

$$\frac{dc_j}{dt} = -\frac{i}{\hbar} \sum_k (j|\mathbf{H}_1|k) c_k \exp(i\omega_{jk} t), \qquad \omega_{jk} \equiv \omega_j - \omega_k. \tag{14–57}$$

This set of equations is completely equivalent to the Schrödinger equation in that it enables the time dependence of the coefficients c_j and hence the time dependence of the wave function to be calculated. The set of equations is exact; no approximation has been made so far. This particular way of expressing the Schrödinger equation will be recognized as the interaction representation (see Chapter 11). Note from Eq. (14–57) that when the perturbing term $\mathbf{H}_1$ vanishes, the c_j's are all constants. Consequently, for small perturbing terms, the rate of change of the c_j's is small. This suggests an approximation in which the initial values of the c_j's are inserted on the right side of Eq. (14–57) and their time dependence is computed without taking into account the implicit time dependence on the right side of the equation.

For example, if at $t = 0$, we have the initial conditions

$$c_0(0) = 1 \qquad \text{and} \qquad c_k(0) = 0, \qquad k \neq 0, \tag{14–58}$$

then an approximate solution for the c_j's is given by

$$c_j(t) = -\frac{i}{\hbar}\int_0^t (j|\mathsf{H}_1|0)\exp(i\omega_{j0}t)\,dt. \tag{14–59}$$

This equation is valid only if the resultant values for the c_j's are all sufficiently small to result in only a very small modification when inserted on the right side of Eq. (14–57). If the perturbing term H_1 is of the form

$$\mathsf{H}_1 = \mathsf{A}\cos\omega t, \tag{14–60}$$

we obtain, as a result of the integration indicated in Eq. (14–59),

$$c_j(t) = -\frac{1}{2\hbar}(j|\mathsf{A}|0)\left\{\frac{\exp[i(\omega_{j0}-\omega)t]-1}{\omega_{j0}-\omega} + \frac{\exp[i(\omega_{j0}+\omega)t]-1}{\omega_{j0}+\omega}\right\}. \tag{14–61}$$

It is apparent from this equation that for there to be an appreciable increase in the probability that the system will be found in a particular energy state, it is necessary that one of the denominators in the expression in braces be very small. In other words, to get an appreciable transition probability (between energy states), a condition of near-resonance must prevail:

$$|\omega_{j0}| \approx \omega. \tag{14–62}$$

This result should be compared with that of Chapter 12, where essentially the same problem was solved exactly.

As we consider Eq. (14–61), it becomes clear that only one of the two terms in the braces can be resonant (of appreciable amplitude) when Eq. (14–62) is satisfied. The other term represents a small high-frequency perturbation on the state that can usually be neglected because of its large denominator ($|\omega_{j0}| + \omega$).

If the system under consideration is that treated exactly in Chapter 12, i.e., a particle of spin one-half in a uniform static magnetic field $\mathcal{B}_0$, the perturbation in Eq. (14–60) can be considered to be of the form

$$\mathrm{H}_1 = -\boldsymbol{\mu}\cdot\boldsymbol{\mathcal{B}}\cos\omega t, \tag{14–63}$$

with $\boldsymbol{\mathcal{B}} \perp \boldsymbol{\mathcal{B}}_0$ representing an oscillating plane-polarized magnetic field at right angles to the large static field acting on the particle. In this case, the antiresonant term of Eq. (14–61) corresponds to the fact that the perturbing field is oscillating, rather than rotating in the direction of the electronic spin precession. The plane-polarized oscillating field can be decomposed into two rotating fields, one rotating with the spin and the other rotating in the opposite sense; in the case above, these correspond to the two terms in the braces in Eq. (14–61).

Note, however, that if a suitable rotating perturbing field is applied, the condition imposed by Eq. (14–61) leads to a resonance regardless of the sign of ω_{j0}. Physically, the case $\omega_{j0} > 0$ corresponds to photon absorption in which energy is transferred to the spin system from the electromagnetic field: the spin undergoes a transition from a lower to a higher energy state. When $\omega_{j0} < 0$, on the other hand, energy is transferred from the spin to the field. This process is known as *induced*, or *stimulated, emission*. It is seen, therefore, that the same perturbing field that causes photon absorption by a lower-energy-state spin causes emission from an upper-state spin with *equal probability*. In a macroscopic system, a net transfer of energy can occur only if there are more spins in one of the two energy levels of interest than in the other.

Because it is nonresonant, one of the terms of Eq. (14–61) will be dropped in the following development. To make things definite, we will assume that $E_j > E_0$, that is, that Eq. (14–61) can be written as

$$c_j(t) = -\frac{1}{2\hbar}(j|\mathsf{A}|0)\frac{\exp[i(\omega_{j0}-\omega)t]-1}{\omega_{j0}-\omega}$$

$$= \frac{-it(j|\mathsf{A}|0)}{2\hbar}\exp\left(\frac{i\Delta\omega t}{2}\right)\frac{\sin(\Delta\omega t/2)}{\Delta\omega t/2}, \tag{14–64}$$

where the substitution

$$\Delta\omega \equiv \omega_{j0} - \omega \tag{14–65}$$

has been made. From this,

$$|c_j(t)|^2 = \frac{t^2|(j|\mathsf{A}|0)|^2}{4\hbar^2}\frac{\sin^2(\Delta\omega t/2)}{(\Delta\omega t/2)^2}. \tag{14–66}$$

This is very sharply peaked about the frequency determined by the resonance condition $\Delta\omega = 0$, as expected.

The quadratic time dependence (for small t) should be noted. This time dependence is at first glance paradoxical, for the number of photons inducing the transition is proportional to the time during which the incident radiation acts, but the transition probability is not proportional to the number of inducing photons, but to the *square* of this number. The paradox is resolved by noting that the (monochromatic) radiation acting for a time t is effectively a pulse of radiation of length t, and such a pulse has its energy distributed over a frequency band whose width is of the order of the reciprocal of the pulse length. Thus in a unit frequency interval at the center of the spectral distribution, the energy of the pulse is proportional to the square of the pulse length.

In many interesting and important situations, one is not concerned with transitions to only a single final state j, but with possible transitions to any of a group of final states, all of approximately the same energy (and hence all "on resonance"). In such a situation, it is possible to define a *transition probability* w, the probability per unit time that a transition has occurred, that is independent of the time. The transition probability is given by

$$w \equiv \frac{1}{t} \sum_j |c_j(t)|^2. \tag{14-67}$$

If the final states of the group are assumed to be distributed (quasi-) continuously in energy, with $n(E)$ being the number of states per unit energy range, the summation of Eq. (14-67) can be replaced by the integration

$$w = \frac{1}{t} \int |c_j(t)|^2 n(E)\, dE, \tag{14-68}$$

where j is a variable determined by $E_j = E$. Combining this with Eq. (14-66) yields

$$w = \frac{t}{4\hbar^2} \int |(j|\mathbf{A}|0)|^2 n(E) \frac{\sin^2 (\Delta\omega t/2)}{(\Delta\omega t/2)^2}\, dE. \tag{14-69}$$

Since

$$E = E_j = E_0 + \hbar\omega_{j0}, \tag{14-70}$$

from Eq. (14-65) we have

$$dE = \hbar\, d(\Delta\omega). \tag{14-71}$$

We see that $\sin^2 (\Delta\omega t/2)/(\Delta\omega t/2)^2$ is sharply peaked about $\Delta\omega = 0$; it is therefore usually a good approximation to treat $n(E)$ as constant over the range where this function is large. Making the further assumption that $|(j|\mathbf{A}|0)|$ is essentially equal for all the contributing final states, we can write Eq. (14-69) as

$$\begin{aligned} w &= \frac{|(j|\mathbf{A}|0)|^2}{2\hbar}\, n(E_j) \int_{-\infty}^{\infty} \frac{\sin^2 (\Delta\omega t/2)}{(\Delta\omega t/2)^2}\, d\left(\frac{\Delta\omega t}{2}\right) \\ &= \frac{\pi |(j|\mathbf{A}|0)|^2 n(E_j)}{2\hbar}. \end{aligned} \tag{14-72}$$

As mentioned above, the transition probability is time-independent.

14–4 Variational techniques. The perturbation methods treated above apply when the problem to be solved differs but little from a situation with a known solution. However, even when this is not the case, important information of a restricted nature can be obtained by using what is known as the *variational method.* This permits a quite accurate estimate of some of the energy levels of a system and in particular its ground-state energy, without the necessity of accurate detailed knowledge of the wave function.

The basic idea behind the variational method is this: the expectation value of the Hamiltonian gives the average energy of the system, in a state corresponding to the particular function used in evaluating the expectation value. Clearly, this average energy must be greater than or equal to the lowest energy state of the system. Consequently,

$$\langle \mathrm{H} \rangle \equiv (\psi, \mathrm{H}\psi) \geq E_0. \tag{14–73}$$

That the lowest energy state is a lower bound on the expectation value enables us to choose a trial wave function containing a number of parameters and then to minimize the expectation value by varying these parameters; hence the name variational method. It is interesting that a function which is a relatively poor approximation to the ground-state wave function may still give a fairly good approximation for the ground-state energy evaluated as the expectation value of Eq. (14–73).

To see how this comes about, assume that the trial function is expanded in terms of the energy eigenstates of the Hamiltonian:

$$\psi = \sum_k c_k u_k. \tag{14–74}$$

If this expansion is substituted into the expression for the expectation value of the Hamiltonian, one obtains

$$\langle \mathrm{H} \rangle = \sum_k |c_k|^2 E_k. \tag{14–75}$$

Note that this contains only the absolute squares of the c_k's. Consequently, a c_k corresponding to an excited state may be of the order of 0.1, and yet contribute to the expectation value of the energy only something of the order of 1%. As a result, a rather badly distorted wave function may give a reasonable value for the lowest energy.

At this state, one must make a judicious guess as to the approximate form of the wave function, assuming some functional form which contains free parameters:

$$\psi = \psi(\lambda_1, \lambda_2, \ldots, r). \tag{14–76}$$

The various free parameters, λ_j, are then varied until the expectation value of the energy takes on a minimum value:

$$\frac{\partial \langle \mathrm{H} \rangle}{\partial \lambda_j} = 0. \tag{14–77}$$

As an example of this technique, consider the ground state of the helium atom. If the nucleus is considered as a fixed center of force, and if we neglect the spin-orbit interaction terms and the interactions between the magnetic moments of the two electrons, the Hamiltonian operator is

$$\mathrm{H} = \frac{1}{2m}(\mathrm{P}_1^2 + \mathrm{P}_2^2) - \frac{2e^2}{r_1} - \frac{2e^2}{r_2} + \frac{e^2}{r_{12}}. \tag{14–78}$$

Let us assume that the wave function for the helium atom is the product of two ground-state wave functions of a hydrogenic atom with Z serving as a free parameter which can be varied. In this case, the normalized wave function is given by

$$\psi = \left(\frac{Z^3}{\pi a_0^3}\right) \exp\left[-\frac{Z}{a_0}(r_1 + r_2)\right]. \tag{14–79}$$

It may be noted, in justification of this choice of wave function, that this would in fact be an exact wave function if the interaction term in the Hamiltonian were dropped and Z were set equal to two. Consequently, if we assume that the electron-interaction term (the last term) in the Hamiltonian has a relatively minor effect on the motion of the electrons, we would expect a somewhat minor change in the wave function to result from the inclusion of this term. To evaluate the expectation value of the Hamiltonian, let us break it up into three parts:

$$\langle \mathrm{H} \rangle = 2\left\langle \frac{1}{2m}\mathrm{P}_1^2 \right\rangle - 4\left\langle \frac{e^2}{r_1} \right\rangle + \left\langle \frac{e^2}{r_{12}} \right\rangle. \tag{14–80}$$

It is clear from the symmetry of the Hamiltonian and the wave function that it is necessary to evaluate the expectation value of only one of the kinetic energies and multiply by two, and that it is necessary to evaluate the expectation value of the potential energy of only one electron relative to the nucleus and then to multiply this result by two, as indicated in Eq. (14–80).

The first two expectation values in Eq. (14–80) can be evaluated very easily by remembering something about the average kinetic energy of an electron moving in a coulomb field of force. It can be shown by the use of the *virial theorem** that for the classical motion of any particle moving

* See, e.g., H. Goldstein, *Classical Mechanics,* Addison-Wesley Publishing Co., Inc., Reading, Mass., 1950, Chapter 3.

in a field of force that obeys an inverse square law, the average kinetic energy of the particle is equal to the negative of its total energy. Consequently, the expectation value of the kinetic energy which appears as the first term in Eq. (14–80) can be evaluated by simply taking the binding energy of a hydrogenic atom in its ground state with a charge Z on the nucleus and changing the sign:

$$\left\langle \frac{1}{2m} \mathrm{P}_1^2 \right\rangle = \frac{1}{2} mc^2 Z^2 \alpha^2 = \frac{1}{2} \frac{Z^2 e^2}{a_0}. \tag{14–81}$$

In similar fashion, the average value of the potential energy of an electron in a hydrogenic atom is equal to twice the binding energy of the electron in the ground state:

$$\left\langle \frac{Ze^2}{r_1} \right\rangle = -\frac{Z^2 e^2}{a_0}. \tag{14–82}$$

Thus,

$$\left\langle \frac{e^2}{r_1} \right\rangle = -\frac{Ze^2}{a_0}. \tag{14–83}$$

The only integral which gives some trouble is that for the last term in Eq. (14–80). A trick can be used in the evaluation of this integral. The form of the integral is identical to that of the interaction of one spherical charge distribution with another superimposed spherical charge distribution. The integral may be evaluated by integrating the product of one charge distribution and the potential function of the other. Evaluating the integral in this way, one obtains

$$\left\langle \frac{e^2}{r_{12}} \right\rangle = \int \bar{\psi} \frac{e^2}{r_{12}} \psi \, dr_1 \, dr_2 = \frac{5}{8} \frac{Ze^2}{a_0}. \tag{14–84}$$

Therefore,

$$\langle \mathrm{H} \rangle = \frac{Z^2 e^2}{a_0} - \frac{4Ze^2}{a_0} + \frac{5}{8} \frac{Ze^2}{a_0}, \tag{14–85}$$

where the parameter Z can be varied to minimize the expectation value of the energy:

$$\frac{\partial \langle \mathrm{H} \rangle}{\partial Z} = 0. \tag{14–86}$$

This gives the result

$$Z \Big|_{\langle \mathrm{H} \rangle = \text{minimum}} = \frac{27}{16} \approx 1.69. \tag{14–87}$$

Substituting this value of Z into Eq. (14–85), we obtain an approximate value for the binding energy of the helium atom:

$$E_0 \approx \langle \mathrm{H} \rangle = -\left(\frac{27}{16}\right)^2 \frac{e^2}{a_0} \approx -2.85 \frac{e^2}{a_0}. \tag{14–88}$$

This is the energy necessary to remove both of the electrons from the helium atom, i.e., the energy necessary to obtain doubly-ionized helium. The experimental value for this energy is

$$E_0 = -2.904 \frac{e^2}{a_0}, \tag{14–89}$$

which is in excellent agreement with the approximation, considering the latter's crudeness.

14–5 The WKB method. As a final type of approximate calculation, consider the *Wentzel-Kramers-Brillouin* (WKB) *approximation.* This applies to situations in which the potential energy is a slowly varying function of position. One-dimensional problems, and three-dimensional problems that can be reduced to an equivalent one-dimensional (radial) problem, can be treated by this method. By a "slowly varying" potential we mean a potential such that the potential V varies but slightly in a region whose length is several de Broglie wavelengths (see Fig. 14–3).

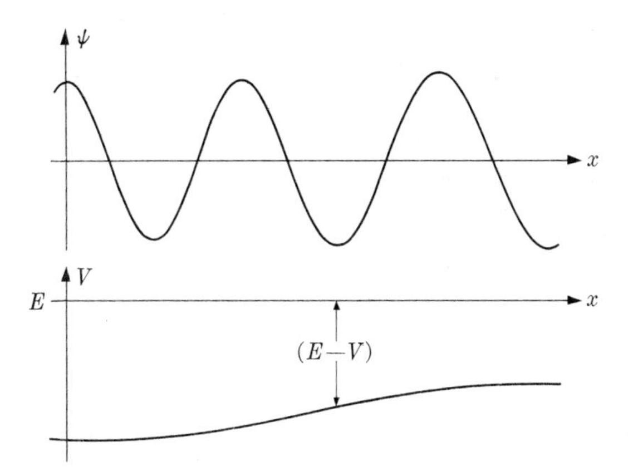

Fig. 14–3. A typical "slowly varying" one-dimensional potential and its associated wave function. Note that the wavelength is a slowly varying function of position, i.e., its fractional change within one wavelength is small.

The de Broglie wavelength associated with a particle moving with energy E in a region of potential V is

$$\lambda = \frac{h}{p} = \frac{h}{[2m(E - V)]^{1/2}}. \tag{14–90}$$

Because the potential varies so slowly with position, we can assume that it is constant over a small region. Then, in this small region, the wave function has the form of a plane wave. The propagation constant for such a plane wave is

$$k = \frac{\{2m[E - V(x)]\}^{1/2}}{\hbar}. \tag{14–91}$$

The condition that the potential be slowly varying can be expressed by the conditions that

$$\left|\frac{1}{k^3}\frac{d^2k}{dx^2}\right| \ll 1 \qquad \text{and} \qquad \left|\frac{1}{k^2}\frac{dk}{dx}\right| \ll 1. \tag{14–92}$$

We expect the wave function to be of the form

$$\psi_\pm(x, t) = \frac{1}{k^{1/2}} \exp\left[\pm i\left(\int^x k\,dx \mp \omega t\right)\right], \tag{14–93}$$

where

$$\omega = \frac{E}{\hbar}; \tag{14–94}$$

that is, we expect a solution in the form of plane waves that travel toward $+x$ and toward $-x$ and whose propagation constants gradually change from one region to another. The factor $1/k^{1/2}$ is used to ensure that the probability of finding the particle at a particular point in space is inversely proportional to the classical speed of the particle at that point. Hence on physical grounds, we expect this to be a suitable solution for a sufficiently slowly varying potential.

If we substitute Eq. (14–93) into the one-dimensional Schrödinger equation,

$$-\frac{\hbar^2}{2m}\frac{\partial^2\psi}{\partial x^2} + V(x)\psi = i\hbar\frac{\partial\psi}{\partial t}, \tag{14–95}$$

we obtain

$$-\frac{\hbar^2}{2m}[-\tfrac{1}{2}k''k^{-3/2} + \tfrac{3}{4}k'^2k^{-5/2} - k^{3/2}]k^{1/2}\psi + V\psi = E\psi. \tag{14–96}$$

Because of the inequalities (14–92), the first two terms in the brackets may be neglected. With substitution from Eq. (14–91), it is apparent that to this approximation Eq. (14–93) is a solution to Schrödinger's equation.

The close relation of the WKB approximation to the classical description of the motion of a particle is apparent, in that the wavelength and amplitude at any point are given by the classical momentum at that point.

In a region where $V > E$, the oscillatory form of solution, Eq. (14–93), is no longer permissible, for the "propagation constant" of Eq. (14–91) becomes imaginary. Instead, the solution must be of an exponential form. For a slowly varying potential, we expect the solution for the classically forbidden region $V > E$ to be, in analogy to Eq. (14–93),

$$\psi_{\pm}(x, t) = \frac{1}{\gamma^{1/2}} \exp\left[\pm \left(\int^x \gamma\, dx \mp i\omega t\right)\right], \tag{14–97}$$

where

$$\gamma = \frac{\{2m[V(x) - E]\}^{1/2}}{\hbar}. \tag{14–98}$$

The wave function thus increases or decreases exponentially as one goes away from the classical "turning point" of the motion, where $V = E$. Assuming that V is a "slowly varying" potential in the classically forbidden region [the inequalities (14–92) are valid], we find that Eq. (14–96) is still valid with k imaginary, and Eq. (14–97) is an approximate solution to Schrödinger's equation.

Approximate solutions have thus been found for the regions where Eq. (14–92) holds, i.e., where the potential changes slowly in a region containing many de Broglie wavelengths. However, it is clear that the regions of $V > E$ and $V < E$, where WKB solutions are valid, are separated by a "turning point" ($V = E$), at which the propagation constant vanishes and the wavelength becomes infinite. Although the above methods fail near this point, a suitable solution can be determined by approximating the actual variation of the potential $V(x)$ around such a point x_0 by a linear variation:

$$V(x) = A(x - x_0) + E \tag{14–99}$$

(see Fig. 14–4). This linear approximation to the potential is assumed valid over a small region on each side of the turning point. Schrödinger's equation can then be solved exactly for this region, and the resulting solutions can be used to join the solutions of the forms of Eqs. (14–93) and (14–97), which are valid away from the turning point.

Assuming that the classically forbidden region is on the $+x$-side of the turning point x_0, the solutions to the Schrödinger equation near x_0 are of the form

$$\psi_{\pm}(x) = C_{\pm} k J_{\pm 1/3}\left(\int_x^{x_0} k\, dx\right), \qquad E > V \quad (\text{or } x < x_0),$$

$$\psi_{\pm}(x) = \mp C_{\pm} \gamma I_{\pm 1/3}\left(\int_{x_0}^{x} \gamma\, dx\right), \qquad V > E, \tag{14–100}$$

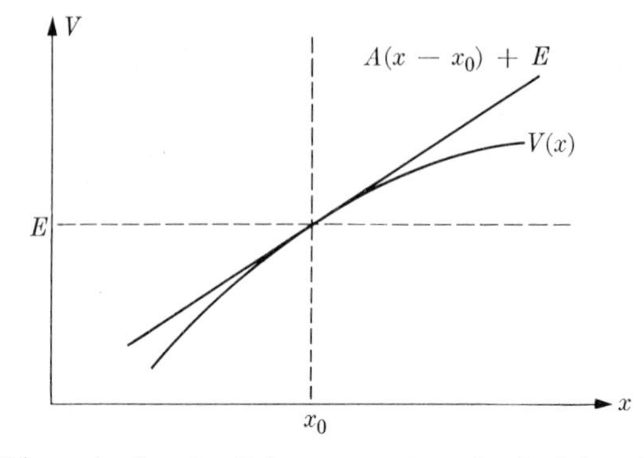

FIG. 14–4. The actual potential energy at a classical turning point and a linear approximation to the actual potential that is valid near the turning point.

where I is the Bessel function of imaginary argument, and the constants have been chosen so as to join the solutions smoothly at the point x_0.

The final step in applying the WKB approximation is to join the solutions $\psi_\pm$ of Eq. (14–100) to those of Eqs. (14–93) and (14–97). To do this, the asymptotic behavior of the solutions near the turning point, Eq. (14–100), is needed:

$$
\begin{aligned}
\psi_+ &\xrightarrow[x\to+\infty]{} -\frac{1}{(2\pi\gamma)^{1/2}}\left[\exp\left(\int_0^x \gamma\,dx\right)+\exp\left(-\int_0^x \gamma\,dx-\frac{5\pi i}{6}\right)\right],\\
\psi_+ &\xrightarrow[x\to-\infty]{} \frac{1}{(2\pi k)^{1/2}}\cos\left[\int_x^0 k\,dx-\frac{5\pi}{12}\right],\\
\psi_- &\xrightarrow[x\to+\infty]{} \frac{1}{(2\pi\gamma)^{1/2}}\left[\exp\left(\int_0^x \gamma\,dx\right)+\exp\left(-\int_0^x \gamma\,dx-\frac{\pi i}{6}\right)\right],\\
\psi_- &\xrightarrow[x\to-\infty]{} \frac{1}{(2\pi k)^{1/2}}\cos\left[\int_x^0 k\,dx-\frac{\pi}{12}\right].
\end{aligned}
\tag{14–101}
$$

These asymptotic formulas cannot be conveniently applied in this form, since they include both increasing and decreasing exponentials for $x \to +\infty$. However, by taking suitable linear combinations of these, the connection relations

$$
\begin{aligned}
\frac{1}{2}\cdot\frac{1}{\gamma^{1/2}}\exp\left(-\int_{x_0}^x \gamma\,dx\right) &\rightarrow \frac{1}{k^{1/2}}\cos\left[\int_x^{x_0} k\,dx-\frac{\pi}{4}\right],\\
\sin\eta\,\frac{1}{\gamma^{1/2}}\exp\left(\int_{x_0}^x \gamma\,dx\right) &\leftarrow \frac{1}{k^{1/2}}\cos\left[\int_x^{x_0} k\,dx-\frac{\pi}{4}+\eta\right]
\end{aligned}
\tag{14–102}
$$

can be found. Here η has any value such that $\sin \eta$ is not approximately zero. The arrows in Eq. (14–102) indicate that the connection should be made in the direction of the increasing exponential. If the connections are made in the reverse direction, in the case of the first formula the slight phase error introduced by the approximation would bring in the (dominant) exponential that increases away from the turning point; in the case of the second formula, neglect of the exponential increasing toward the turning point introduces a large phase error in the oscillatory solution.

As an example of the use of the WKB method, consider the α-decay of a radioactive nucleus. The problem can be simplified by assuming that the α-particle is a particle of charge $Z = 2e$ and mass M inside a nuclear potential well surrounded by a coulomb barrier. The α-particle then "tunnels through" the barrier, as discussed in Chapter 3. The further assumption will be made that the α-particle emerges in an S-state; there is therefore no contribution to the effective potential barrier from centrifugal effects. The potential energy of the particle as a function of the distance from the center of the nucleus is plotted in Fig. 14–5. Here the nuclear potential is assumed constant ($V = -V_0$), the nuclear radius is r_0, and r_c designates the radius at which the kinetic energy of the α-particle is zero outside the nucleus. To undergo decay, the α-particle must have a positive energy E.

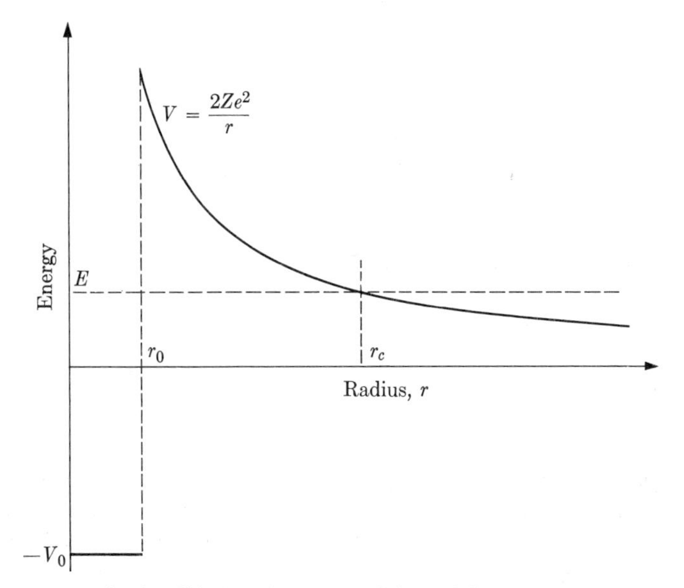

Fig. 14–5. A simplified radial-potential model corresponding to a nucleus capable of undergoing α-decay. The α-particle experiences a strong attractive potential well at the nucleus. The charge on the nucleus provides the strong "coulombic barrier" that the α-particle must penetrate in leaving the nucleus.

As discussed in Chapter 10, the problem reduces to a one-dimensional (radial) problem, with the energy-eigenvalue equation becoming

$$\left[-\frac{\hbar^2}{2M}\frac{d^2}{dr^2} + V(r)\right]u = Eu, \tag{14–103}$$

where

$$u = r\psi, \qquad u(0) = 0. \tag{14–104}$$

Solutions to this equation can be written for the three regions separated at r_0 and r_c; these can then be matched across these points.

$$\begin{aligned} u(r) &= \sin(kr), & 0 < r < r_0, \\ &= \frac{A}{\gamma^{1/2}} \exp\left(\pm\int_{r_0}^{r} \gamma\, dr\right), & r_0 < r < r_c, \\ &= \frac{B}{(k')^{1/2}} \exp\left(\pm i\int_{r_c}^{r} k'\, dr\right), & r > r_c. \end{aligned} \tag{14–105}$$

The solution in the interior of the nucleus, $0 < r < r_0$, is exact; WKB solutions have been used for the other two regions. The constants k, γ, and k' are defined by

$$\begin{aligned} k &\equiv \frac{[2M(E + V_0)]^{1/2}}{\hbar}, & 0 < r < r_0, \\ \gamma &\equiv \frac{[2M(V - E)]^{1/2}}{\hbar}, & r_0 < r < r_c, \\ k' &\equiv \frac{[2M(E - V)]^{1/2}}{\hbar}, & r > r_c. \end{aligned} \tag{14–106}$$

It is convenient to rewrite the solution for the region $r_0 < r < r_c$ as

$$\begin{aligned} u(r) &= \frac{A}{\gamma^{1/2}} \exp\left(\mp\int_{r_0}^{r_c} \gamma\, dr\right) \exp\left(\pm\int_{r}^{r_c} \gamma\, dr\right) \\ &= \frac{A'}{\gamma^{1/2}} \exp\left(\pm\int_{r}^{r_c} \gamma\, dr\right). \end{aligned} \tag{14–107}$$

In α-decay, standing waves are not set up in the region $r > r_c$, but instead the solution here corresponds to an outward-moving spherical wave. It will be seen in Chapter 16 that this means it must have the asymptotic behavior

$$u(r) \xrightarrow[r\to\infty]{} \frac{B}{(k')^{1/2}} \exp\left(i\int_{r_c}^{r} k'\, dr + \beta\right), \tag{14–108}$$

where β is a physically meaningless phase constant. One can obtain such a solution in this outer region by making use of the second of equations (14-102). In this joining relation, letting $\eta = \pi/4$ gives

$$\frac{1}{(k')^{1/2}} \cos\left(\int_{r_c}^{r} k'\, dr\right) \to \frac{1}{(2\gamma)^{1/2}} \exp\left(\int_{r}^{r_c} \gamma\, dr\right). \tag{14-109}$$

If, instead, $\eta = -\pi/4$ is taken, the result is

$$\frac{1}{(k')^{1/2}} \sin\left(\int_{r_c}^{r} k'\, dr\right) \to -\frac{1}{(2\gamma)^{1/2}} \exp\left(\int_{r}^{r_c} \gamma\, dr\right). \tag{14-110}$$

When this is multiplied by $i \equiv \sqrt{-1}$ and added to Eq. (14-109), we find

$$\frac{i}{(k')^{1/2}} \exp\left[i\left(\int_{r_c}^{r} k'\, dr - \frac{\pi}{4}\right)\right] \to -\frac{i}{\gamma^{1/2}} \exp\left(\int_{r}^{r_c} \gamma\, dr\right), \tag{14-111}$$

which is of the required form. Application of this joining condition to the wave functions of Eqs. (14-105) and (14-107) across the point $r = r_c$ gives the matching relation

$$\frac{A'/\gamma^{1/2}}{B/(k')^{1/2}} = \frac{-i/\gamma^{1/2}}{[1/(k')^{1/2}] \exp(-i\pi/4)} \tag{14-112}$$

or

$$B = i \exp\left(-i\frac{\pi}{4}\right) A' = (i)^{1/2} A \exp\left(-\int_{r_0}^{r_c} \gamma\, dr\right). \tag{14-113}$$

[The solutions of Eqs. (14-105) and (14-107) with negative exponents are absent in this case.]

The proper joining of the solutions at $r = r_0$, where there is a step discontinuity (but where the WKB solution is valid up to the point $r = r_0$), is obtained by equating the logarithmic derivatives. This gives

$$\begin{aligned} \frac{1}{\sin kr} \frac{d}{dr} \sin kr &= k \cot kr_0 = -\gamma_0, \\ \tan kr_0 &= -\frac{k}{\gamma_0}, \end{aligned} \tag{14-114}$$

where

$$\gamma_0 \equiv \gamma(r_0). \tag{14-115}$$

In addition, the wave function must be continuous at $r = r_0$, so we find that

$$\frac{A}{\gamma_0^{1/2}} = \sin kr_0 = \left(\frac{\tan^2 kr_0}{1 + \tan^2 kr_0}\right)^{1/2} = \left[\frac{(k/\gamma_0)^2}{1 + (k/\gamma_0)^2}\right]^{1/2}, \tag{14-116}$$

$$A = \left[\frac{\gamma_0 (k/\gamma_0)^2}{1 + (k/\gamma_0)^2}\right]^{1/2}.$$

Using the above values for A and B, we find that the function for the wave which has leaked through the barrier is

$$u(r) = \left(\frac{i\gamma_0}{k'}\right)^{1/2} \left[\frac{(k/\gamma_0)^2}{1 + (k/\gamma_0)^2}\right]^{1/2} \exp\left(-\int_{r_0}^{r_c} \gamma \, dr\right) \exp\left(i \int_{r_c}^{r} k' \, dr\right), \quad r > r_c \tag{14-117}$$

Under the conditions encountered in a nucleus, $(k/\gamma_0)^2$ is rather small compared with unity; that is, the height of the coulomb barrier seen by an α-particle in the nucleus is greater than its kinetic energy in the nucleus. Consequently, from Eq. (14–114),

$$\tan kr_0 \approx 0, \qquad kr_0 \approx \pi, 2\pi, \ldots \tag{14-118}$$

In this case, the external wave function becomes

$$u(r) = \left(\frac{ik^2}{k'\gamma_0}\right)^{1/2} \exp\left(-\int_{r_0}^{r_c} \gamma \, dr\right) \exp\left(i \int_{r_c}^{r} k' \, dr\right). \tag{14-119}$$

It is convenient to "normalize" the solution to a unity probability of finding the α-particle inside the nucleus. (The function, which extends throughout all space and for large r has the asymptotic form

$$\psi \xrightarrow[r \to \infty]{} \frac{A}{r} \exp\left[i \, \frac{(2ME)^{1/2}}{\hbar} \, r\right], \tag{14-120}$$

is, of course, not normalizable in the usual sense, since $\int |\psi|^2 \, d\tau$ over all space diverges.) The nucleus will have a unity probability for containing the α-particle when

$$4\pi \int_0^{r_0} |cu|^2 \, dr = 1, \tag{14-121}$$

where c is a normalizing factor to be applied to the wave functions obtained for each of the three regions. This can be evaluated readily:

$$4\pi |c|^2 \int_0^{r_0} \sin^2 kr \, dr = 2\pi |c|^2 r_0 = 1, \qquad |c|^2 = \frac{1}{2\pi r_0}. \tag{14-122}$$

The α-decay rate of the nucleus is clearly related to the outward flux of particles across some spherical surface $r = R > r_c$. This can be found by using the probability-density flux introduced in Chapter 3. From Eq. (3–73),

$$\mathbf{S} = -\frac{i\hbar}{2M} (\bar{\psi} \nabla \psi - \nabla \bar{\psi} \cdot \psi). \tag{14-123}$$

From Eqs. (14–119) and (14–122),

$$\psi(r) = \frac{1}{r}\left(\frac{k^2}{2\pi k'\gamma_0 r_0}\right)^{1/2} \exp\left(-\int_{r_0}^{r_c} \gamma\, dr\right) \exp\left(i\int_{r_c}^{r} k'\, dr\right), \qquad r > r_c. \tag{14–124}$$

Evaluation of the radial probability-density flux from this and Eq. (14–123) gives

$$S_r(r) = \frac{\hbar k^2}{2\pi M\gamma_0 r_0 r^2} \exp\left(-2\int_{r_0}^{r_c} \gamma\, dr\right). \tag{14–125}$$

The outward particle flux across the shell $r = R$ is

$$F = 4\pi R^2 S_r(R)$$

$$= \frac{2\hbar k^2}{M\gamma_0 r_0} \exp\left(-2\int_{r_0}^{r_c} \gamma\, dr\right). \tag{14–126}$$

Expressed in terms of the energy E, r_0, and V_0, the particle flux is

$$F = 2\left(\frac{2}{M}\right)^{1/2} \frac{E + V_0}{[V(r_0) - E]^{1/2}} \frac{1}{r_0} \exp\left\{-2\int_{r_0}^{r_c} \frac{[2M(V - E)]^{1/2}}{\hbar}\, dr\right\}. \tag{14–127}$$

This particle flux must be the rate of decrease of the probability that the α-particle will be inside the nucleus (when the probability is unity). This probability, P, varies with time as

$$\frac{dP}{dt} = -FP. \tag{14–128}$$

Therefore

$$P = \exp(-Ft). \tag{14–129}$$

The *half-life* of the nucleus for α-decay is defined as that time at which $P = \frac{1}{2}$:

$$T_{1/2} \equiv \frac{\ln 2}{F}. \tag{14–130}$$

This can readily be obtained from Eq. (14–127).

14–6 Summary. The need for approximation methods in making quantum-mechanical calculations in nearly all cases of nontrivial interest was pointed out. Perturbation situations in which the system of interest differs but little from a system whose behavior can be calculated were first discussed. Time-independent perturbation theory, in which the Hamiltonian does not depend on the time explicitly, was developed and applied to an anharmonic oscillator, paramagnetic ions in crystals, and spin-orbit coupling effects in alkali atoms. The modifications of perturbation theory necessary to handle the case of degenerate energy states were indicated.

Time-dependent perturbations were next handled, and the transition probability between the unperturbed energy states brought about by the perturbation was calculated to first order for the case of a transition between two energy levels induced by an oscillating electromagnetic field. Variational techniques were developed and used to estimate the ground-state energy of a helium atom. Finally, the case of a slowly varying potential was examined with the aid of the WKB approximation. This approximation was used to derive an expression giving the half-life of a nucleus for α-decay in terms of the parameters of the system: the energy of the α-particle, the depth of the nuclear potential well, and the electrostatic potential set up by the charges of the decaying atom.

Problems

14–1. Derive an approximate expression for the splitting of the $(n = 2)$ energy level of a hydrogen atom under the influence of a uniform electric field (linear Stark effect). The unperturbed eigenfunctions can be obtained from Table 10–1 and Eq. (9–66). Neglect the fine-structure splitting.

14–2. Use the variational method to calculate the lowest energy of the hydrogen atom, assuming that as a result of an interaction with a new type of nuclear field the coulomb interaction is modified to become $V = -e^2/(r + r_0)$, where $0 < r_0 \ll a_0$.

14–3. It was found empirically by Geiger and Nuttal that the energy of an α-particle could be related to the corresponding decay constant $\gamma = 1/T_{1/2}$ with a formula of the general type $\ln E = a \ln \gamma + b$, where a takes on nearly the same value for all three radioactive series, and b differs from one series to the next. (a) Evaluate the integral in the barrier-penetration term of the theoretical expression for γ and compare the theoretical γ thus obtained with the empirical formula. What can be concluded? (b) By consulting a table giving both decay constants and decay energies for various α-emitters, compute a rough value for the size of the nucleus.

14–4. Tritium (H^3) is radioactive and decays to He^3 with the emission of an electron. Assuming that the β-decay electron can be ignored since it quickly leaves the atom, the effect of the β-decay can be represented as an instantaneous change in the magnitude of the nuclear charge without any change in the orbital-electron wave function. (This is known as the "sudden" approximation.) (a) Assuming that the tritium atom is initially in its ground state, calculate the probability of finding the resulting He^+ ion in its ground state immediately after the β-decay. (b) Calculate the mean energy radiated by the atom after the decay.

14–5. The potential energy of interaction for a diatomic molecule is sometimes taken to be of the form

$$V = \frac{A}{r^2} - \frac{B}{r}.$$

Calculate the vibrational energy levels of such a molecule by making use of a "parabolic fit" to this effective potential. Put in the numerical values characteristic of HCl, expressing energies in electron volts.

14–6. Consider an anharmonic one-dimensional oscillator with a potential energy given by $V = \frac{1}{2}kx^2 + Ax^4$. (a) Use the variational method to calculate the lowest energy level by choosing as a trial function $\psi = \alpha u_0 + \beta u_2$, where u_0 and u_2 are simple harmonic oscillator functions. Choose β/α and ω as the variational parameters. (b) Compare this result with the perturbation calculation in the text.

14–7. (a) In time-independent perturbation theory, the Hamiltonian can be written as $\mathrm{H} = \mathrm{H}_0 + \mathrm{H}'$. Show that

$$\sum_m |H'_{nm}|^2 = (\mathrm{H}'^2)_{nn}.$$

Consider a hydrogen atom in its ground state in a uniform electric field which polarizes it. For a field in the z-direction, $\mathrm{H}' = -e\mathcal{E}z$, where $\mathcal{E}$ is the electric field strength. (b) Show that the first-order correction to the ground-state energy H'_{11} is zero.

The change in the ground-state energy is $\Delta W = \frac{1}{2}\alpha\mathcal{E}^2$, where α is the polarizability and is known to be about 0.68×10^{-24} cm^3. (c) Show that the matrix element H'_{1q} is nonzero only for $l = 1$.

Simple order-of-magnitude estimates show that $|H'_{1q}|^2$ decreases rapidly in size as the n associated with the state q increases:

$$\tfrac{1}{2}\alpha\mathcal{E}^2 = +\sum_{q\neq 1} \frac{|H'_{1q}|^2}{E_q - E_1}.$$

(d) Show that

$$\tfrac{1}{2}\alpha\mathcal{E}^2 < \frac{(\mathrm{H}'^2)_{11}}{E_2 - E_1},$$

where E_2 is the lowest P-state energy. (e) Calculate this upper limit on α and compare it with the experimental value. The agreement is good because of the rapid convergence of the series.

14–8. Two hydrogen atoms separated from each other by a distance large compared with a Bohr radius a_0 are attracted toward each other by the van der Waals interaction. This represents the interaction due to a mutual polarization of the two atoms by each other. (a) Write the Hamiltonian for a two-hydrogen-atom system in terms of the distance R between the nuclei and r_1 and r_2, the coordinates of the electrons respectively associated with nuclei 1 and 2 *relative to the positions of these nuclei.* Treat the system by perturbation theory, taking the two separate but not interacting atoms as the unperturbed system and all the interaction terms as the perturbation. (b) Show that in an expansion of the perturbation in powers of R^{-1}, the leading term is the term in R^{-3}. (c) Using the first result of Problem 14–7, compute a lower limit to the strength of the interaction as a function of R^{-1}.

14–9. The one-dimensional energy-eigenvalue equation

$$\frac{d^2u_n}{dx^2} - x^2u_n = E_nu_n$$

has eigenvalues $E_n = 2n + 1$ and matrix elements

$$x_{mn} = \sqrt{\frac{m}{2}}\,\delta_{m,n+1} + \sqrt{\frac{n}{2}}\,\delta_{m+1,n}.$$

(a) Use perturbation theory to find the terms in α and α^2 in the eigenvalues of

$$\frac{d^2v}{dx^2} - x^2v - \alpha xv = E'v.$$

(b) Determine the eigenvalues exactly and compare with the perturbation calculation. (c) If the original system corresponds to a simple harmonic oscillator oscillating about $x = 0$, what is the corresponding interpretation of the revised system? (d) Does this interpretation fit in with the energy-eigenvalue calculation for this system?

14–10. The unperturbed wave functions for Problem 14–9 are

$$u_n = \frac{H_n(x)\exp(-x^2/2)}{\pi^{1/4}\sqrt{2^n n!}}.$$

(a) Find the terms in α by which v_n, the eigenfunction for the revised system, differs from u_n. (b) Compare this approximate v_n with the Taylor-series expansion in α for the exact solution. (c) Obtain in this way a recurrence relation for H_n and H_n'.

14–11. Calculate an approximate energy value for the lowest P-state of a particle of mass m moving in a potential of the form $A/\sqrt{r}$.

14–12. A hydrogen atom is placed in a static electric field of strength 10^3 statvolts/cm $= 3 \times 10^5$ volts/cm. This field is instantaneously turned off. Calculate the probability that the atom will thereafter emit a photon with a wavelength of the first member of the Lyman series ($n = 2 \rightarrow n = 1$).

$$\psi_{100} = \frac{1}{(\pi a_0^3)^{1/2}}\exp\left(-\frac{r}{a_0}\right);$$

$$\psi_{210} = \frac{1}{(32\pi a_0^5)^{1/2}}\,z\exp\left(-\frac{r}{2a_0}\right).$$

$$e = 4.8 \times 10^{-10}\,\text{statcoul} = 1.6 \times 10^{-19}\,\text{coul},$$

$$a_0 = 0.53 \times 10^{-8}\,\text{cm},$$

$$\int_0^\infty x^n \exp(-x)\,dx = n!.$$

14–13. A one-dimensional anharmonic oscillator has a classical equation of motion of the form

$$m\ddot{x} + kx + ax^3 = 0.$$

(a) Calculate its possible energies, using first-order perturbation theory. (b) Compute the eigenfunction corresponding to the lowest energy state of this system.

14–14. A one-dimensional oscillator in the form of a mass m suspended from a spring with spring constant k is in its lowest energy state. The upper end of the spring is suddenly raised a distance d, and after a time T is quickly returned to its original position. (a) Assuming the validity of first-order perturbation theory, calculate the probability that a transition has occurred to the first excited state. (b) Show that in first order, this is the only transition that occurs.

14–15. Obtain an approximate value for the lowest energy of the hydrogen atom, using the variational technique with the wave function for the ground state of the three-dimensional oscillator as the trial function:

$$\psi = \left(\frac{2a}{\pi}\right)^{3/4} \exp(-ar^2).$$

14–16. (a) For the one-dimensional potential well shown in Fig. 14–6, calculate the possible energies (one-dimensional motion only) subject to the conditions $2mE_0a^2 \ll \hbar^2$ and $2mV_0a^2 \ll \hbar^2$.

(b) Show that for particle energies in a range for which the central barrier has a small transmission probability (see Chapter 3), the energy levels of the system occur in pairs, each pair consisting of an even and an odd state.

(c) Form an energy-superposition state from such a pair of states, for which the particle is almost certain to be found on the left side of the well. This state

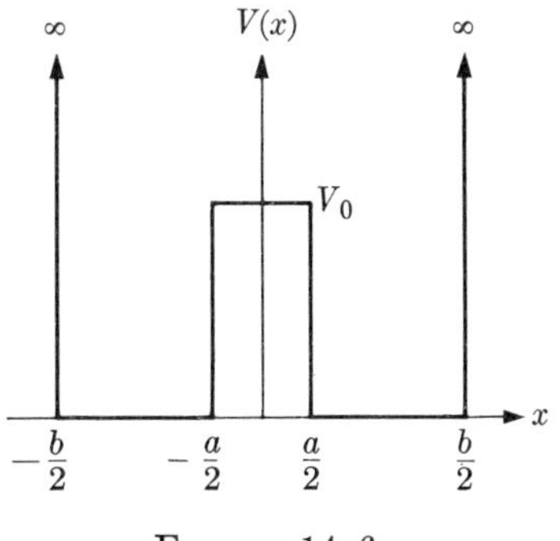

FIGURE 14–6

is analogous to the classical motion of a particle with $E < V_0$. Examine the time dependence of this state, and show that the time required for the particle to get to the right side of the well is of the same order of magnitude as obtained from the following semiclassical argument. Assume that the particle is classical, traveling back and forth on the left side of the well, with a probability of transmission through the barrier given by the quantum calculation of Chapter 3. Compare this calculation of the time dependence of probability for the occupancy of the right side of the box with the quantum-mechanical calculation.

CHAPTER 15

INTERACTION WITH A STRONG ELECTROMAGNETIC FIELD

15–1 The Hamiltonian of a particle in an electromagnetic field. In this chapter, the interaction of a charged particle with an externally produced electromagnetic field will be considered. In a complete treatment, the electromagnetic field must be considered as a dynamical system, with its coordinates and momenta treated according to quantum-mechanical formalism.* When the field is treated in this fashion, it is found that it possesses many of the properties of particles; as mentioned earlier, these electromagnetic quanta are called photons. The problem of the interaction of the field with a charged particle is essentially the problem of the creation and destruction of photons under the influence of the interaction with the charged particle. However, for a sufficiently strong electromagnetic field, the specifically quantum-mechanical effects become small fluctuations on large, classically determined quantities, and it is possible to describe the effect of the electromagnetic field on charged particles as an interaction between the charged particles and the given variables which characterize the externally applied electromagnetic field. In this type of description, the effect of the charged particles on the electromagnetic field is neglected; thus such a description is fundamentally incapable of describing the radiation processes of an atom. It is capable, however, of describing the effect of the field on charged particles; for example, we can evaluate the action of an electromagnetic field in causing an atom to jump from one energy state to another.

To properly introduce the electromagnetic interaction into the equations of motion of a charged particle, we start with the classical Hamiltonian of the particle (see Chapter 5),

$$H = \frac{1}{2m}\left(\boldsymbol{p} - \frac{q}{c}\boldsymbol{A}\right)^2 + q\phi, \tag{15–1}$$

where $\boldsymbol{p}$ is the canonical momentum and is related to the ordinary linear momentum $m\boldsymbol{v}$ by

$$\boldsymbol{p} = m\boldsymbol{v} + \frac{q}{c}\boldsymbol{A}. \tag{15–2}$$

---

* W. Heitler, *The Quantum Theory of Radiation*, Oxford University Press, Oxford, 3rd ed., 1958.

This Hamiltonian may be substituted into the Schrödinger equation

$$\mathrm{H}\psi = i\hbar \frac{\partial \psi}{\partial t}. \tag{15–3}$$

Since we treat the fields as externally applied entities, the operators $\boldsymbol{A}$ and ϕ in Eq. (15–1) are simply ordinary functions of position and time.

15–2 Motion of a free electron in a uniform magnetic field. As a first example of the interaction of a charged particle with an electromagnetic field, consider the interaction of an electron with a uniform static magnetic field. In this case, the Hamiltonian can be written as

$$\mathrm{H} = \frac{1}{2m}\left(\mathbf{P} + \frac{e}{c}\boldsymbol{A}\right)^2, \tag{15–4}$$

since there is no electrostatic potential.

The magnetic field strength is given by

$$\boldsymbol{\mathcal{B}} = \nabla \times \boldsymbol{A}, \tag{15–5}$$

and the Lorentz condition, Eq. (5–20), reduces to

$$\nabla \cdot \boldsymbol{A} = 0. \tag{15–6}$$

Since

$$[f(x), \mathrm{P}_x] = i\hbar \frac{\partial f(x)}{\partial x}, \tag{15–7}$$

it is seen that

$$\boldsymbol{A} \cdot \mathbf{P} - \mathbf{P} \cdot \boldsymbol{A} = i\hbar\, \nabla \cdot \boldsymbol{A}. \tag{15–8}$$

This, together with Eq. (15–6), shows that the momentum operator and the vector potential commute with each other:

$$\mathbf{P} \cdot \boldsymbol{A} = \boldsymbol{A} \cdot \mathbf{P}. \tag{15–9}$$

Expanding Eq. (15–4) and making use of this commutation, one obtains

$$\mathrm{H} = \frac{\mathrm{P}^2}{2m} + \frac{e}{mc}\boldsymbol{A} \cdot \mathbf{P} + \frac{e^2}{2mc^2} A^2. \tag{15–10}$$

Furthermore, since the vector potential represents a uniform magnetic field, it can be written as

$$\boldsymbol{A} = -\tfrac{1}{2}\boldsymbol{r} \times \boldsymbol{\mathcal{B}}. \tag{15–11}$$

The second term in the Hamiltonian can then be written, apart from the factor e/mc, as

$$\boldsymbol{A} \cdot \mathbf{P} = -\tfrac{1}{2}(\boldsymbol{r} \times \boldsymbol{\mathcal{B}}) \cdot \mathbf{P} = \tfrac{1}{2}\boldsymbol{\mathcal{B}} \cdot (\boldsymbol{r} \times \mathbf{P}) = \tfrac{1}{2}\boldsymbol{\mathcal{B}} \cdot \mathbf{L}, \tag{15–12}$$

since $\mathbf{\mathcal{B}}$ and $\mathbf{r}$ commute. Also

$$A^2 = \tfrac{1}{4}|\mathbf{r} \times \mathbf{\mathcal{B}}|^2 = \tfrac{1}{4}[r^2\mathcal{B}^2 - (\mathbf{r} \cdot \mathbf{\mathcal{B}})^2]. \tag{15–13}$$

To simplify the notation, assume that the uniform magnetic field is in the z-direction and of magnitude $\mathcal{B}$. In this case, the Hamiltonian reduces to

$$\mathrm{H} = \frac{1}{2m}\,\mathrm{P}^2 + \frac{e}{2mc}\,\mathcal{B}\mathrm{L}_z + \frac{e^2\mathcal{B}^2}{8mc^2}\,(x^2 + y^2). \tag{15–14}$$

It can be seen from this equation that the operator L_z commutes with the Hamiltonian and that both these operators commute with the operator P_z. Consequently, the three operators H, P_z, and L_z commute with one another, and it is possible to choose wave functions which are simultaneously eigenfunctions of all three operators. [Remember from Eq. (15–2) that the momentum is no longer only the kinetic momentum $m\mathbf{v}$, and the z-component of angular momentum L_z now also contains a part corresponding to the $\mathbf{A}$-term of the generalized momentum.] The energy represented by this Hamiltonian can be separated into three parts: the energy associated with motion in the z-direction, the term involving L_z, and the remainder of the energy associated with motion in the x- and y-directions. This latter part will be designated by the operator H_0:

$$\mathrm{H}_0 = \frac{1}{2m}\,(\mathrm{P}_x^2 + \mathrm{P}_y^2) + \tfrac{1}{2}\left(\frac{e^2\mathcal{B}^2}{4mc^2}\right)(x^2 + y^2). \tag{15–15}$$

Note that this is simply the Hamiltonian of a two-dimensional simple harmonic oscillator and has an energy which is the sum of the energies of two linear harmonic oscillators. The wave function which is simultaneously an eigenfunction of all three mutually commuting operators H_0, L_z, and P_z can be written in the form

$$\psi = \psi_{nm_lp_z}. \tag{15–16}$$

The three subscripts are the quantum numbers appearing in the eigenvalue equations

$$\begin{aligned} \mathrm{H}_0\psi_{nm_lp_z} &= (n+1)\hbar\omega\psi_{nm_lp_z}, \\ \mathrm{L}_z\psi_{nm_lp_z} &= m_l\hbar\psi_{nm_lp_z}, \\ \mathrm{P}_z\psi_{nm_lp_z} &= p_z\psi_{nm_lp_z}. \end{aligned} \tag{15–17}$$

The ω appearing in the first of these equations is given by

$$\omega = +\frac{e\mathcal{B}}{2mc}\cdot \tag{15–18}$$

The ground-state wave function for the two-dimensional oscillator is an even function under a change of sign of the x- and y-coordinates:

$$\psi_{0m_lp_z}(x, y) = \psi_{0m_lp_z}(-x, -y). \tag{15-19}$$

The first excited state, with $n = 1$, is an odd function under a change in sign of both x and y. It is seen that even wave functions are associated with even quantum numbers n, and odd wave functions are associated with odd quantum numbers. Also, in Eq. (15–17), even values of m_l are associated with wave functions which are even under a change in sign of x and y, and odd values of m_l are associated with odd wave functions. Therefore, n and m_l are either both even or both odd. From the above discussion, the energy-eigenvalue equation for the total Hamiltonian can be written as

$$\begin{aligned} \mathrm{H}\psi_{nm_lp_z} &= \left[\frac{1}{2m}\,p_z^2 + (n+1)\hbar\omega + m_l\hbar\omega\right]\psi_{nm_lp_z} \\ &= \left[\frac{1}{2m}\,p_z^2 + (n + m_l + 1)\hbar\omega\right]\psi_{nm_lp_z}. \end{aligned} \tag{15-20}$$

We could also use ladder operators to obtain the same wave function (see Problem 15–9). Since n and m_l are both either even or odd, and since the total energy of the electron in a uniform magnetic field cannot be negative [H being the square of a Hermitian operator, Eq. (15–4)], we see that

$$n + m_l = 2r \geq 0; \tag{15-21}$$

therefore

$$n \geq -m_l. \tag{15-22}$$

The total energy eigenvalue can thus be written as

$$E_{nm_lp_z} = (2r+1)\hbar\omega + \frac{1}{2m}\,p_z^2, \qquad r = 0, 1, 2\ldots \tag{15-23}$$

The quantity p_z represents the momentum in the z-direction of the particle. The total energy of the electron is composed of the kinetic energy associated with motion along the z-direction and the energy associated with motion in the xy-plane, as given by $(2r + 1)\hbar\omega$. Note from Eq. (15–23) that the motion in the x- and y-directions has a zero-point fluctuation effect connected with it, as in the case of the simple harmonic oscillator, and that the lowest energy of an electron in a uniform magnetic field is not zero but is equal to $\hbar\omega$. This result is a bit surprising, inasmuch as the electron is not confined to a small region of space by the magnetic field, but can exist anywhere in a rather large volume; it might at first appear that the uncertainty principle should not lead to an uncertainty in momentum and the resulting contribution to the kinetic energy of the particle.

The Hamiltonian of Eq. (15–14) is not unique for the problem of the motion of an electron in a uniform magnetic field; an infinite number of vector potentials $\boldsymbol{A}$ can be used to represent a uniform magnetic field along the z-direction. The only restrictions necessary for Eq. (15–10) to be valid are that Eqs. (15–5) and (15–6) must be satisfied. It is readily seen that any vector potential $\boldsymbol{A}'$ related to the vector potential of Eq. (15–11) by

$$\boldsymbol{A}' = \boldsymbol{A} + \nabla f, \tag{15–24}$$

where f is any differentiable scalar function of position $[f = f(x, y, z)]$ satisfying

$$\nabla^2 f = 0, \tag{15–25}$$

also represents the same uniform magnetic field as $\boldsymbol{A}$. [The transformation of Eq. (15–24) is a special case of a *gauge* transformation in which both scalar (ϕ) and vector ($\boldsymbol{A}$) electromagnetic potentials are transformed in such a way as to keep the electromagnetic fields unchanged. Such a transformation does not alter the physical situation.]

Formally, it can be shown by direct substitution that if the vector-potential transformation of Eq. (15–24) is made, the original form of the energy-eigenvalue equation is obtained if the wave-function transformation

$$\psi' = \psi \exp\left(\frac{ie}{\hbar c} f\right) \tag{15–26}$$

is simultaneously made.

As an example of an alternative vector potential, consider

$$A'_x = -\mathcal{B}y, \qquad A'_y = A'_z = 0. \tag{15–27}$$

This can be obtained from Eqs. (15–11), (15–24), and the scalar function

$$f = -\frac{\mathcal{B}}{2}\, xy. \tag{15–28}$$

With this choice of vector potential, the energy-eigenvalue equation is

$$\left[\frac{1}{2m}\left(\mathrm{P}_x - \frac{e\mathcal{B}y}{c}\right)^2 + \frac{\mathrm{P}_y^2}{2m} + \frac{\mathrm{P}_z^2}{2m}\right]\psi = E\psi. \tag{15–29}$$

As before, z is a cyclic coordinate, and P_z is a constant of the motion. Now, however, x is also cyclic, and H, P_z, and P_x commute. The wave functions can thus be chosen to be simultaneous eigenfunctions of these operators; such a wave function will be of the form

$$\psi = \exp\left(\frac{ip_x x}{\hbar}\right) \exp\left(\frac{ip_z z}{\hbar}\right) G(y). \tag{15–30}$$

The function $G(y)$ satisfies

$$\left[\frac{\mathrm{P}_y^2}{2m} - \frac{2ep_x\mathcal{B}y}{c} + \frac{e^2\mathcal{B}^2}{c^2}\,y^2\right]G(y) = E'G(y), \tag{15-31}$$

where

$$E' = E - \frac{p_z^2}{2m} - \frac{p_x^2}{2m}. \tag{15-32}$$

Equation (15–31) can be simplified by making the substitution

$$y_0 \equiv \frac{cp_x}{e\mathcal{B}}; \tag{15-33}$$

it becomes

$$\left[\frac{\mathrm{P}_y^2}{2m} + \frac{e^2\mathcal{B}^2}{2mc^2}\,(y - y_0)^2\right]G(y) = \left(E' + \frac{p_x^2}{2m}\right)G(y)$$

$$= \left(E - \frac{p_z^2}{2m}\right)G(y). \tag{15-34}$$

This can be recognized as the equation for a one-dimensional simple harmonic oscillator of (circular) frequency

$$\omega_1 = \frac{e\mathcal{B}}{mc}. \tag{15-35}$$

[Compare Eq. (15–34) with Eqs. (3–55) and (3–57).] The energy associated with this motion can be written immediately, using the results obtained earlier:

$$E' + \frac{p_x^2}{2m} = E - \frac{p_z^2}{2m} = (n + \tfrac{1}{2})\hbar\omega_1 \tag{15-36}$$

or

$$E = (n + \tfrac{1}{2})\hbar\omega_1 + \frac{p_z^2}{2m}. \tag{15-37}$$

In terms of the (circular) frequency introduced in the discussion of the same problem using the other gauge, Eq. (15–18),

$$\omega = \frac{\omega_1}{2} \tag{15-38}$$

and

$$E = (2n + 1)\hbar\omega + \frac{p_z^2}{2m}. \tag{15-39}$$

This is identical to the previously obtained result, Eq. (15–23), as of course it must be. The eigenenergy E is seen to be independent of the momentum in the x-direction, p_x. This, however, is now a constant of the motion and can assume any value in the continuous range $-\infty \leq p_x \leq +\infty$. Thus there is an infinite degeneracy to be associated with each energy state. This was also the case for the alternative gauge discussed earlier. From Eq. (15–20) it can be seen that for each value of the energy there is an infinite number of possibilities for the two quantum numbers n and m_l. All that is required is that $n + m_l$ be constant, and n can assume any integral value in the range $n \geq 0$, while m_l can take on any integral value in the range $n \geq -m_l \geq -\infty$.

The Hamiltonian for either gauge can readily be modified to include a term for the interaction of the spin magnetic moment of the particle with the external field. If the term

$$+\frac{e}{mc}\,\mathcal{B}\cdot\mathbf{S} = +\frac{e}{mc}\,\mathcal{B}S_z \tag{15–40}$$

is added, the resulting energy for the particle (assumed to be an electron) is

$$E_{nm_lp_z\pm} = (2r + 1 \pm \tfrac{1}{2})\hbar\omega + \frac{1}{2m}\,p_z^2. \tag{15–41}$$

The sign $(\pm)$ refers to the two possible orientations of the electron spin relative to the magnetic field.

15–3 The weak-field Zeeman effect. The *Zeeman effect* splits a spectral line into a number of components under the influence of a magnetic field acting on the emitting atom. The relevant problem here is that of calculating the effect of an externally applied magnetic field on the energy levels of an atom. The Hamiltonian of the one-electron atom, or the one-valence-electron atom as in the case of an alkali metal, can be written, as in Eq. (14–46), as

$$\mathrm{H} = \frac{1}{2m}\,\mathrm{P}^2 + V(r) + \frac{1}{2m^2c^2}\,\frac{1}{r}\,\frac{dV}{dr}\,\mathbf{L}\cdot\mathbf{S}. \tag{15–42}$$

When a uniform magnetic field is present, this becomes

$$\mathrm{H} = \frac{1}{2m}\left(\mathbf{P} + \frac{e}{c}\,\boldsymbol{A}\right)^2 + V(r) + f(r)\mathbf{L}\cdot\mathbf{S} + \frac{e}{mc}\,\mathcal{B}\cdot\mathbf{S}. \tag{15–43}$$

For the magnetic field strengths commonly encountered in the laboratory,

$$\left|\frac{e^2A^2}{mc^2}\right| \ll V(r) \tag{15–44}$$

is satisfied in those regions where the electron is nearly always found.

Consequently, the square of the vector potential can be neglected in comparison with the potential energy of the electron. If we neglect this term and again take the magnetic field to be in the z-direction, we can write the Hamiltonian of Eq. (15–43) as

$$\mathrm{H} = \frac{1}{2m}\,\mathrm{P}^2 + V(r) + f(r)\mathbf{L}\cdot\mathbf{S} + \frac{e\mathcal{B}}{2mc}\,(\mathrm{J}_z + \mathrm{S}_z). \qquad (15\text{–}45)$$

Assume that the magnetic field is weak in a sense to be described later; the Zeeman splitting of the energy level will be calculated in this weak-field approximation. If we use perturbation theory, the change in the energy level which results from the inclusion of the last term in Eq. (15–45) can be written, in first order, from Eq. (15–18):

$$\Delta E = +\,\omega\langle \mathrm{J}_z + \mathrm{S}_z\rangle = m_j\hbar\omega + \omega\langle \mathrm{S}_z\rangle. \qquad (15\text{–}46)$$

Here the wave function is characterized by the quantum numbers l, j, m_j, and n. To evaluate $\langle \mathrm{S}_z\rangle$, it is necessary to calculate explicitly the spin dependence of such wave functions. To do this, we introduce the ladder operator

$$\mathrm{J}_- = \mathrm{J}_x - i\mathrm{J}_y. \qquad (15\text{–}47)$$

From Eq. (9–59), replacing $\mathbf{L}$ by $\mathbf{J}$, we have

$$\mathrm{J}_-\psi_{l,j,m_j+1} = [(j - m_j)(j + m_j + 1)]^{1/2}\hbar\psi_{ljm_j}. \qquad (15\text{–}48)$$

For simplicity, the index n has been dropped because it is common to all the levels in question. Also, from Eq. (9–60) we see that

$$\psi_{ljm_j} = \left[\frac{(j + m_j)!}{(2j)!(j - m_j)!}\right]^{1/2}\left(\frac{1}{\hbar}\right)^{j-m_j}\mathrm{J}_-^{j-m_j}\psi_{ljj}. \qquad (15\text{–}49)$$

It is clear that the largest value of m_j is equal to $l + \frac{1}{2}$, when both the orbital angular momentum and the spin angular momentum of the electron have their largest possible component in the positive z-direction. This can occur only for $j = l + \frac{1}{2}$. Consequently, this energy state is also an eigenstate of L_z and S_z and can be characterized by the quantum numbers $l = j - \frac{1}{2}$ and $m_j = j$. Inasmuch as the wave function for which j and m_j take on their largest possible values is also an eigenfunction of L^2, L_z, and S_z, the wave function can be written explicitly in the form

$$\psi_{l,l+1/2,l+1/2} = Y_{ll}(\theta, \phi)\,R_+(r). \qquad (15\text{–}50)$$

The subscript (+) on the radial function signifies that the spin of the electron is in the positive z-direction. By using the ladder operator, all the other eigenfunctions with the same value of j can be generated as in Eq. (15–49). In particular, for $m_j = j - 1$, the function has the form

$$\psi_{j-1/2,j,j-1} = \frac{1}{\hbar\sqrt{2j}}\, J_-\psi_{j-1/2,j,j}. \tag{15-51}$$

There are two eigenfunctions with this particular value of m_j; the one which is orthogonal to that of Eq. (15–51) can be written as

$$\frac{1}{\sqrt{2l(2l+1)}}\,(L_- - 2lS_-)\psi_{j-1/2,j,j}. \tag{15-52}$$

[It may be verified directly that the functions of Eqs. (15–51) and (15–52) are orthogonal to each other.] Consequently, the function of Eq. (15–52) cannot be an eigenfunction of the largest possible value of j and must be an eigenfunction of the smaller value, namely $j = l - \frac{1}{2}$. This function then can be taken to be the leading function for a chain of all the various possible values of m_j with this particular value of j. Starting either with the function of Eq. (15–50) or with the function of Eq. (15–52), one can generate all the eigenfunctions with this particular value of l and total quantum number n:

$$\begin{aligned}
\psi_{l,l+1/2,m_j} &= \left[\frac{(l+\frac{1}{2}+m_j)!}{(2l+1)!(l+\frac{1}{2}-m_j)!}\right]^{1/2} \\
&\quad \times \left(\frac{1}{\hbar}\right)^{l+1/2-m_j} J_-^{l+1/2-m_j}\psi_{l,l+1/2,l+1/2}, \\
\psi_{l,l-1/2,m_j} &= \left[\frac{(l-\frac{1}{2}+m_j)!}{(2l+1)!(l-\frac{1}{2}+m_j)!}\right]^{1/2} \\
&\quad \times \left(\frac{1}{\hbar}\right)^{l-1/2-m_j} J_-^{l-1/2-m_j}(L_- - 2lS_-)\psi_{l,l+1/2,l+1/2}.
\end{aligned} \tag{15-53}$$

The ladder operators appearing in these equations can be simplified by making use of

$$\begin{aligned}
J_-^{l+1/2-m_j} &= (L_- + S_-)^{l+1/2-m_j} \\
&= L_-^{l+1/2-m_j} + (l+\tfrac{1}{2}-m_j)L_-^{l-1/2-m_j}S_-,
\end{aligned} \tag{15-54}$$

where the operator S_- appears only to the first power. The effect of this operator is either to "turn the spin down" or to give zero; consequently, its square and all higher powers are equal to zero. By a suitable combination of the above equations, one obtains

$$\begin{aligned}\psi_{l,l+1/2,m_j} &= \left(\frac{l+\frac{1}{2}+m_j}{2l+1}\right)^{1/2} Y_{l,m_j-1/2}R_+ \\ &\quad + \left(\frac{l+\frac{1}{2}-m_j}{2l+1}\right)^{1/2} Y_{l,m_j+1/2}R_-, \\ \psi_{l,l-1/2,m_j} &= \left(\frac{l+\frac{1}{2}-m_j}{2l+1}\right)^{1/2} Y_{l,m_j-1/2}R_+ \\ &\quad - \left(\frac{l+\frac{1}{2}+m_j}{2l+1}\right)^{1/2} Y_{l,m_j+1/2}R_-.\end{aligned} \tag{15–55}$$

These equations represent the expansion of the wave functions characterized by the quantum numbers l and m_j in terms of wave functions characterized by the quantum numbers l, m_l, and m_s. Thus a transformation of the representation from one set of basis functions to another has been effected.

This way of expressing the wave functions ψ_{ljm_j} is particularly useful for calculating $\langle \mathrm{S}_z\rangle$, since the terms in the decompositions given by Eq. (15–55) are separately eigenfunctions of S_z and are orthogonal to each other. Consequently, the cross terms in computing $\langle \mathrm{S}_z\rangle$ are zero, and this expectation value is

$$\begin{aligned}\langle \mathrm{S}_z\rangle_{j=l+1/2} &= \frac{1}{2}\hbar\,\frac{l+\frac{1}{2}+m_j}{2l+1} - \frac{1}{2}\hbar\,\frac{l+\frac{1}{2}-m_j}{2l+1} \\ &= \frac{m_j\hbar}{2l+1},\end{aligned} \tag{15–56}$$

$$\begin{aligned}\langle \mathrm{S}_z\rangle_{j=l-1/2} &= \frac{1}{2}\hbar\,\frac{l+\frac{1}{2}-m_j}{2l+1} - \frac{1}{2}\hbar\,\frac{l+\frac{1}{2}+m_j}{2l+1} \\ &= -\frac{m_j\hbar}{2l+1}.\end{aligned} \tag{15–57}$$

Substituting these results into Eq. (15–46), we find

$$\Delta E_{ljm_j} = m_j\hbar\omega\left(\frac{2j+1}{2l+1}\right) \tag{15–58}$$

for the shift in energy of a particular energy level under the influence of an external magnetic field.

This result has a simple physical interpretation. Note that each energy level characterized by a particular m_j is shifted in energy by an amount proportional to m_j. In other words, all the energy levels corresponding to a particular j (which represent the possible orientations of this total angular momentum with respect to the magnetic field) are, for zero magnetic field, equal in energy, but when a magnetic field is applied, each level is shifted in energy by an amount proportional to the component of the total angular momentum along the direction of the magnetic field. This is just the result one would expect if the atomic angular momentum is thought of as associated with a rotating top having a certain magnetic moment. The interaction of such a magnetic moment with the magnetic field is proportional to the component of the angular momentum in the direction of the field, leading to the equal splittings found.

The magnetic moment associated with the total angular momentum vector $\mathbf{J}$ arises from contributions from the orbital motion of the electron, which can be thought of as a circular current, and from the electron spin. These two contributions are added vectorially, since the corresponding angular momenta are added vectorially.

15–4 The *g*-factor. One quantity of importance in the analysis of spectra is the ratio of the magnetic moment to the associated angular momentum of an atom. This is known as the *gyromagnetic ratio*, and can be written as $g(e/2mc)$, where $|g|$ is called the *g-factor* and is a dimensionless number.

The g-factor for spin momentum is different from that for orbital angular momentum. Consequently, for a vector model, the direction of the magnetic moment of the atom is different from the direction of the angular momentum of the atom. One can imagine the electron spin and orbital momentum as each rapidly precessing about the total angular

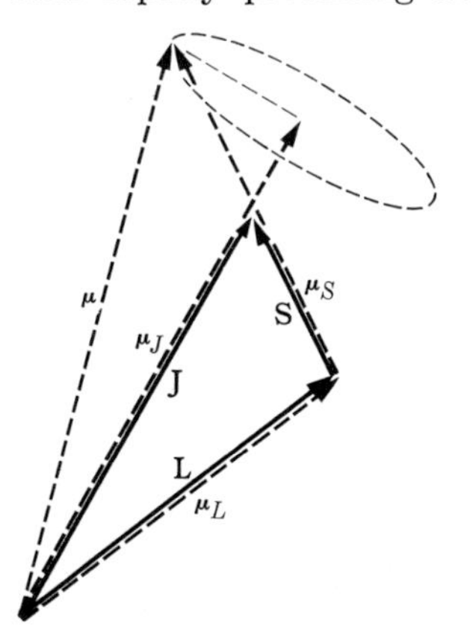

FIG. 15–1. A vector model of the addition of two angular momenta, showing the corresponding addition of the accompanying magnetic moments. Dashed vectors represent magnetic moments; solid vectors represent angular momenta. The g-factor for the combined system can be obtained from this model.

momentum of the atom, leading to a precession of the magnetic moment about the direction of the total angular momentum. This rapid precession can be pictured as averaging out all components except the component along the total angular momentum, thus leading to an effective magnetic moment for the atom which is in the direction of the total angular momentum. On the other hand, the complicated vectorial way in which the magnetic moment is added leads to a g-factor which lies between that of the orbital motion and that of the spin angular momentum. In Eq. (15–58), the term in parentheses is the g-factor, namely,

$$g = \frac{2j+1}{2l+1}. \qquad (15\text{–}59)$$

This is seen to be equal to two in the case of l equal to zero, since then $j = s = \frac{1}{2}$. For large values of l, this g-factor becomes equal to unity. Figure 15–1 is a vector diagram showing how the two angular momenta combine to give a total angular momentum and how the two magnetic moments combine vectorially to give the correct component of magnetic moment along the axis of the total angular momentum, thus giving the g-factor of Eq. (15–59).

15–5 The strong-field Zeeman effect. The energy shifts given by Eq. (15–58) are correct only so long as the field is sufficiently weak; the shift in energy must be small compared with the fine-structure splitting between the states $j = l + \frac{1}{2}$ and $j = l - \frac{1}{2}$. Another interesting special case is that of the strong-field limit, in which the magnetic field is so strong that the external magnetic field is larger than the effective internal magnetic field acting on the electron. In this case, the spin-orbit term in Eq. (15–45) is regarded as a perturbation term and the Zeeman term is taken as part of the unperturbed Hamiltonian. It is now advantageous to write the Hamiltonian in the form

$$\mathrm{H} = \frac{1}{2m}\mathrm{P}^2 + V(r) + \frac{e\mathcal{B}}{2mc}(\mathrm{L}_z + 2\mathrm{S}_z) + f(r)\mathbf{L}\cdot\mathbf{S}. \qquad (15\text{–}60)$$

The first three terms constitute the unperturbed Hamiltonian. All commute with the operators L_z and S_z, so wave functions for the unperturbed Hamiltonian can be taken to be simultaneously eigenfunctions of L^2, L_z, and S_z, with quantum numbers l, m_l, and m_s. The energy of the atom in a state with quantum numbers l, m_l, m_s, and n can now be written as

$$E_{nlm_lm_s} = E_n + \hbar\omega(m_l + 2m_s) + \langle f(r)\mathbf{L}\cdot\mathbf{S}\rangle. \qquad (15\text{–}61)$$

The last term represents the contribution from the perturbing spin-orbit term, in the form of the expectation value of this operator. Inasmuch as the average value of L_x and L_y is zero for a state of definite L_z, the contribution from the perturbing term can be simplified:

$$\langle f(r)\mathbf{L}\cdot\mathbf{S}\rangle = \langle f(r)L_zS_z\rangle = \langle f(r)\rangle m_l m_s \hbar^2. \tag{15–62}$$

This contribution to the energy can be expressed in terms of the zero-field fine-structure splitting of the level δE. Using Eq. (9–71), we find, for zero applied magnetic field, that this splitting is

$$\begin{aligned}\delta E &\equiv E_{n,l,j=l+1/2} - E_{n,l,j=l-1/2} = \langle f(r)\mathbf{L}\cdot\mathbf{S}\rangle \\ &= \langle f(r)\rangle \tfrac{1}{2}[j(j+1) - l(l+1) - \tfrac{3}{4}]\,\hbar^2 \Big|_{j=l-1/2}^{j=l+1/2} \\ &= \langle f(r)\rangle(l+\tfrac{1}{2})\hbar^2.\end{aligned} \tag{15–63}$$

Expressed in this way, the energy in the strong-field limit for the various

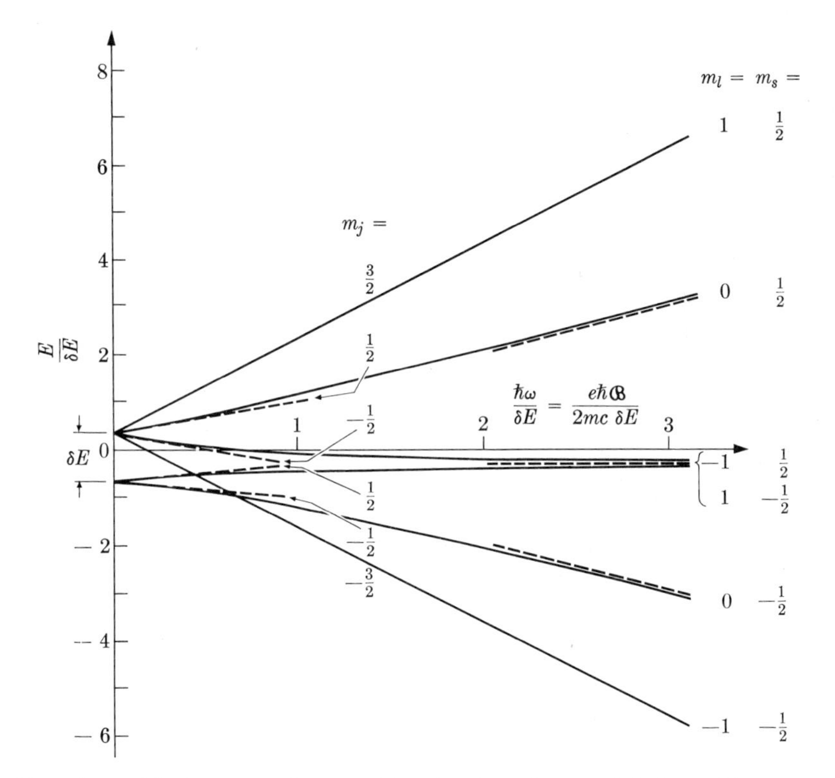

Fig. 15–2. The Zeeman effect in a P-state of an alkali metal atom. The curves have been plotted from an expression valid for all values of the magnetic field. Also shown, as broken lines, are the Zeeman splittings in the "weak-field" and "strong-field" limits as calculated in the text, using perturbation theory.

angular-momentum states is

$$E_{nljm_j} = E_n + \hbar\omega(m_l + 2m_s) + \delta E \frac{m_l m_s}{l + \frac{1}{2}}. \tag{15-64}$$

A corresponding equation that is valid in the weak-field limit is obtained from Eqs. (15–45), (15–58), (15–63), and (9–71):

$$E_{nljm_j} = E_n + \delta E \left[\frac{j(j+1) - l(l+1) - \frac{3}{4}}{2l+1}\right] + \hbar\omega m_j \left(\frac{2j+1}{2l+1}\right). \tag{15-65}$$

These expressions are plotted as broken curves in Fig. 15–2 as functions of the magnetic field strength for the case $l = 1$. The curves are labeled by the quantum numbers which are valid in the strong- and weak-field limits respectively. In the region of weak fields, note that the energies branch out from a common point at zero magnetic field and that the curves are all equally separated for a given j. Equations (15–64) and (15–65) are valid only in the limits of very strong and very weak fields respectively; the solid curves of Fig. 15–2 have been plotted from an exact expression good for all magnetic field strengths. Inasmuch as the figure is plotted for $l = 1$, these energy levels represent the behavior of the energy levels in an alkali metal, such as sodium, for P-states.

15–6 Interaction of an atomic electron with a plane electromagnetic wave. In this section, the rate at which an atom absorbs energy from a plane electromagnetic wave incident upon it, and also the rate at which stimulated emission takes place if the atom happens to be in an excited state, will be calculated. Note that, in accordance with the approximation that is being used, the natural (spontaneous) emission of the atom is ignored. For a plane wave in free space, the magnitude of the magnetic field strength is equal to the magnitude of the electric field strength (in cgs units); from this, we can estimate the order of magnitude of the interaction energies.

The first to be calculated is the interaction energy of the electron with the electric field due to the electronic charge. This has the order of magnitude given by $ea_0\mathcal{E}$, where a_0 is a measure of the radius of the atom. On the other hand, the magnetic dipole interaction has an energy of the order of $(e\hbar/mc)\mathcal{B}$. This represents the energy of interaction between the magnetic dipole moment of the electron and the magnetic field. If a_0 is taken to be the Bohr radius for a hydrogen atom, we have

$$a_0 = \frac{e^2}{mc^2} \cdot \frac{1}{\alpha^2} = \frac{\hbar}{mc} \cdot \frac{1}{\alpha}, \tag{15-66}$$

where α, the fine-structure constant, is given by

$$\alpha \equiv \frac{e^2}{\hbar c} \approx \frac{1}{137}. \tag{15-67}$$

Comparing the electric and magnetic interaction magnitudes, we see that the magnetic interaction energy is about 1/137 of the electric interaction energy and may therefore, to a good approximation, be neglected. This leaves the expression

$$\mathrm{H}' = +\frac{e}{mc}\,\boldsymbol{A}\cdot\mathbf{P} \tag{15-68}$$

as the only interaction energy which need be considered.

For a plane wave, the vector potential may be assumed to be

$$\boldsymbol{A} = \{\boldsymbol{A}_0 \exp\,[i(\boldsymbol{k}\cdot\boldsymbol{r} - \omega t)]\}_{\text{real part}}. \tag{15-69}$$

For a choice of Lorentz gauge, and with the scalar potential ϕ equal to zero, the plane of polarization of the wave is perpendicular to the direction of propagation; hence

$$\boldsymbol{A}_0\cdot\boldsymbol{k} = 0. \tag{15-70}$$

Also, the divergence of the vector potential is zero:

$$\operatorname{div}\boldsymbol{A} = 0. \tag{15-71}$$

For a plane electromagnetic wave having a wavelength which is large compared with the diameter of the atom, it is possible to introduce a further simplification known as the *dipole approximation*. In this case, $\boldsymbol{k}\cdot\boldsymbol{r} \ll 1$ for all values of $\boldsymbol{r}$ where the atomic electron is apt to be. The term $\exp\,(i\boldsymbol{k}\cdot\boldsymbol{r})$ in Eq. (15–69) can therefore be replaced by unity. Taking the center of the atom to be at the point $\boldsymbol{r} = 0$, the interaction energy of Eq. (15–68) can be approximated by

$$\mathrm{H}' = +\frac{e}{mc}\,\boldsymbol{A}_0\cdot\mathbf{P}\cos\omega t. \tag{15-72}$$

Here the *electric* dipole part of the interaction is considered. This approximation is equivalent to assuming that the electromagnetic field is uniform over a region large compared with the size of the atom.

The problem to be considered is the calculation of transitions of the atom between energy states caused by its interaction with the electromagnetic wave given in Eq. (15–72). We will apply time-dependent perturbation theory, and direct use will be made of the expression for the expansion coefficients c_j developed in Chapter 14. From Eq. (14–61), assuming that the resonance condition

$$\omega_{j0} \approx \omega \tag{15-73}$$

is satisfied, and dropping small terms, we obtain

$$c_j(t) = -\frac{ie}{2mc\hbar} A_0 \cdot (j|\mathbf{P}|0) \exp\left[\tfrac{1}{2}i(\omega_{j0} - \omega)t\right] \frac{\sin \frac{1}{2}(\omega_{j0} - \omega)t}{\frac{1}{2}(\omega_{j0} - \omega)}. \tag{15–74}$$

To simplify the notation, assume that the direction of polarization of the electromagnetic wave is in the z-direction; we then obtain, as the probability that the atom will be in state j at time t,

$$|c_j(t)|^2 = \frac{e^2}{4m^2c^2\hbar^2} A_0^2 |(j|P_z|0)|^2 \frac{\sin^2 \frac{1}{2}(\omega_{j0} - \omega)t}{\frac{1}{4}(\omega_{j0} - \omega)^2}. \tag{15–75}$$

Note that this implies that at time $t = 0$, when the electromagnetic radiation is imagined to be suddenly switched on, the atom is in the state 0. The probability of being in state j at the later time t is a sinusoidally oscillating function of t. In practice, there is usually some damping mechanism which stops this oscillation between energy states.

An example of such a mechanism is collision damping, in which collisions with other atoms disturb the atom in such a way as to produce random phase shifts in the various c_k's of the expansion, Eq. (14–54). After such *random* phase shifts, the behavior of the atom is, on the average, as if it were in any one of the several (pure) energy states, with probabilities given by the absolute squares of the corresponding c_k's. Thus all that is required is to calculate the average probability that a transition will have been made between the state 0 and state j at the time of the first collision. To do this, it is first necessary to obtain a distribution function for collisions. An atom observed at time $t = 0$ will eventually suffer a collision at some later time t. The probability per unit time, dW/dt, that the collision will occur at a certain time t after the initial observation, a collision not having previously occurred in the interval between $t = 0$ and $t = t$, is given by

$$\frac{dW}{dt} = \gamma \exp(-\gamma t). \tag{15–76}$$

This expression can be obtained by dividing the time interval from $t = 0$ to $t = t$ into infinitesimal intervals dt and multiplying together the probabilities that the atom will not suffer a collision in each of these time intervals. If Eq. (15–76) represents the probability per unit time that a collision will occur at a time t, then the mean transition probability in the time interval from zero to infinity is

$$\overline{W} = \int_0^\infty |c_j(t)|^2 \gamma \exp(-\gamma t)\, dt. \tag{15–77}$$

This is the average probability that a transition will have occurred from the state 0 to the state j at the time of the first collision after $t = 0$. The integral which must be evaluated is

$$\int_0^\infty \gamma \exp(-\gamma t) \sin^2 \tfrac{1}{2}\alpha t \, dt = \frac{1}{2} \frac{\alpha^2}{\gamma^2 + \alpha^2}. \tag{15–78}$$

Using this result, one obtains for the transition probability per collision

$$\overline{W} = \int_0^\infty |c_j(t)|^2 \gamma \exp(-\gamma t) \, dt = \frac{e^2 A_0^2}{4m^2c^2\hbar^2} |(j|\mathrm{P}_z|0)|^2 \frac{2}{(\omega_{j0} - \omega)^2 + \gamma^2}. \tag{15–79}$$

Note from this expression that the probability that an atom initially in state 0 will be thrown into state j is exactly equal to the probability that an atom initially in state j will be thrown into state 0, since

$$|(0|\mathrm{P}_z|j)|^2 = |(j|\mathrm{P}_z|0)|^2 \tag{15–80}$$

must be satisfied. Equation (15–79) gives the transition probability per collision that an atom will be thrown from one state into the other; from this expression, we can readily obtain the probability per second that a transition from one energy state to the other will occur. We do this by multiplying by the average number of collisions per second, which is simply γ. Knowing the probability per second that a transition will occur from one state to the other, we can write directly the energy absorbed per second by a gas which contains populations n_0 and n_j of atoms in states 0 and j respectively. The rate at which energy is absorbed by the gas is

$$U = (n_0 - n_j)\hbar\omega \frac{e^2 A_0^2}{4m^2c^2\hbar^2} |(j|\mathrm{P}_z|0)|^2 \frac{2\gamma}{(\omega_{j0} - \omega)^2 + \gamma^2}. \tag{15–81}$$

It is sometimes desirable to express the rate at which an atom initially in state 0 absorbs energy from the electromagnetic wave in terms of a collision cross section. This represents the effective cross-sectional area presented by the atom to incident photons. It is equal to the average energy per second absorbed by the atom in the state 0, divided by the energy flux per second per square centimeter in the incident electromagnetic wave. This ratio, which has the dimensions of an area, can be thought of as an effective cross-sectional area σ of the atom. The energy flux in the plane wave is

$$S = \frac{\mathcal{E}^2}{8\pi} c = \frac{\omega^2 A_0^2}{8\pi c}. \tag{15–82}$$

Therefore

$$\sigma = \frac{\hbar\omega(e^2A_0^2/4m^2c^2\hbar^2)|(j|\mathrm{P}_z|0)|^2\{2\gamma/[(\omega_{j0} - \omega)^2 + \gamma^2]\}}{\omega^2 A_0^2/8\pi c}$$

$$= 2\pi \frac{e^2}{\hbar c} \frac{|(j|\mathrm{P}_z|0)|^2}{m^2\omega^2} \frac{2\gamma\omega}{(\omega_{j0} - \omega)^2 + \gamma^2}. \tag{15–83}$$

The matrix element can be written as

$$(j|P_z|0) = m\frac{i}{\hbar}(j|[H, z]|0) = im\omega_{j0}(j|z|0). \tag{15–84}$$

Then

$$\sigma = 2\pi\frac{e^2}{\hbar c}|(j|z|0)|^2\left(\frac{\omega_{j0}}{\omega}\right)\frac{2\gamma\omega_{j0}}{(\omega_{j0}-\omega)^2+\gamma^2}\cdot \tag{15–85}$$

Consequently, the cross section at resonance is

$$\sigma = 4\pi\frac{e^2}{\hbar c}|(j|z|0)|^2\frac{\omega_{j0}}{\gamma}\cdot \tag{15–86}$$

Since the matrix element $|(j|z|0)|$ has a magnitude, for a strong transition, of the order of the diameter of the atom, this is of the order of the "area" of the atom increased by the factor $\alpha(\omega_{j0}/\gamma)$.

The matrix element may sometimes be estimated from convenient sum rules:

$$\sum_j \omega_{j0}|(j|z|0)|^2 = \frac{\hbar}{2m}\cdot \tag{15–87}$$

Also,

$$\sum_j |(j|z|0)|^2 = (0|z^2|0) = \langle z^2\rangle_0. \tag{15–88}$$

Equation (15–87) is easily derived by first computing explicitly the commutator of z with the Hamiltonian and then forming the commutator of z with this commutator. This yields

$$2zHz - Hz^2 - z^2H = \frac{\hbar^2}{m}\cdot \tag{15–89}$$

Equation (15–87) then results from taking the matrix element (0, 0) of this equation in a representation with H diagonal.

Equation (15–88) follows simply from an application of the matrix multiplication rule. If 0 refers to the ground state, all the terms of the summation of Eq. (15–87) are positive, and we obtain the inequalities

$$\begin{aligned} \omega_{j0}|(j|z|0)|^2 &\leq \frac{\hbar}{2m}, \\ |(j|z|0)|^2 &\leq \langle z^2\rangle_0. \end{aligned} \tag{15–90}$$

The expression $(2m\omega_{j0}/\hbar)|(j|z|0)|^2$ is called the *oscillator strength* of the transition. The peak cross section is proportional to the oscillator strength. Equation (15–87) states that the sum of all oscillator strengths of transitions to a given level is unity. It is interesting to note that in sodium, the oscillator strength of the two yellow D-lines is 0.976 and the first inequality of Eq. (15-90) is very nearly an equality. For unity oscillator strength, the cross section at resonance can be written as

$$\sigma = 2\pi \frac{e^2}{\gamma mc} \cdot \tag{15-91}$$

This is the radiation absorption cross section of a classical oscillator. This is the origin of the term *oscillator strength.*

Equation (15-91) implies that the cross section is infinite when the time between collisions is infinite. In this situation, however, the strong-field approximation is inadequate and it is necessary to include the effect of spontaneous radiation and the corresponding radiation damping. If such effects are included, it is found that σ at resonance is only of the order of λ^2.

The absorption coefficient for a gas in which the population of state j relative to state 0 is determined by a Boltzmann factor (see Chapter 18)

$$\frac{n_0}{n_j} = \exp\left[\frac{-(E_0 - E_j)}{kT}\right] \tag{15-92}$$

can be written as

$$\Gamma = (n_0 + n_j)\, \frac{1 - \exp(-\hbar\omega_{j0}/kT)}{1 + \exp(-\hbar\omega_{j0}/kT)} \cdot \hbar\omega\sigma, \tag{15-93}$$

where n_0 and n_j represent the number of atoms in states 0 and j in a column of the gas one square centimeter in cross section, and Γ is the absorption coefficient, that is, the fraction of the electromagnetic radiation incident upon the gas which is absorbed by it. Note, from Eq. (15-83), that the maximum absorption occurs at resonance, that is, when the incident frequency is equal to the frequency associated with the energy difference between the two energy states. In this case, we note that the smaller γ,

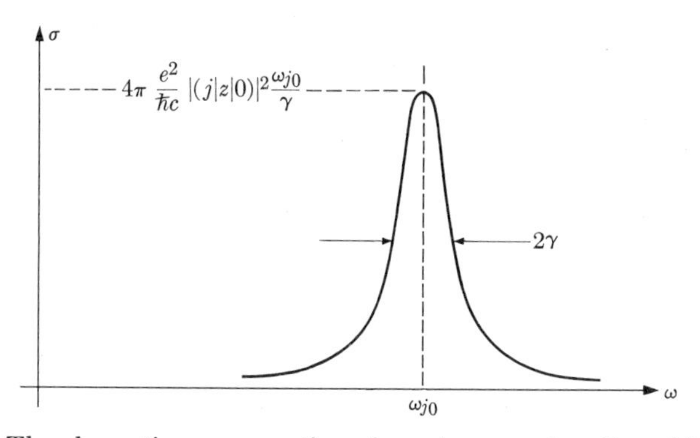

FIG. 15-3. The absorption cross section of an atom as a function of frequency, for the case of collision broadening. This absorption line has a *Lorentz* line shape.

the larger the absorption cross section; consequently, when the gas is at resonance, the less frequent the collisions are, the greater the absorption is. On the other hand, for frequencies that are off resonance by more than γ, the absorption becomes larger with increasing values of γ. The line contour of the absorption is obtained by plotting the absorption cross section as a function of frequency; this is done in Fig. 15–3. The absorption-line contour given by Eq. (15–83) is known as the *Lorentz line shape.*

As indicated above, the absorption has been computed only for the strong-field limit. However, the expressions obtained actually are correct also for weak incident electromagnetic fields, provided that the time between collisions is short compared with the natural time required for an atom to radiate a photon spontaneously in jumping from state j to state 0. If the time is not comparatively short, it is necessary to modify Eq. (15–83) as indicated above by adding to γ^2 another term, γ_r^2, representing the damping resulting from the spontaneous radiation process.

15–7 Selection rules. In the preceding section, it was shown by computation of the transitions which occur from one energy level to another as a result of electromagnetic radiation incident on an atom that the probability that a transition will occur is proportional to the square of the matrix element of the interaction term in the Hamiltonian which couples the two energy states in question. We shall now consider the conditions which must be satisfied for the matrix element in question to be nonzero. These conditions are known as *selection rules.* If the spin-orbit interaction is included as part of the unperturbed Hamiltonian and the radiation interaction term is treated as a perturbing term in the Hamiltonian, the stationary energy states will be characterized by the quantum numbers j, l, m_j, and n. The matrix element determining the transitions from one energy state to another is, in the electric-dipole approximation, of the form $(jlm_jn|\mathbf{P}|j'l'm_j'n')$.

Remember that the momentum operator $\mathbf{P}$ falls in the class of vectors which we have previously designated class $\mathbf{T}$, with respect to the angular-momentum operators $\mathbf{L}$ and $\mathbf{J}$ (see Chapter 9). Thus the commutation relations of Eqs. (9–81) through (9–86) hold. In considering the matrix elements of the vector $\mathbf{P}$, it is useful to represent the three components of this vector in terms of the combinations

$$\begin{aligned} \mathrm{P}_+ &= \mathrm{P}_x + i\mathrm{P}_y, \\ \mathrm{P}_- &= \mathrm{P}_x - i\mathrm{P}_y, \\ \mathrm{P}_z&. \end{aligned} \tag{15–94}$$

Consider now the selection rule satisfied with respect to m_j. From Eq. (9–81), J_z and P_z commute with each other. Consequently, the only nonvanishing matrix elements which can be obtained for P_z are with $\Delta m_j = 0$. To prove this formally, we need only write the commutation relation in matrix form:

$$\mathsf{J}_z\mathsf{P}_z - \mathsf{P}_z\mathsf{J}_z = 0. \qquad (15\text{–}95)$$

The matrix elements of J_z are known, since the representation employed is one for which the functions are eigenfunctions of J_z; they are

$$(jlm_jn|\mathrm{J}_z|j'l'm_j'n') = m_j\hbar\,\delta_{m_jm_j'}\,\delta_{ll'}\,\delta_{jj'}\,\delta_{nn'}. \qquad (15\text{–}96)$$

Computing the matrix elements of the commutator, we obtain from Eq. (15–95),

$$(jlm_jn|[\mathrm{J}_z,\mathrm{P}_z]|j'l'm_j'n') = 0. \qquad (15\text{–}97)$$

By writing out the matrix products occurring here explicitly and making use of Eq. (15–96), we find that

$$(m_j\hbar - m_j'\hbar)(jlm_jn|\mathrm{P}_z|j'l'm_j'n') = 0. \qquad (15\text{–}98)$$

It is clear from this that the matrix elements of P_z vanish if $m_j \neq m_j'$. Thus the selection rule $\Delta m_j = 0$ applies.

In similar fashion, by replacing **T** with **P** in Eq. (9–85), we can obtain

$$(\mathrm{J}_z - \hbar)\mathrm{P}_+ - \mathrm{P}_+\mathrm{J}_z = 0. \qquad (15\text{–}99)$$

Again making use of the matrix elements given by Eq. (15–96), we find that

$$(m_j\hbar - m_j'\hbar - \hbar)(jlm_jn|\mathrm{P}_+|j'l'm_j'n') = 0. \qquad (15\text{–}100)$$

From this, it is clear that the matrix elements of P_+ will vanish unless the change in m_j is such as to increase m_j by one unit:

$$\Delta m_j = m_j - m_j' = 1. \qquad (15\text{–}101)$$

In similar fashion, for P_- the only nonvanishing matrix elements occur for

$$\Delta m_j = -1. \qquad (15\text{–}102)$$

These results can be summarized by saying that

$$(jlm_jn|\mathbf{P}|j'l'm_j'n') = 0 \qquad (15\text{–}103)$$

unless

$$\Delta m_j = 0, \pm 1. \qquad (15\text{–}104)$$

This selection rule has a simple physical interpretation. Consider a quantized radiation field. A circularly polarized photon carries one unit of angular momentum; it thus behaves like a particle of spin one. Consequently, when it is absorbed it can change the z-component of the total angular momentum of the atom, j, by one unit either way or it can leave it unchanged. This assumes that for a dipole transition no orbital angular momentum is transferred.

Consider now a selection rule for j. From Eq. (9–81) one can obtain, after a great deal of laborious algebra,

$$\mathrm{J}^4\mathbf{T} - 2\mathrm{J}^2\mathbf{T}\mathrm{J}^2 + \mathbf{T}\mathrm{J}^4 - 2\hbar^2(\mathrm{J}^2\mathbf{T} + \mathbf{T}\mathrm{J}^2) + 4\hbar^2\mathbf{J}(\mathbf{J}\cdot\mathbf{T}) = 0. \tag{15–105}$$

From Eq. (9–82) it is clear that $\mathbf{J}\cdot\mathbf{T}$ commutes with J^2. Consequently, the only nonvanishing matrix elements of this dot product are for $j = j'$. Because this is also true for $\mathbf{J}$, the term $\mathbf{J}(\mathbf{J}\cdot\mathbf{T})$ in Eq. (15–105) has nonvanishing matrix elements only for $j = j'$. Assuming that $j \neq j'$, we can write the general matrix element of the operator of Eq. (15–105), for $\mathbf{T} \equiv \mathbf{P}$, as

$$\{[j(j+1)]^2 - 2j(j+1)j'(j'+1) + [j'(j'+1)]^2 - 2[j(j+1) + j'(j'+1)]\} \times (jlm_jn|\mathbf{P}|j'l'm_j'n') = 0. \tag{15–106}$$

This can be simplified to

$$[(j + j' + 1)^2 - 1][(j - j')^2 - 1](jlm_jn|\mathbf{P}|j'l'm_j'n') = 0. \tag{15–107}$$

Thus the matrix elements of $\mathbf{P}$ must vanish except for a change in j of ± 1. The case in which $j = j'$ was explicitly excluded in the considerations leading to Eq. (15–107).

From the above discussion, it can be seen that the only nonvanishing matrix elements of $\mathbf{P}$ are those for which j changes by ± 1 or 0:

$$\Delta j = \pm 1, 0. \tag{15–108}$$

This selection rule also has a simple physical interpretation. The photon absorbed or emitted during a transition has many of the properties of a particle of spin one, as seen earlier. There are three ways in which the angular momentum of the photon may add vectorially to the total angular momentum of the atom: it increases the total angular momentum by one unit; it leaves it unchanged; or it decreases it by one unit. These three cases clearly correspond to the selection rules of Eq. (15–108).

There is one further condition to be imposed on the selection rule for j. If we admit for the moment the possibility that the particle spin is integral, so that j is integral, then there is the question of whether a transition can occur between one state of $j = 0$ and another state of $j = 0$. Such a transition is forbidden. The proof of this is the following. The state

$j = 0$ is an eigenfunction of all three components of the vector $\mathbf{J}$. Also, for a total angular momentum $j = 0$, the state is nondegenerate, there being only one "orientation" for such a vector. In such a case, the direction taken for the axis of quantization is arbitrary; there is no change in the wave function for the state $j = 0$ in going from one axis of quantization to another. However, because of the selection rule on Δm_j, we have for the z-axis of quantization

$$(0l0n|\mathrm{P}_{\pm}|0l'0n') = 0. \tag{15–109}$$

This implies that the matrix elements of P_x and P_y vanish. Because of the arbitrariness of the direction of quantization, the matrix element of P_z must also vanish. Therefore, the matrix elements of all three components of P vanish for a transition $j = 0$ to $j = 0$.

Since the commutation relations of Chapter 9 hold for $\mathbf{L}$ as well as for $\mathbf{J}$, it follows that we have the same selection rules on l; namely, the only allowed changes in l are

$$\Delta l = \pm 1, 0, \tag{15–110}$$

with $l = 0$ to $l = 0$ forbidden. These conditions are actually not restrictive enough, in that *any* transition for which $\Delta l = 0$ is forbidden. To see this, note that the operator $\mathbf{P}$ is an odd operator: it changes sign with a change in sign of the three coordinates of the particle. Consequently, the matrix elements of P joining states of the same l must be zero because an eigenfunction of $\mathbf{L}$ is an even or odd function, depending on whether l is even or odd. This rules out the possibility of a transition for which l does not change. Hence, the selection rule on l is that

$$\Delta l = \pm 1. \tag{15–111}$$

It is also clear from the above that the parity of the wave function must change during a transition.

The above selection rules are for electric-dipole transitions. These occur when the leading term in the interaction of Eq. (15–68) can be written in the form of Eq. (15–72). In the event that the selection rules given above indicate that transitions between two levels are forbidden, it may be that higher-order terms in the expansion of Eq. (15–69) give nonvanishing matrix elements. In such a case, the transition is said to be of a *higher multipole order* (e.g., an electric-quadrupole transition) and, although *first-order forbidden,* it is not *strictly forbidden,* that is, forbidden to all orders of approximation. Transitions from $j = 0$ to $j = 0$ are strictly forbidden in all orders ($I = 0$). This is because of the angular momentum of a photon or, equivalently, because an S-wave does not exist for electromagnetic waves.

15–8 Summary. This chapter has dealt with the interaction of particles with a strong electromagnetic field, one of such amplitude that it can be treated classically without appreciable error. The Hamiltonian of a particle in a strong field was presented in terms of the classical vector and scalar field potentials, $\boldsymbol{A}$ and ϕ. Several important illustrative examples were then worked out. The first of these, the case of an electron in a uniform magnetic field, was shown to have a close formal analogue in the two-dimensional simple harmonic oscillator.

The Zeeman effect was next considered for fields in which the magnetic interaction was weak compared with the fine-structure splitting. The gyromagnetic ratio or g-factor was defined and discussed in terms of a vector model. The strong-field Zeeman effect was also treated, using perturbation methods.

Finally, the extremely important case of resonant transitions between two atomic energy states induced by an applied electromagnetic field was treated in the dipole approximation. The absorption cross section and absorption coefficient were defined and expressions for them were derived. Selection rules for electric-dipole transitions indicating which atomic states can be coupled by radiatively induced transitions were derived and discussed. Higher-order multipole transitions were briefly mentioned.

Problems

15–1. The ground state of positronium, the hydrogenlike system composed of a positron and an electron bound together by their coulomb interaction, consists of one singlet and three triplet substates. The singlet level is the most stable and lies 8×10^{-4} ev below the triplet levels, which are degenerate in zero field. Calculate the effects of a magnetic field on this system. (A positron has a charge and a magnetic moment equal in magnitude but opposite in sign to those of an electron.)

15–2. An electron moves in a central electrostatic field. Each negative energy state is characterized by a definite value of the orbital angular momentum. The degeneracy of each level is $2(2l + 1)$. Show that the inclusion of the spin-orbit interaction and an interaction with an external uniform magnetic field completely removes the degeneracy but does not change the "center of gravity" of each unperturbed energy level.

15–3. An atom with no permanent magnetic moment is said to be *diamagnetic*. Neglect the spin of the electron and proton, and show how to calculate the induced diamagnetic moment for a hydrogen atom in its ground state when a weak magnetic field is applied.

15–4. (a) Show that the dielectric constant of HCl gas depends only upon the population of the ground rotational level. (b) Assuming that the molecules consist of two ions (H^+ and Cl^-) a fixed distance d apart, with each ion carrying one electric charge, calculate the temperature dependence of the dielectric constant. (c) Assume a reasonable value for d and compute the dielectric constant. (d) Compare this result with the experimental value.

15–5. A radiofrequency field acts upon HCl gas. (a) Assuming that the frequency is in the neighborhood of the resonant frequency for transitions between the ground and first excited rotational states, calculate the rate at which the gas absorbs the radio energy. Make the following assumptions: (1) the HCl molecule consists of two ions held a fixed distance d apart; each ion carries one electric charge; (2) a collision between two molecules establishes thermal equilibrium; the cross section for a collision is σ. (b) Show how the absorption varies with frequency, pressure, and temperature.

15–6. Describe the Zeeman effect in atomic hydrogen.

15–7. If the nucleus of an atom possesses a spin $\mathbf{I}$ and associated magnetic moment $\boldsymbol{\mu}$, the interaction of this moment with the magnetic moment associated with the electronic angular momentum $\mathbf{J}$ can split the levels into various sublevels corresponding to different total angular-momentum $\mathbf{F} = \mathbf{J} + \mathbf{I}$ states. Such splittings, which are generally very small, are known as *hyperfine splittings*. The proton in a hydrogen atom has $I = \frac{1}{2}$, leading to a ground state composed of two levels, corresponding to $F = 1$ and $F = 0$. The hyperfine separation of the ground state of hydrogen is 1420 Mc/sec. (a) Calculate the probability that a transition will be induced from one hyperfine energy level to another by a radiofrequency magnetic pulse. (b) Show that if the magnetic field vector is polarized parallel to the axis of quantization, the only transition which can occur is from $m_F = 0$ to $m_F = 0$. (c) Show that if the radiofrequency pulse is followed $(n/2.84) \times 10^{-9}$ sec later (n is an odd integer) by an identical pulse, no first-order transitions can occur.

15–8. (a) Calculate an approximate value for the dielectric constant of helium at normal temperature and pressure. (b) Compare the result with the experimental value. [*Hint:* Use the sum rule of Eq. (15–87).]

15–9. (a) Make use of ladder operators such as were developed in Chapter 6 (Eq. 6–74) to obtain operators which will generate the wave functions of Eq. (15–20). (b) In this connection, show that the operator

$$\mathrm{R}^2 \equiv \mathrm{R}_{x+}^2 + \mathrm{R}_{y+}^2$$

increases the quantum number n by two units and leaves m_l unchanged. Here the operator

$$\mathrm{R}_{x+} = \frac{1}{\sqrt{2m}}\,\mathrm{P}_x + i\sqrt{\frac{k}{2}}\,x, \qquad \text{etc.}$$

(c) Also show that the operators $(\mathrm{R}_{x+} \pm i\mathrm{R}_{y+})$ increase n by one unit and increase or decrease m_l by one unit. (d) Write an explicit operator generator of the function $\psi_{nm_lp_z}$, assuming that the operator acts on the function ψ_{00p_z}.

15–10. Show that the functions of Eqs. (15–51) and (15–52) are orthogonal to each other.

15–11. From Sections 10–2, 12–2, and 15–2, the wave functions for stationary states of the hydrogen atom can be written as

$$\psi_{n,l,j=l\pm 1/2,m_j} = \frac{1}{\sqrt{2l+1}}\begin{bmatrix} \sqrt{l+\frac{1}{2}\pm m_j}\; Y_{l,m_j-1/2} \\ \pm\sqrt{l+\frac{1}{2}\mp m_j}\; Y_{l,m_j+1/2} \end{bmatrix} R_{nl}.$$

This includes the spin-orbit interaction, treated in lowest approximation (see Section 14–2). Use Eq. (14–51) to compute the fine-structure splitting in the $2P$-state.

CHAPTER 16

SCATTERING

16–1 Physical concepts. A simple one-dimensional scattering problem has already been considered in Chapter 3, where the case of a (quantum-mechanical) wave incident on a rectangular potential barrier was treated. The general subject of the scattering, or deflection, of one or more particles by an interaction with a scattering center is extremely important in modern physics. Perhaps the most striking examples are in nuclear physics, where the scattering of beams of particles such as protons, electrons, or mesons by various target particles provides much of the basic data of nuclear physics. In the case of nuclear forces, the form of the interaction between the particles is not known, and the experimental scattering data are used to derive information about which forms of the force law are possible, i.e., are consistent with the data, and which are not.

The concept of *scattering cross section* is very useful in dealing with the interaction of a beam of particles with a scattering center. When a beam with a particle flux of N particles/cm^2/sec is incident on a scattering center, particles can usually be found leaving the center in all directions. Let dN be the flux of particles scattered into an element of solid angle $d\omega$ about the direction described by the polar angles θ and ϕ. We expect dN to be proportional to the incident flux N and the size of the solid angle $d\omega$:

$$dN = \sigma(\theta, \phi)N\, d\omega. \tag{16–1}$$

Here the proportionality constant, which is in general a function of the angles θ and ϕ, is designated by $\sigma(\theta, \phi)$. Consideration of this equation shows that $\sigma(\theta, \phi)$ has the dimensions of an area. Since the distribution of particles over a plane perpendicular to the beam is assumed uniform, it is clear that a consistant interpretation is that $\sigma(\theta, \phi)$ is the area of the cross section of the incident beam through which pass all particles that are scattered into $d\omega$ about θ and ϕ. For this reason, the proportionality constant is known as the *differential scattering cross section* of the beam. If Eq. (16–1) is integrated over all solid angles to give the total flux of particles scattered by the center, the result defines the *total scattering cross section*, σ_t:

$$\begin{aligned} N_{\text{scat}} &= \int dN = \int \sigma(\theta, \phi)N\, d\omega \\ &= N\int \sigma(\theta, \phi)\, d\omega \\ &= N\sigma_t. \end{aligned} \tag{16–2}$$

In some cases, one deals with a situation in which the target, as well as scattering the incident beam, absorbs particles from it. It is clear that a *total absorption cross section* can be defined in analogous fashion. The concept of cross section can be further generalized in an obvious way to include particle and photon production, target transmutation, etc.

In the above discussion, the target is assumed to consist of a fixed scattering center, and the angles θ and ϕ, used to characterize the scattering, are given in relation to a system of spherical coordinates whose origin is at the scattering center. In practice, however, scattering centers are never absolutely fixed, but recoil under the forces of the interaction causing the scattering; the recoiling scattering center absorbs some energy (and momentum) from the incident particle, the exact amount depending on the scattering angle and the relative masses of incident and target particles. In this more realistic situation, there are two coordinate systems in relation to which the scattering can be described and which are of practical significance.

One, known as the *laboratory system*, is fixed in space, with the target particles (before recoil) at rest. This is the system to which all angles actually measured in the laboratory in performing an experiment are referred.

In analyzing scattering measurements in terms of an interaction potential between beam and target particles, however, the *center-of-mass system* is more convenient. As the name implies, in this system the center of mass of the "incident particle-target particle" system is stationary. In the center-of-mass system, the scattering can be described as taking place from a fixed scattering center (the center of mass), with the two particles (incident and target) remaining collinear with this center and both moving either toward or away from the center with equal momenta.

The collinearity arises because of momentum conservation, and the azimuthal angle ϕ must be the same for both systems. However, the angles θ which measure the change in direction between the initial (before scattering) and final (after scattering) momenta of the incident particles differ in the two systems. A straightforward geometrical argument (see Fig. 16-1) shows that the relation between the two angles is given by

$$\tan \theta_{\text{lab}} = \frac{\sin \theta_{\text{c.m.}}}{\cos \theta_{\text{c.m.}} + m_1/m_2}, \tag{16-3}$$

where m_1 is the mass of the incident particle and m_2 that of the target. It is clear that when $m_2 \gg m_1$, the conversion from laboratory-measured angles to the physically more significant center-of-mass angles produces but small changes in angle.

Equation (16-3) is based on the classical picture of particle trajectories. However, the relationship between the two systems of reference is deter-

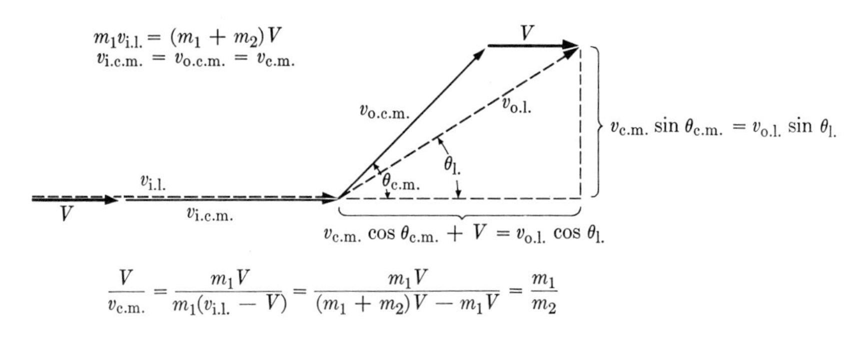

FIG. 16–1. The relation between scattering angle in the laboratory system and in the center-of-mass system. Subscripts i., o., l., and c.m. refer respectively to *incident* and *outgoing* particles, and to the *laboratory* and *center-of-mass* systems. V is the velocity of the center of mass.

mined solely by the two fundamental principles of conservation of energy and conservation of momentum, and because these hold equally in quantum and classical theory, Eq. (16–3) is equally applicable to quantum and classical scattering problems.

As seen earlier, a beam of monoenergetic particles can be described quantum-mechanically by means of a plane wave. Such a plane wave is of infinite extent in space, whereas the beam actually used in any scattering experiment is of necessity limited in extent in the transverse direction and hence, from the uncertainty relation, cannot be composed of free particles whose momenta and energy are precisely known. This does not destroy the usefulness of the description of a monoenergetic beam by a plane wave, however, for with beams of macroscopic cross section, the uncertainty in the momentum is negligible.

In the quantum-mechanical description of scattering, the total wave function describing the "trajectory" of a particle can be separated into two parts, one representing the incoming particle and one the particle after scattering. As noted above, the incident part can be taken to be a plane wave. The total wave function can then be written as

$$\psi = \exp(i\boldsymbol{k} \cdot \boldsymbol{r}) + v, \tag{16–4}$$

where v represents the scattered wave (particle). Let the origin of the coordinate system be at the scattering center. The center of mass is the appropriate origin for nonfixed scattering centers. Far from the scatterer, the scattered wave must represent a flux of particles moving radially outward. The scattered wave v must therefore have the asymptotic form

$$v \xrightarrow[r\to\infty]{} f(\theta, \phi) \frac{\exp(ikr)}{r}, \tag{16–5}$$

where $f(\theta, \phi)$ specifies the angular dependence of the scattered wave. From its form, it is clear that v represents an outgoing wave. It is easily verified that, asymptotically, Eq. (16–5) obeys the Schrödinger equation for a free particle. The particle flux $\boldsymbol{S}$ in the scattered wave can be computed from

$$\boldsymbol{S} = -\frac{i\hbar}{2m}[\bar{v}\boldsymbol{\nabla}v - (\boldsymbol{\nabla}\bar{v})v]. \tag{16–6}$$

This is

$$\boldsymbol{S} = \frac{\hbar k}{m}\frac{|f(\theta, \phi)|^2}{r^2}\,\boldsymbol{r}_0 - \frac{i\hbar}{mr^3}\,\mathrm{Im}\left[\bar{f}(\theta, \phi)\frac{\partial f}{\partial\theta}\right]\boldsymbol{\theta}_0 - \frac{i\hbar}{mr^3\sin\theta}\,\mathrm{Im}\left[\bar{f}(\theta, \phi)\frac{\partial f}{\partial\phi}\right]\boldsymbol{\phi}_0, \tag{16–7}$$

where $\boldsymbol{r}_0$, $\boldsymbol{\theta}_0$, and $\boldsymbol{\phi}_0$ are respectively unit vectors in the direction of increasing r, θ, and ϕ. At the very large r's for which Eq. (16–5) is valid, only the radial component is important. This is

$$S_r = \frac{\hbar k}{m}\frac{|f|^2}{r^2} = \frac{v|f|^2}{r^2}. \tag{16–8}$$

(In this expression, v represents the classical particle velocity and not the scattered wave.) Note that this is numerically the probability density times the velocity; for the unit incident flux implicit in Eq. (16–4), this is the particle density times the velocity. The particles can all be considered to be moving outward. The function $f(\theta, \phi)$ can be related to the differential cross section $\sigma(\theta, \phi)$ for the scattering center by comparing Eqs. (16–1) and (16–8). From Eq. (16–1), the radial flux outward into a solid angle element $d\omega$ is $N\sigma\, d\omega$, where N is the incident flux. This can be converted to the outward flux per unit area at a radius r from the scattering center by

$$d\omega = \frac{dA}{r^2}. \tag{16–9}$$

The outward flux at angles θ and ϕ per unit area, S_{scat}, is thus

$$S_{\mathrm{scat}} = \frac{N\sigma}{r^2}. \tag{16–10}$$

The incident flux N is obtained by applying Eq. (16–6) to $\exp(ikz)$, the incident part of Eq. (16–4). This yields

$$N = S_{\mathrm{inc}} = \frac{\hbar k}{m} = v. \tag{16–11}$$

Therefore

$$S_{\text{scat}} = \frac{v\sigma}{r^2} = \frac{v|f|^2}{r^2} \tag{16–12}$$

and

$$\sigma(\theta, \phi) = |f(\theta, \phi)|^2. \tag{16–13}$$

Note that in computing the probability density fluxes, we took the two parts of Eq. (16–4) separately, thus ignoring the interference terms between exp (ikz) and v which would arise if Eq. (16–4) itself were used in computing the flux $\mathbf{S}$. That this is the correct procedure can be seen as follows. The incident beam of particles is represented by the term exp (ikz), corresponding to a beam infinite in extent in the direction transverse to its direction of propagation. This is physically impossible, and in fact in the laboratory one deals with beams confined to a sharply defined region of space. The interference terms between exp (ikz) and v represent a situation in which both incident and scattered beams are present at the particle detector. The incident beam is absent, however, at the place (far from the target) at which the scattered beam is usually experimentally detected. The interference terms apply only to regions in which the incident and scattered waves overlap, and the most important effect of such interference is the loss, by scattering, of particles from the original beam. If the measurement were made in a region where both incident and scattered particles were present, it would be necessary to use some momentum-selection device to admit only scattered particles, and again the interference effect would disappear.

In the above discussion, the nonradial terms in Eq. (16–7) have been ignored because they decrease more rapidly with increasing r than the radial term does. They have an important physical interpretation, however. As will be seen in detail shortly, an incident plane wave contains components corresponding to nonzero angular momentum about the scattering center. Classically, these correspond to the nonzero *impact parameters* of particles making up the parts of the incoming beam not directed exactly at the scatterer. The $1/r^3$ radial dependence of the nonradial scattered wave flux is essential to preserve angular momentum. Since S can be interpreted as the density of particles times their velocity, rS can be interpreted as the angular-momentum density. From Eq. (16–7), this angular-momentum density has a radial dependence of $1/r^2$, just as has the radial particle-flux component, leading to conservation of the angular momentum of the particles as they move outward from the center after scattering.

An interesting aspect of scattering can be seen by considering the scattering of particles by a large obstacle when the energy of the incoming particles is high enough for the de Broglie wavelength of the beam particles to be small compared with the dimensions of the obstacle. By analogy with the classical case of light scattered from a large opaque object, it is clear that there will exist a "shadow" region behind the scatterer, in which no particles will be found. Therefore in the wave-function description of the scattering process (Eq. 16–4), the scattered wave must be such as to cancel the incident wave exp $(i\boldsymbol{k} \cdot \boldsymbol{r})$ in this shadow region. In other words, in the region behind the scatterer, the scattered wave must be equal in amplitude, and hence in flux, (though opposite in phase) to the incident wave, *even though no particles are to be found in this region.* This paradoxical situation leads to a phenomenon known as *shadow scattering.*

Since it exists only over the cross section of the scatterer, the forward-scattered wave is diffracted. Because it is diffracted, this shadow-scattered wave represents scattered particles. The shadow-scattered wave is diffracted only through very small angles if the scatterer is large, but the

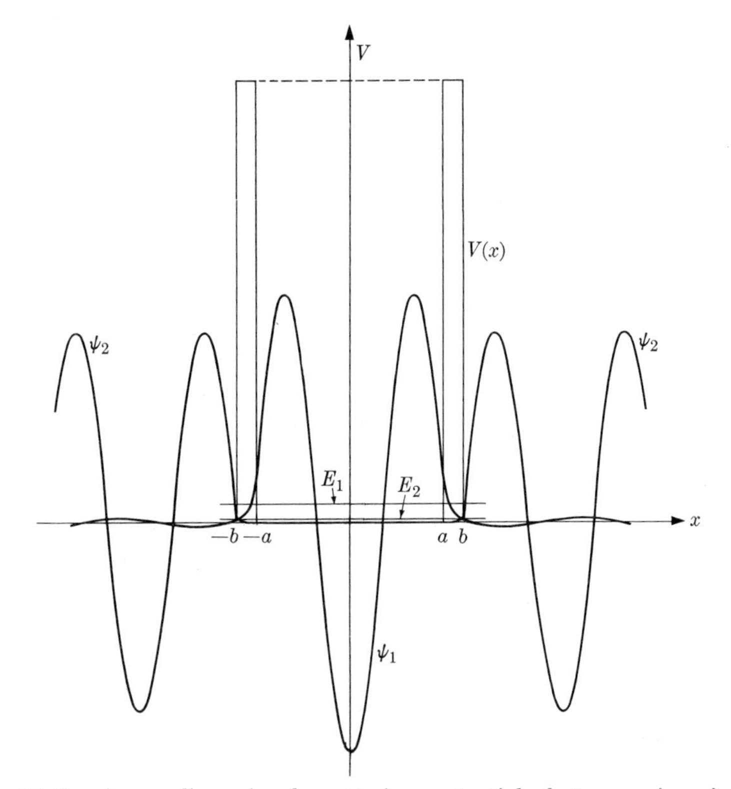

FIG. 16–2. A one-dimensional scattering potential that can give rise to "virtual states" when (quasi-) standing waves are set up between the two potential hills in the region $-a \leq x \leq +a$. ψ_1 is a wave function corresponding to a virtual energy state, while ψ_2 is a typical wave function for an energy "off resonance."

cross section for the scattering is equal to the projected area of the scatterer. In addition to the forward shadow-scattered particles, all particles striking the front surface of the scatterer are also scattered (assuming no absorption of particles). The total scattering cross section of the obstacle is hence twice its projected area.

The concept of a *virtual energy level* or *virtual state* is also of value in discussing certain scattering situations. Consider the one-dimensional situation illustrated in Fig. 16–2. As was seen in Chapter 3, solutions of the Schrödinger equation can be found for such a potential for all positive values E of the energy. However, if the potential barriers between $x = \pm a$ and $x = \pm b$ are relatively impenetrable, that is, if

$$(V - E)^{1/2}(b - a) \gg 1, \tag{16–14}$$

then for certain values of the energy the probability amplitude $|\psi|^2$ will, within the barriers ($-a \leq x \leq a$), assume values that are large compared with those outside $|x| > |b|$. A detailed calculation shows that these values of E are just those for which bound states would exist in the inner region if the barriers were indeed impenetrable. Such states are known as *virtual energy states.* They are important in scattering problems, for when the energy of the incoming particles corresponds to such a state, a *resonant* condition is said to occur, in which the scattering cross section is markedly greater than for nonresonant energies. Such virtual states are not infinitely sharp, but correspond to a range of particle energies, the breadth of the resonance increasing as the transmission through the barriers is increased. In certain three-dimensional cases where the potential $V(r)$ is everywhere less than zero, $V(r) < 0$, virtual states can occur for positive energies for particles approaching the scattering center with nonzero angular momentum; in such a case the "centrifugal potential" (see Chapter 10) may provide the necessary potential barrier.

16–2 The Born approximation. An important class of scattering centers can be categorized by having a potential that is localized and weak: localized in that no appreciable scattering occurs far from the center of the scatterer, and weak in that the scattered wave is much weaker than the incident wave. This latter condition can be expressed with reference to Eq. (16–4) by the condition that

$$|\exp(ikz)| = 1 \gg |v|. \tag{16–15}$$

If Eq. (16–4) is substituted into the Schrödinger equation

$$-\frac{\hbar^2}{2m}\nabla^2\psi + V\psi = E\psi, \tag{16–16}$$

the result is

$$-\nabla^2 v - k^2 v = -U \exp(ikz) - Uv, \tag{16–17}$$

where

$$U \equiv \frac{2m}{\hbar^2} V. \tag{16–18}$$

The Born approximation consists of using the condition of Eq. (16–15) to approximate Eq. (16–17) by

$$\nabla^2 v + k^2 v = U \exp(ikz). \tag{16–19}$$

Physically, this is equivalent to saying that scattering occurs as if each part of the scattering potential had a wave of full strength $\exp(ikz)$ incident on it. This, of course, corresponds to the assumption that the scattering potential is weak. Equation (16–19) can be solved by using a Green's function w which is a solution to the equation

$$\nabla^2 w + k^2 w = -4\pi\,\delta(\mathbf{r} - \mathbf{r}'). \tag{16–20}$$

(In all the following development, the δ-function is to be considered as a nonsingular function sharply peaked at $\mathbf{r} = \mathbf{r}'$. The passage to the singular limit will be taken at a later appropriate stage, when the function appears under a suitable integral.) In a suitable limit, the solution to Eq. (16–20) can be written as

$$w = \frac{\exp(ik|\mathbf{r} - \mathbf{r}'|)}{|\mathbf{r} - \mathbf{r}'|}. \tag{16–21}$$

With this Green's function, the solution to Eq. (16–19) can be written as

$$v(\mathbf{r}) = -\frac{1}{4\pi}\int \frac{\exp(ik|\mathbf{r} - \mathbf{r}'|)}{|\mathbf{r} - \mathbf{r}'|}\, U(\mathbf{r}') \exp(ikz')\, d\mathbf{r}', \tag{16–22}$$

as can be seen from the following.

Multiply Eq. (16–20) by v, multiply Eq. (16–19) by w, and subtract:

$$(v\nabla^2 w - w\nabla^2 v) = -4\pi\,\delta(\mathbf{r} - \mathbf{r}')v - wU \exp(ikz). \tag{16–23}$$

Integrating this over all space and applying Green's theorem,* we find

* H. Margenau and G. M. Murphy, *Mathematics of Physics and Chemistry*, D. Van Nostrand Co., Inc., New York, 1949, p. 156. P. M. Morse and H. Feshbach, *Methods of Theoretical Physics, Part I*, McGraw-Hill Book Co., Inc., New York, 1953, pp. 803 ff.

$$\int_{\text{all space}} (v\nabla^2 w - w\nabla^2 v)\,d\mathbf{r} = \int_{\substack{\text{sphere at}\\ R=\infty}} (v\boldsymbol{\nabla} w - w\boldsymbol{\nabla} v)\cdot d\mathbf{S}$$

$$= -4\pi v(\mathbf{r}') - \int_{\text{all space}} wU \exp(ikz)\,d\mathbf{r}. \tag{16–24}$$

The surface integral at infinity can be evaluated by using the appropriate asymptotic expressions for the integrand. For $r \to \infty$, the following asymptotic relations are valid (see Fig. 16–3):

$$\begin{aligned}
v &\xrightarrow[r\to\infty]{} \frac{\exp(ikr)}{r} f(\theta, \phi),\\
|\mathbf{r} - \mathbf{r}'| &\xrightarrow[r\to\infty]{} r - r'\cos\alpha,\\
\frac{1}{|\mathbf{r} - \mathbf{r}'|} &\xrightarrow[r\to\infty]{} \frac{1}{r} + \frac{r'\cos\alpha}{r^2},\\
w &\xrightarrow[r\to\infty]{} \exp(-ikr'\cos\alpha)\frac{\exp(ikr)}{r}\left(1 + \frac{r'\cos\alpha}{r}\right),\\
\boldsymbol{\nabla} w &\xrightarrow[r\to\infty]{} \left(ik - \frac{1}{r} - \frac{r'\cos\alpha}{r^2}\right) w\mathbf{r}_0,\\
\boldsymbol{\nabla} v &\xrightarrow[r\to\infty]{} \left(ik - \frac{1}{r}\right) v\mathbf{r}_0 + \frac{\exp(ikr)}{r^2}\left(\frac{\partial f}{\partial\theta}\boldsymbol{\theta}_0 + \frac{1}{\sin\theta}\frac{\partial f}{\partial\phi}\boldsymbol{\phi}_0\right),
\end{aligned} \tag{16–25}$$

where $\mathbf{r}_0$, $\boldsymbol{\theta}_0$, and $\boldsymbol{\phi}_0$ are orthogonal unit vectors. From these relations it is readily seen that

$$(v\boldsymbol{\nabla} w - w\boldsymbol{\nabla} v) \xrightarrow[r\to\infty]{} -\frac{\exp(2ikr)\exp(-ikr'\cos\alpha)}{r^3}\left(\frac{\partial f}{\partial\theta}\boldsymbol{\theta}_0 + \frac{1}{\sin\theta}\frac{\partial f}{\partial\phi}\boldsymbol{\phi}_0\right) \tag{16–26}$$

and

$$\int (v\boldsymbol{\nabla} w - w\boldsymbol{\nabla} v)\cdot d\mathbf{S} \xrightarrow[r\to\infty]{} 0. \tag{16–27}$$

Equation (16–24) is thus seen to be equivalent to Eq. (16–22). Equation (16–22) can be put into a different form by the further use of the approximations of Eq. (16–25):

$$\begin{aligned}
v &\xrightarrow[r\to\infty]{} -\frac{1}{4\pi}\int \frac{U(\mathbf{r}')\exp(ikz')\exp[ik(r - r'\cos\alpha)]}{r}\,d\mathbf{r}'\\
&\longrightarrow -\frac{\exp(ikr)}{4\pi r}\int \exp[ik(z' - r'\cos\alpha)]U(\mathbf{r}')\,d\mathbf{r}'.
\end{aligned} \tag{16–28}$$

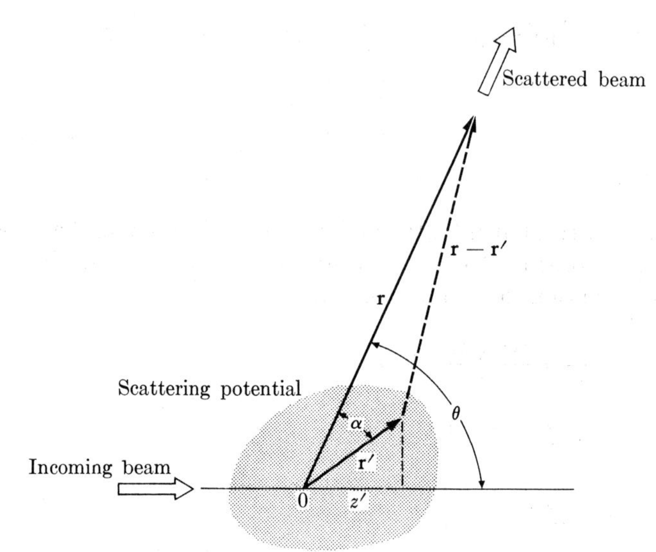

FIG. 16–3. The geometric relations between the vectors $\boldsymbol{r}$ and $\boldsymbol{r}'$ used in computing the scattering of particles in the *Born approximation.* Here $\boldsymbol{r}$ is the vector from the center of the coordinate system, taken at the center of the scatterer, to the point at which the scattered wave is being computed; $\boldsymbol{r}'$ is the position vector of a point in the scattering potential; and α is the angle between $\boldsymbol{r}$ and $\boldsymbol{r}'$.

Denoting the wave vector of the incoming beam by $\boldsymbol{k}_0$ and that of the scattered beam by $\boldsymbol{k}$, we have

$$kz' = \boldsymbol{k}_0 \cdot \boldsymbol{r}', \qquad kr' \cos \alpha = \boldsymbol{k} \cdot \boldsymbol{r}'. \tag{16–29}$$

Therefore

$$v \xrightarrow[r\to\infty]{} -\frac{\exp(ikr)}{4\pi r} \int \exp[i(\boldsymbol{k}_0 - \boldsymbol{k}) \cdot \boldsymbol{r}']U(\boldsymbol{r}')\, d\boldsymbol{r}'. \tag{16–30}$$

Define the vector $\boldsymbol{K}$ by

$$\boldsymbol{K} \equiv \boldsymbol{k}_0 - \boldsymbol{k}. \tag{16–31}$$

It thus represents the change in the wave vector of the incident particle caused by the scattering. Then

$$v \xrightarrow[r\to\infty]{} -\frac{\exp(ikr)}{4\pi r} \int \exp(i\boldsymbol{K} \cdot \boldsymbol{r}')U(\boldsymbol{r}')\, d\boldsymbol{r}'. \tag{16–32}$$

The scattering is thus determined by the Fourier transform of the scattering potential, taken with respect to the change in wave vector $\boldsymbol{K}$. By

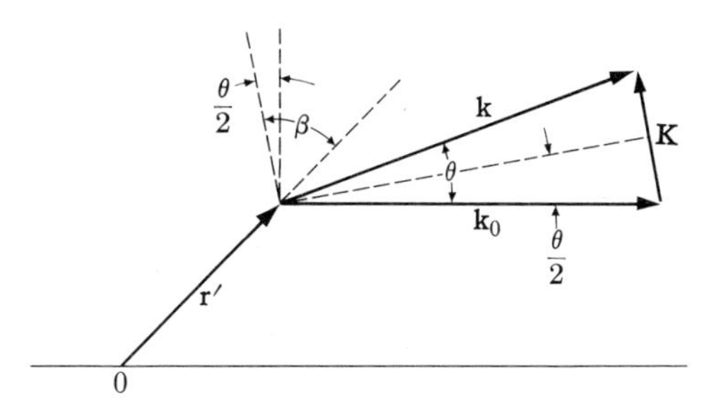

FIG. 16–4. Geometrical relations used in computing the scattering from a (shallow) spherical potential in the Born approximation. θ is the angle of scattering, and β is the angle between the vector change of momentum $\boldsymbol{K}$ and the position vector $\boldsymbol{r}'$.

comparing this equation with Eq. (16–5), we see that

$$f(\theta, \phi) = -\frac{1}{4\pi}\int \exp\,(i\boldsymbol{K}\cdot\boldsymbol{r}')U(\boldsymbol{r}')\,d\boldsymbol{r}'. \tag{16–33}$$

The corresponding differential scattering cross section is

$$\sigma(\theta, \phi) = \frac{1}{(4\pi)^2}\left|\int \exp\,(i\boldsymbol{K}\cdot\boldsymbol{r}')U(\boldsymbol{r}')\,d\boldsymbol{r}'\right|^2. \tag{16–34}$$

As an illustration of the application of this formula, consider the scattering of high-energy particles by the (shallow) spherical potential

$$\begin{aligned} V &= V_0, \qquad r \le a, \\ &= 0, \qquad r > a. \end{aligned} \tag{16–35}$$

It can be seen by reference to Fig. 16–4 that the integral in Eq. (16–34) can be written in the form

$$\int = \int_{r'=0}^{a}\int_{\beta=0}^{2\pi} \exp\left(2ik_0 \sin\frac{\theta}{2}\, r' \cos\beta\right)\frac{2m}{\hbar^2}\, V_0\cdot 2\pi r'^2\, dr' \sin\beta\, d\beta. \tag{16–36}$$

This is readily evaluated:

$$\int = \frac{\pi m V_0}{\hbar^2 k_0^3 \sin^3(\theta/2)}\left[\sin\left(2k_0 a \sin\frac{\theta}{2}\right) - 2k_0 a \sin\frac{\theta}{2}\cos\left(2k_0 a \sin\frac{\theta}{2}\right)\right]. \tag{16–37}$$

For small scattering angles, this approaches

$$\int \xrightarrow[\theta\to 0]{} \frac{8\pi m V_0 a^3}{3\hbar^2}, \tag{16–38}$$

while the differential cross section approaches

$$\sigma(\theta) \xrightarrow[\theta\to 0]{} \frac{4m^2 V_0^2 a^6}{9\hbar^4}. \tag{16–39}$$

Thus the small-angle scattering increases much faster than the geometrical cross section as the scatterer radius is increased.

If $k_0 a \gg 1$, then for all angles such that $k_0 a\theta \gg 1$, the second term in the brackets of Eq. (16–37) dominates the scattering, and

$$\int \approx -\frac{2\pi m V_0 a}{\hbar^2 k_0^2 \sin^2(\theta/2)} \cos\left(2k_0 a \sin\frac{\theta}{2}\right). \tag{16–40}$$

This corresponds to a differential cross section of

$$\sigma(\theta) = \frac{m^2 V_0^2 a^2}{4\hbar^4 k_0^4 \sin^4(\theta/2)} \cos^2\left(2k_0 a \sin\frac{\theta}{2}\right). \tag{16–41}$$

The cross section is thus a rapidly fluctuating function of θ. Averaging over these rapid fluctuations gives

$$\overline{\sigma(\theta)} = \frac{m^2 V_0^2 a^2}{8\hbar^4 k_0^4 \sin^4(\theta/2)}. \tag{16–42}$$

Comparing this with the expression for Rutherford scattering of a charged particle by a coulombic field,*

$$\sigma(\theta) = \frac{m^2 (ZZ'e^2)^2}{4\hbar^4 k_0^4 \sin^4(\theta/2)}, \tag{16–43}$$

we see that there is a striking resemblance in the (averaged) angular dependence of the scattering. Indeed, the two cross sections are identical if the height of the spherical potential V_0 is chosen equal to the coulombic energy of the incident particle in Rutherford scattering when the incident particle is a distance a (the spherical potential radius) away from its scatterer.

---

* H. Goldstein, *Classical Mechanics*, Addison-Wesley Publishing Co., Inc., Reading, Mass., 1950, Chapter 3.

16–3 Partial waves. Another treatment of scattering problems is particularly useful when the scattering potential is spherically symmetric and localized. This is known as the method of *partial waves* because it employs a decomposition of the wave function into spherical waves.

Before considering the method of partial waves for the treatment of scattering problems, the spherical-wave representation of the wave function of a free particle will be considered. This has already been discussed briefly in Section 10–4. The Hamiltonian of a free particle is

$$\mathrm{H} = \frac{1}{2m}\,\mathrm{P}^2 = -\frac{\hbar^2}{2m}\,\nabla^2. \tag{16–44}$$

As was discussed in Chapter 9, this H commutes with the angular momentum operator **L** and consequently also with L^2. The three operators H, L_z, and L^2 are a mutually commuting set, and wave functions can be chosen which are simultaneously eigenfunctions of these three operators. Such wave functions can be written as

$$\psi_{klm}(r, \theta, \phi) = R_{kl}(r)\,Y_{lm}(\theta, \phi). \tag{16–45}$$

The energy of the particle is

$$E_k = \frac{\hbar^2 k^2}{2m}, \tag{16–46}$$

and $Y_{lm}(\theta, \phi)$ is, as usual, a spherical harmonic. As in Eq. (10–4), the radial function $R_{kl}(r)$ satisfies the equation

$$\frac{1}{2m}\,\mathrm{P}_r^2 R + \frac{l(l+1)^2}{2mr^2}\,R = E_k R, \tag{16–47}$$

with

$$\mathrm{P}_r = -i\hbar\,\frac{1}{r}\,\frac{\partial}{\partial r}\cdot r. \tag{16–48}$$

For $l = 0$, the solution is

$$R_{k0} = \begin{cases} \dfrac{\sin kr}{kr}, \\[2ex] \dfrac{\cos kr}{kr}. \end{cases} \tag{16–49}$$

The cosine form of solution must be excluded for a free particle because it is singular at the origin.

The solutions of Eq. (16–49) are sometimes defined as *zeroth-order spherical Bessel* and *Neumann functions*:

$$j_0(kr) \equiv \frac{\sin kr}{kr},$$
$$n_0(kr) \equiv -\frac{\cos kr}{kr}. \tag{16–50}$$

The radial function j_0 satisfies a delta-function normalization relation:

$$\int_0^\infty j_0(kr)j_0(k'r)r^2\,dr = \frac{\pi}{2k^2}\,\delta(k-k'). \tag{16–51}$$

It may also be normalized in terms of a particle flux:

$$j_0 = \frac{\exp(ikr)}{2ikr} - \frac{\exp(-ikr)}{2ikr} = \frac{1}{2}\,h_0^{(1)}(kr) + \frac{1}{2}\,h_0^{(2)}(kr), \tag{16–52}$$

where

$$h_0^{(1)}(kr) = j_0(kr) + in_0(kr) \tag{16–53}$$

and

$$h_0^{(2)}(kr) = j_0(kr) - in_0(kr) \tag{16–54}$$

are defined as *spherical Hankel functions.* Note that Eq. (16–52) represents a standing wave consisting of the sum of an ingoing and an outgoing part. The total flux of the outgoing part is

$$W = 4\pi r^2 S_r = -4\pi r^2\,\frac{i\hbar}{2m}\left[\frac{1}{4}\,\overline{h_0^{(1)}}\,\frac{d}{dr}\,h_0^{(1)} - \frac{1}{4}\,\frac{d}{dr}\,\overline{h_0^{(1)}}\cdot h_0^{(1)}\right]\cdot|Y_{00}|^2$$
$$= \frac{\hbar}{4mk}. \tag{16–55}$$

To find solutions to the radial equation (16–47) for all values of l, it is convenient to make use of the class **T** operators of Chapter 9 to generate other solutions from the two solutions of Eq. (16–49) that have already been obtained. The momentum operator $\mathbf{P} = -i\hbar\nabla$ commutes with the Hamiltonian, and the operator $P_+ = P_x + iP_y$ is of the class T_+. As shown in Chapter 9, the operator P_+ operating on an eigenfunction of L^2 and L_z with $m = l$ gives a new eigenfunction of these operators with the m and l indices both increased by one unit. Since P_+ commutes with H, the resulting function is also an eigenfunction of H. Hence the function

$$\psi_{kll} = P_+^l\psi_{k00} \tag{16–56}$$

is a solution to the eigenvalue equations of H, L^2, and L_z. Since ψ_{k00} is a function of r only, this can be written as

$$\psi_{kll}(kr) = (-i\hbar)^l \left(\frac{x+iy}{r}\right)^l r^l \left(\frac{1}{r}\frac{d}{dr}\right)^l \psi_{k00}. \tag{16-57}$$

Omitting normalization factors, this is

$$\psi_{kll} \sim Y_{ll}(\theta, \phi)\left(\frac{r}{k}\right)^l \left(\frac{1}{r}\frac{d}{dr}\right)^l \psi_{k00}. \tag{16-58}$$

It is clear that the nonsingular radial function may be written as

$$j_l(kr) = \left(-\frac{r}{k}\right)^l \left(\frac{1}{r}\frac{d}{dr}\right)^l j_0(kr) \tag{16-59}$$

(the sign has been chosen to agree with the usual definition of the spherical Bessel function). The singular Neumann and Hankel functions are generated in the same way by substituting the corresponding singular function on the right. Equation (16-59) can be taken as the definition of these functions. From the way in which these functions have been generated, it is clear that they satisfy the radial equation (16-47). This can be simplified to give

$$\frac{d^2 j_l(x)}{dx^2} + \frac{2}{x}\frac{dj_l(x)}{dx} + \left[1 - \frac{l(l+1)}{x^2}\right] j_l(x) = 0. \tag{16-60}$$

Spherical Bessel and Neumann functions for the first three values of l are

$$\begin{aligned}
j_0(x) &= \frac{\sin x}{x}, & n_0(x) &= -\frac{\cos x}{x}, \\
j_1(x) &= \frac{\sin x}{x^2} - \frac{\cos x}{x}, & n_1(x) &= -\frac{\cos x}{x^2} - \frac{\sin x}{x}, \\
j_2(x) &= \left(\frac{3}{x^3} - \frac{1}{x}\right)\sin x - \frac{3}{x^2}\cos x, & & \\
& & n_2(x) &= -\left(\frac{3}{x^3} - \frac{1}{x}\right)\cos x - \frac{3}{x^2}\sin x.
\end{aligned} \tag{16-61}$$

These are plotted in Fig. 16-5. As the order of the spherical Bessel function increases, the values of x at which the function differs appreciably from zero also increase. For small values of r, Eq. (16-59) becomes

$$\begin{aligned}
j_l(x) &\xrightarrow[x\to 0]{} \frac{x^l}{1\cdot 3\cdot 5\cdots(2l+1)}, \\
n_l(x) &\xrightarrow[x\to 0]{} -\frac{1\cdot 1\cdot 3\cdot 5\cdots(2l-1)}{x^{l+1}}.
\end{aligned} \tag{16-62}$$

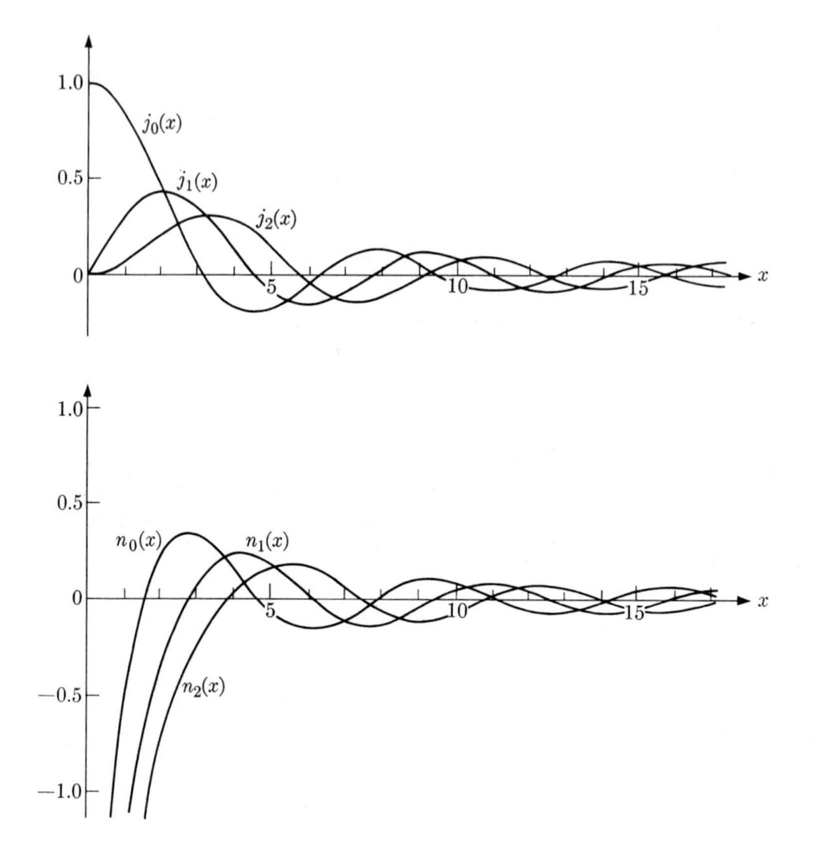

FIG. 16–5. Spherical Bessel and Neumann functions for $l = 0, 1, 2$.

Asymptotically, the expressions for j_l and n_l are

$$\begin{aligned} j_l(x) &\xrightarrow[x\to\infty]{} \frac{1}{x}\cos\left[x - \frac{\pi}{2}(l+1)\right], \\ n_l(x) &\xrightarrow[x\to\infty]{} \frac{1}{x}\sin\left[x - \frac{\pi}{2}(l+1)\right]. \end{aligned} \tag{16–63}$$

A convenient expression for the wave function corresponding to definite values for H, L^2, and L_z is

$$\psi_{klm} = Y_{lm}(\theta, \phi) j_l(kr). \tag{16–64}$$

This is normalized so that the total outward (or inward) particle flux is

$$W = \int r^2 S_r \, d\Omega, \tag{16–65}$$

where

$$S_r = -\frac{i\hbar}{2m}\left[\overline{\psi_{klm}^{+}}\frac{\partial}{\partial r}\psi_{klm}^{+} - \frac{\partial}{\partial r}\overline{\psi_{klm}^{+}}\cdot\psi_{klm}^{+}\right]. \tag{16-66}$$

Here

$$\psi_{klm}^{+} = \tfrac{1}{2}Y_{lm}(\theta,\,\phi)h_l^{(1)}(kr) \tag{16-67}$$

is the outward-moving part of ψ; the radial part is a Hankel function. The integration of Eq. (16–65) is over all solid angles at a fixed radius. S_r is most conveniently evaluated in the asymptotic region. From Eq. (16–63), the outward particle flux is independent of l and is given by

$$W = \frac{\hbar}{4mk}. \tag{16-68}$$

A plane wave may be expanded in functions of the form of Eq. (16–64), since these constitute a complete set. It is convenient to take the plane wave in the z-direction; in this case the wave function is independent of the angle ϕ, and the expansion consists only of terms with $m = 0$:

$$\exp(ikz) = \sum_{l=0}^{\infty} c_l Y_{l0}(\theta) j_l(kr). \tag{16-69}$$

As shown in Chapter 9, Y_{l0} can be obtained from

$$Y_{l0}(\theta,\,\phi) = \frac{1}{(2l!)^{1/2}}\frac{1}{\hbar^l}\,\mathrm{L}_-^l Y_{ll} \tag{16-70}$$

and

$$Y_{ll} = \frac{1}{(2\pi)^{1/2}}(-1)^l\left[\frac{(2l+1)!}{2}\right]^{1/2}\frac{1}{2^l l!}\exp(il\phi)\sin^l\theta. \tag{16-71}$$

To evaluate the expansion coefficient c_l, Eq. (16–69) is multiplied by $\overline{Y_{l0}}$ and integrated over all solid angles for fixed r:

$$c_l j_l(kr) = \int \overline{Y_{l0}}\exp(ikz)\sin\theta\,d\theta\,d\phi. \tag{16-72}$$

Substituting Eq. (16–70) for Y_{l0}, we find that

$$\begin{aligned} c_l j_l(kr) &= \frac{1}{(2l!)^{1/2}}\frac{1}{\hbar^l}\int \overline{\mathrm{L}_-^l Y_{ll}}\exp(ikz)\sin\theta\,d\theta\,d\phi \\ &= \frac{1}{(2l!)^{1/2}}\frac{1}{\hbar^l}\int \overline{Y_{ll}}\mathrm{L}_+^l\exp(ikr\cos\theta)\sin\theta\,d\theta\,d\phi \\ &= \frac{i^l\pi^{1/2}(2l+1)^{1/2}}{2^l l!}(kr)^l\int_0^{\pi}\sin^{2l}\theta\exp(ikr\cos\theta)\sin\theta\,d\theta. \end{aligned} \tag{16-73}$$

Here use has been made of the expression for L_+ given in Eq. (9–39).

It is evident that the right side must be a way of generating a spherical Bessel function. In particular, going to the limit $r \to 0$ and making use of Eq. (16–62) on the left side gives

$$c_l = i^l[4\pi(2l + 1)]^{1/2}. \tag{16–74}$$

Hence

$$\exp(ikz) = \sum_{l=0}^{\infty} i^l[4\pi(2l + 1)]^{1/2} Y_{l0}(\theta) j_l(kr). \tag{16–75}$$

Y_{l0} may be expressed as a Legendre polynomial (see Chapter 9):

$$Y_{l0}(\theta) = \left[\frac{2l + 1}{4\pi}\right]^{1/2} P_l(\cos\theta). \tag{16–76}$$

Thus

$$\exp(ikz) = \sum_{l=0}^{\infty} i^l(2l + 1) P_l(\cos\theta) j_l(kr). \tag{16–77}$$

Note that

$$j_l(kr) = \tfrac{1}{2}[h_l^{(1)}(kr) + h_l^{(2)}(kr)] \tag{16–78}$$

and each of the spherical partial waves in Eq. (16–77) consists of an ingoing and an outgoing wave. The total ingoing probability flux of the lth wave, from Eqs. (16–68) and (16–75), is

$$W_l = \frac{\pi\hbar}{mk}(2l + 1). \tag{16–79}$$

The probability density flux of the plane wave is

$$S = \frac{\hbar k}{m}\cdot \tag{16–80}$$

The ratio of these two probability fluxes is

$$\sigma_l = \frac{W_l}{S} = \frac{\pi}{k^2}(2l + 1) = \frac{\lambda^2}{4\pi}(2l + 1). \tag{16–81}$$

We will call σ_l the *lth partial-wave cross section*. Physically, it is the effective area around the origin of the coordinate system to be hit by a particle in the lth angular-momentum state.

Equation (16–81) can be obtained in the following "classical" way. A particle with a momentum $\boldsymbol{p} = \hbar\boldsymbol{k}$ must classically pass the origin at a distance of $[l(l + 1)]^{1/2}k^{-1}$ if its squared angular momentum is to be $l(l + 1)\hbar^2$. If the area of an annular ring with inner radius

$$[(l - \tfrac{1}{2})(l + \tfrac{1}{2})]^{1/2}k^{-1}$$

and outer radius

$$[(l + \tfrac{1}{2})(l + \tfrac{3}{2})]^{1/2} k^{-1}$$

is assumed to be the target area σ_l for approaching the scattering center in this angular-momentum state, then

$$\begin{aligned} \sigma_l &= \frac{\pi}{k^2} [(l + \tfrac{1}{2})(l + \tfrac{3}{2}) - (l - \tfrac{1}{2})(l + \tfrac{1}{2})] \\ &= \frac{\pi}{k^2} (2l + 1). \end{aligned} \tag{16–82}$$

This is illustrated in Fig. 16–6.

Thus far, only free-particle wave functions have been considered. Now assume that there is a spherically symmetric scatterer at the origin. The angular-momentum operators commute with the Hamiltonian, and the ingoing lth partial wave is reflected out as the same type of wave; i.e., there is no scattering of particles out of their angular-momentum states. Consider an ingoing spherical wave

$$\psi_{klm}^{-} = \tfrac{1}{2} Y_{lm}(\theta, \phi) h_l^{(2)}(kr). \tag{16–83}$$

With no scatterer present at the origin, this wave collapses upon the origin and becomes the outgoing wave

$$\psi_{klm}^{+} = \tfrac{1}{2} Y_{lm}(\theta, \phi) h_l^{(1)}(kr) \tag{16–84}$$

[see Eq. (16–78)]. With a spherically symmetrical scatterer, assuming no particle absorption at the center, the only effect the scatterer can have is

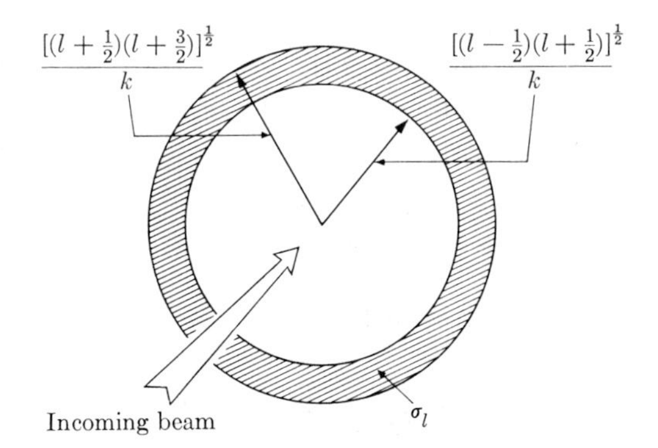

FIG. 16–6. "Classical" cross section for a particle approaching a scattering center with an impact parameter such that its angular momentum squared is approximately $l(l + 1)\hbar^2$.

that of producing a phase shift in the outgoing wave. With the scatterer present, the outgoing wave thus becomes

$$\psi_{klm}^{+} = \tfrac{1}{2} \exp (2i\delta_l) Y_{lm} h_l^{(1)}(kr). \tag{16-85}$$

The phase shift δ_l is related to the interaction with the scatterer, as will be seen in detail later.

In terms of Hankel functions, the plane-wave expansion of Eq. (16–75) is

$$\exp (ikz) = \tfrac{1}{2} \sum_{l=0}^{\infty} i^l [4\pi(2l + 1)]^{1/2} Y_{l0}(\theta)[h_l^{(1)}(kr) + h_l^{(2)}(kr)]. \tag{16-86}$$

With a scatterer present, the outgoing waves are phase-shifted, and the wave function becomes

$$\begin{aligned} \psi &= \tfrac{1}{2} \sum_{l=0}^{\infty} i^l [4\pi(2l + 1)]^{1/2} Y_{l0}(\theta)[\exp (2i\delta_l) h_l^{(1)}(kr) + h_l^{(2)}(kr)] \\ &= \exp (ikz) + \tfrac{1}{2} \sum_{l=0}^{\infty} i^l [4\pi(2l + 1)]^{1/2} [\exp (2i\delta_l) - 1] Y_{l0}(\theta) h_l^{(1)}(kr). \end{aligned} \tag{16-87}$$

Thus the effect of the scatterer is to give an outgoing scattered wave

$$v = \tfrac{1}{2} \sum_{l=0}^{\infty} i^l [4\pi(2l + 1)]^{1/2} [\exp (2i\delta_l) - 1] Y_{l0}(\theta) h_l^{(1)}(kr) \tag{16-88}$$

in addition to the original plane wave. Note that the total outgoing flux in the lth wave is the same as without the scatterer, but now the outgoing wave has been split into two parts, the scattered wave and the outgoing part of the incident plane wave.

From Eq. (16–88), the outgoing probability flux of the lth *scattered* wave is equal to the inward flux of the lth partial wave multiplied by the factor $|\exp (2i\delta_l) - 1|^2$. Hence the scattering cross section into the lth partial wave, from Eq. (16–81), is

$$\sigma_l^{(s)} = \frac{\lambda^2}{4\pi} (2l + 1) \cdot 4 \sin^2 \delta_l, \tag{16-89}$$

and the total scattering cross section is

$$\begin{aligned} \sigma_{\text{scat}} &= \sum_l \frac{\lambda^2}{\pi} (2l + 1) \sin^2 \delta_l \\ &= \frac{4\pi}{k^2} \sum_l (2l + 1) \sin^2 \delta_l. \end{aligned} \tag{16-90}$$

The maximum scattering cross section occurs when the scattering phase shift is $\pm\pi/2$, $\pm 3\pi/2$, . . . , and is four times as great as the input cross section. Thus four times as many particles can be scattered in the lth partial wave as strike the scatterer with this angular momentum. This paradoxical behavior is related to shadow scattering and the way in which the scattered wave is defined.

In nuclear physics, particles are sometimes absorbed by the nucleus (the scatterer); particles may also be emitted. In computing the scattering in the case of particle absorption, we can ignore the particles lost to the nucleus, and the outgoing particle flux in the lth partial wave may be less than the ingoing flux. Equation (16–87) is still valid, with δ_l now having a positive imaginary part.

An absorption cross section can be defined as

$$\sigma_{\text{abs}} \equiv \sum_l \frac{\lambda^2}{4\pi}(2l+1)[1 - |\exp(2i\delta_l)|^2], \tag{16–91}$$

and the scattering cross section is, as before,

$$\sigma_{\text{scat}} = \sum_l \frac{\lambda^2}{4\pi}(2l+1)|1 - \exp(2i\delta_l)|^2. \tag{16–92}$$

Note that the maximum absorption cross section of the lth partial wave is

$$\sigma_{\text{abs}}^{(l)} = \frac{\lambda^2}{4\pi}(2l+1). \tag{16–93}$$

If the absorption is a maximum, there is an equal amount of scattering. This again is a paradoxical situation: the absorption of all particles incident in the lth wave results in an equal number of scattered particles.

So far, nothing has been said about how the phase shifts δ_l can be computed. From Eq. (16–87), the radial part of the lth partial-wave function with the scatterer present is given by

$$R_l = \exp(2i\delta_l)h_l^{(1)}(kr) + h_l^{(2)}(kr). \tag{16–94}$$

This can be put into the form

$$R_l = 2\exp(i\delta_l)\,[j_l(kr)\cos\delta_l - n_l(kr)\sin\delta_l]. \tag{16–95}$$

This is the most general solution (apart from a multiplicative factor) to the radial equation (16–47) for the region in which the scattering potential vanishes. Since the scattering potential was assumed to be localized, we can find a sphere of radius r_0 outside of which Eq. (16–95) is valid. The phase shift δ_l is found by matching this solution to that valid within the sphere at $r = r_0$. This can be done by equating logarithmic derivatives of the wave functions at the sphere.

As an example of the partial-wave method, consider the scattering of a beam by a rigid sphere of radius a. The matching condition in this case is particularly simple: the wave function must vanish at $r = a$:

$$j_l(ka) \cos \delta_l - n_l(ka) \sin \delta_l = 0, \tag{16–96}$$

or

$$\tan \delta_l = \frac{j_l(ka)}{n_l(ka)}. \tag{16–97}$$

For low-energy incident particles, $ka \ll 1$ and we can use the approximations of Eq. (16–62):

$$\begin{aligned} \tan \delta_l &= \frac{(ka)^l}{1 \cdot 3 \cdot 5 \cdots (2l+1)} \left[- \frac{(ka)^{l+1}}{1 \cdot 1 \cdot 3 \cdot 5 \cdots (2l-1)} \right] \\ &= - \frac{(ka)^{2l+1} \cdot 2^{2l-1} l!(l-1)!}{(2l+1)!(2l-1)!}. \end{aligned} \tag{16–98}$$

From this, it is seen that δ_l falls off very rapidly as l increases, and so the series expression of Eq. (16–90) converges rapidly. Thus for low-energy particles, where $ka \ll 1$, most of the scattering arises from the $l = 0$ partial wave and the scattering is spherically symmetric [see Eq. (16–87)]. The phase shift δ_0 is given by

$$\begin{aligned} \tan \delta_0 &= \frac{j_0(ka)}{n_0(ka)} = \tan ka, \\ \delta_0 &= ka. \end{aligned} \tag{16–99}$$

Substitution of this into Eq. (16–90) gives

$$\sigma_{\text{scat}} \approx \frac{4\pi}{k^2} (ka)^2 = 4\pi a^2. \tag{16–100}$$

Thus for low-energy particles, the scattering is isotropic and the cross section is four times the geometrical cross section of the rigid sphere.

For high-energy bombarding particles, the method of partial waves usually loses most of its utility, because in this case many l-values must be considered and the computation becomes very laborious. However, the case of the rigid spherical scatterer can be treated by this method as follows. From Eq. (16–97), it can be seen that

$$\sin^2 \delta_l = \frac{j_l^2(ka)}{j_l^2(ka) + n_l^2(ka)}. \tag{16–101}$$

Using the asymptotic expressions (16-63) for the spherical Bessel functions, we find that

$$\sin^2 \delta_l \xrightarrow[ka \to \infty]{} \cos^2 \left[ka - \frac{\pi}{2}(l + 1) \right] \cdot \qquad (16\text{-}102)$$

For high-energy particles, $ka \gg 1$, and the de Broglie wavelength for the incident particles is much smaller than the radius of the scatterer. From the "classical" argument leading to Eq. (16-82), it can be seen that in the "classical" limit of $ka \gg 1$ (de Broglie wavelength small compared with the radius of the scatterer), the incident particles will not "see" the scatterer for $l > ka$, but for $l < ka$ appreciable phase shifts are to be expected.

This result can also be seen by referring to Eqs. (16-62) and (16-63). The asymptotic result, Eq. (16-102), is valid only for $l \ll ka$. For $l \gg ka$, it must be replaced by the equation obtained by substituting Eq. (16-62) into Eq. (16-101). The result is that δ_l is negligibly small if $l \gg ka$. Thus for $ka \gg 1$, the sum in Eq. (16-90) can be cut off at $l = ka$, with Eq. (16-102) substituted for the nonzero terms. Thus

$$\sigma \approx \frac{4\pi}{k^2} \sum_{l=0}^{ka} (2l + 1) \cos^2 \left[ka - \frac{\pi}{2}(l + 1) \right] \cdot \qquad (16\text{-}103)$$

Since $ka \gg 1$, the argument of the cosine in this equation is a rapidly varying function of k, and it is reasonable in computing the sum to replace these $\cos^2$ terms by their average value of one-half. This gives

$$\sigma = \frac{2\pi}{k^2} \sum_{l=0}^{ka} (2l + 1), \qquad (16\text{-}104)$$

which for $ka \gg 1$ is approximately

$$\sigma = 2\pi a^2. \qquad (16\text{-}105)$$

In other words, for high-energy particles the cross section is twice the geometrical scatterer area. As mentioned previously, the factor of two arises from the inclusion of shadow scattering.

Earlier in this chapter, virtual energy levels and resonance scattering were briefly discussed. We saw that virtual states arise when the effective potential, including the "centrifugal potential," is such that a particle of energy corresponding to the virtual state can be trapped for a relatively long time before it "leaks out" of the potential. Since the centrifugal potential can contribute in a decisive way to the formation of such states, a virtual state corresponds to a definite angular-momentum state for the "trapped" particle. A virtual level, in general, gives rise to a large phase shift for the appropriate partial wave when the bombarding particle energy coincides with the energy of the virtual state. In this case, the partial wave is said to be *in resonance*, and the resonant wave is apt to dominate the scattering at energies at and near resonance. The longer a particle can stay trapped before escaping, the *sharper* the energy level is. The sharper an energy level, the narrower is the spread of incident particle energies that are effectively in resonance. The phase shift is also likely to be greater at resonance for a sharp energy level than for one whose lifetime for trapping is short. At resonance the phase shift is likely to be nearly $\pm\pi/2$ and, as has been seen, in such a case the scattering cross section takes on its maximum value.

16–4 Summary. This chapter considered scattering, beginning with a brief discussion of various physical concepts connected with scattering. The idea of scattering cross section was introduced, and differential and total cross sections were defined. The laboratory and center-of-mass coordinate systems and the relation between them were described. The quantum description of the scattering process in terms of an incident plane wave and a scattered wave was presented, and an interpretation of the various terms in the probability flux corresponding to the scattered wave was given. The relation between the scattering cross section and the angular dependence of the scattered wave was shown. Shadow scattering and virtual energy levels were briefly mentioned.

Two methods for treating scattering problems were discussed: the Born approximation and the method of partial waves. The first is most applicable when the kinetic energy of the incoming beam is large compared with the scattering potential, whereas the second method is most readily applied when the energy of the incoming particles is low. The two methods thus tend to complement each other. Scattering by a shallow spherical potential well was used to illustrate the Born approximation, and scattering by a rigid sphere was treated by partial-wave methods. The relation of virtual levels to the resonant scattering of appropriate partial waves was discussed briefly.

Problems

16–1. Compute an approximate expression for the scattering cross section of a square potential well when the potential depth is adjusted to introduce a new level at $E = 0$. Consider low-energy incident particles.

16–2. The capture cross section of a certain nucleus for neutrons having an energy of 0.1 ev is measured to be 2.5×10^{-18} cm^2. Give upper and lower bounds for the elastic scattering cross section.

16–3. Show that the limiting expressions of Eqs. (16–62) and (16–63) for spherical Bessel and Neumann functions are valid.

16–4. Given a spherical wave $\psi = Y_{lm}j_l(kr)$, expand it in terms of plane waves, and calculate the expansion coefficients $A(\boldsymbol{k})$:

$$Y_{lm}j_l(kr) = \frac{1}{(2\pi)^{3/2}} \int A(\boldsymbol{k}) \exp(i\boldsymbol{k} \cdot \boldsymbol{r})\, d\boldsymbol{k}.$$

16–5. Why is the inelastic scattering (scattering accompanied by a loss of energy of the scattered particles) of a stream of particles always accompanied by some elastic scattering?

16–6. Use the Born approximation to obtain the differential scattering cross section for a spinless particle of energy E by a potential field of the form $V(r) = A \exp(-br)$, where A and b are given constants.

16–7. The scattering of high-energy particles by a spherical potential barrier was considered in the text. Use the method of partial waves to compute the scattering in the limit of very low-energy incident particles.

16–8. (a) Use the results of Problem 16–7 to show that for a suitable V_0 (the depth of a square potential well of radius a), it is possible for the phase shift of the $l = 0$ partial wave to be equal to 180° while higher-order phase shifts are negligibly small because of the low energy of the incident particles. (b) What happens to the scattering cross section in this case? This effect was observed by Ramsauer in the scattering of low-energy (0.7 ev) electrons by rare-gas atoms. (c) Using an atomic radius of 10^{-8} cm, what must be the depth of the effective potential well for helium, to explain the observations of Ramsauer?

16–9. (a) What is the maximum capture cross section for monoenergetic thermal (0.025 ev) neutrons? (b) What is the accompanying elastic scattering cross section?

16–10. Consider a scattering situation in which only the $l = 0$ and $l = 1$ partial waves have appreciable phase shift. (a) Discuss how the contribution of the $l = 1$ wave affects the total cross section. (b) How does it affect the angular distribution of scattered particles? (c) What sort of measurements should be made to obtain an accurate value of δ_0? (d) of δ_1? (e) How might a small $l = 2$ phase shift be detected?

16–11. Show that the sum in Eq. (16–103) can be evaluated directly (without replacing the $\cos^2$ term by one-half) to give

$$\sum_{l=0}^{ka} (2l+1)\cos^2\left[ka - \frac{\pi}{2}(l+1)\right] = \tfrac{1}{2}(ka+1)ka + \tfrac{1}{2}ka\cos 2ka, \qquad ka \gg 1.$$

Note that this result shows that the total cross section does not vary greatly with k.

CHAPTER 17

IDENTICAL PARTICLES

17–1 The particle-exchange operator. In Chapter 6, we discussed the treatment of systems composed of more than one particle. However, all particles were there assumed to be distinguishable from one another. In this chapter, the effect on the formalism of assuming that the system of interest consists of *indistinguishable* particles is considered. By "indistinguishable particles" we mean that if the position and spin coordinates of two of them are interchanged, *there is no physical way of measuring that a change has been made* in the system. Consequently, this symmetry under an interchange of two particles should appear somewhere in the formalism.

We can approach the question of particle symmetry and the effect of identical particles by introducing the particle interchange operator P_{12} defined through the equation

$$\mathrm{P}_{12}\psi(r_1, \boldsymbol{S}_1; r_2, \boldsymbol{S}_2) \equiv \psi(r_2, \boldsymbol{S}_2; r_1, \boldsymbol{S}_1). \tag{17–1}$$

The effect of this operator is to interchange the subscripts of the spin and position variables of the wave function for particles 1 and 2. (The wave function has been indicated as a function of only these two classes of variables, but it may, in addition, be a function of the coordinates describing other particles.) If the two particles are truly identical, it is clear that the Hamiltonian must be symmetric with respect to the positions and spins of the identical particles. In other words, there should be no change in the energy of a system if we merely relabel the particles: if what was formerly called particle 2 is now called particle 1 and what was formerly called particle 1 is now called particle 2, the energy of the system and consequently the Hamiltonian should be left unchanged. Thus the particle-interchange operator commutes with the Hamiltonian:

$$[\mathrm{P}_{12}, \mathrm{H}] = 0. \tag{17–2}$$

The eigenvalue equation for the interchange operator is

$$\mathrm{P}_{12}\psi = \alpha\psi. \tag{17–3}$$

The eigenvalues are clearly

$$\alpha = \pm 1, \tag{17–4}$$

just as they are for the parity operator (see Section 10–5), inasmuch as the interchange operator applied twice brings the particles back to their original configuration and hence produces no change in the wave function. (The square of the eigenvalue must be equal to unity.)

Since the interchange operator commutes with the Hamiltonian, it is possible to choose eigenfunctions to be simultaneously eigenfunctions of the Hamiltonian and the interchange operator. Consequently, energy states of the mechanical system can be labeled as being either even or odd under particle interchange. Inasmuch as the commutation relation Eq. (17–2) is satisfied for any Hamiltonian, perturbed or not, it is clear that the rate of change of the expectation value of the interchange, or symmetry, operator is zero:

$$\frac{d}{dt}\langle \mathrm{P}_{12}\rangle = 0. \tag{17–5}$$

Thus, two particles that are in a state for which the interchange eigenvalue is $+1$ will remain in this state for all time; there is no interaction which can change the two particles into the other state. This property of evenness or oddness under the symmetry operator is therefore *completely permanent* and can be considered as a fixed property of the particles themselves, rather than of the various possible states the particles can assume.

Those particles for which the eigenvalue of Eq. (17–3) is $+1$ are said to be particles which satisfy *Bose-Einstein statistics.* Those particles for which the sign is minus are said to be particles satisfying *Fermi-Dirac statistics.* So far as is now known, all particles (or quanta) having integral (or zero) spin obey Bose statistics, and all with half-integral spin obey Fermi statistics. Photons, which have an effective spin of 1, obey Bose statistics.

17–2 The Pauli principle. The character of the statistics satisfied by the particles is very definitely reflected in their motion. This can be seen, for example, by examining the wave function for two particles which satisfy Fermi statistics. Consider the possibility that two such identical particles might occupy the same point in space and have the same z-component for their spin angular momenta. It is seen from the effect of the interchange operator on such a function that under these conditions the function must vanish:

$$\begin{aligned}\mathrm{P}_{12}\psi(r_1, S_1; r_2, S_2) &= \psi(r_2, S_2; r_1, S_1)\\ &= -\psi(r_1, S_1; r_2, S_2)\\ &= 0 \quad \text{if} \begin{cases} r_1 = r_2,\\ S_1 = S_2.\end{cases}\end{aligned} \tag{17–6}$$

The vanishing of the wave function under these conditions implies that there is zero probability that the particles will occupy the same point in space and have identical spin orientations.

Equation (17–6) is one form in which the physical principle known as the *Pauli exclusion principle* can appear. Historically, the principle was first expressed as *no two particles obeying Fermi statistics can exist in the same quantum state.* That this is true can be seen by considering the case of two Fermi particles moving in a common field of force. If we neglect the interactions between the particles, we can write the wave function for a stationary state as

$$\psi = \frac{1}{\sqrt{2}}\,[u_1(\mathbf{r}_1, \mathbf{S}_1)u_2(\mathbf{r}_2, \mathbf{S}_2) - u_1(\mathbf{r}_2, \mathbf{S}_2)u_2(\mathbf{r}_1, \mathbf{S}_1)]. \tag{17–7}$$

Here u_1 and u_2 are single-particle stationary states for this force field. [See the discussion of Eq. (6–115).]

The wave function of Eq. (17–7) satisfies

$$\mathrm{P}_{12}\psi = -\psi. \tag{17–8}$$

It has been properly symmetrized to be odd under the interchange operator. Note that the wave function vanishes identically if the two functions u_1 and u_2 are identical. A more physical way of saying this is that the two identical particles cannot be in a state in which they move in the same orbit with their spins parallel. Thus there can be but two electrons moving in one particular atomic "orbit," and these two electrons must have oppositely directed spins. This statement of the Pauli principle helps to explain the periodic system of the elements.

The Pauli principle also provides an explanation for the chief features of the optical spectra of the alkali metals. As an example, consider the energy levels of potassium. These are shown in Fig. 17–1. Potassium has nineteen electrons. The ground-state wave function will be discussed first in the crude approximation of neglecting the electron-electron interactions. Symmetry effects, however, will be included. In this approximation, two electrons with antiparallel spins occupy the hydrogenlike $1S$-state; eight electrons occupy the $(n = 2)$-shells, two (antiparallel) in the $2S$-state and six in the $2P$-states (in three antiparallel pairs corresponding to the three possible values of m_l); and the remaining nine electrons occupy the S-, P-, and D-states of the $(n = 3)$-shell.

In actuality, the situation is not quite this simple: interelectron interactions must be considered. The tightly bound inner electrons in the $(n = 1)$- and $(n = 2)$-shells, orbiting very close to the nucleus, tend to neutralize the positive nuclear charge experienced by the outer electrons. However, the outer S-electrons, and, to a lesser extent, the P- (and D-) electrons, tend to penetrate this electron space charge. Thus the effective

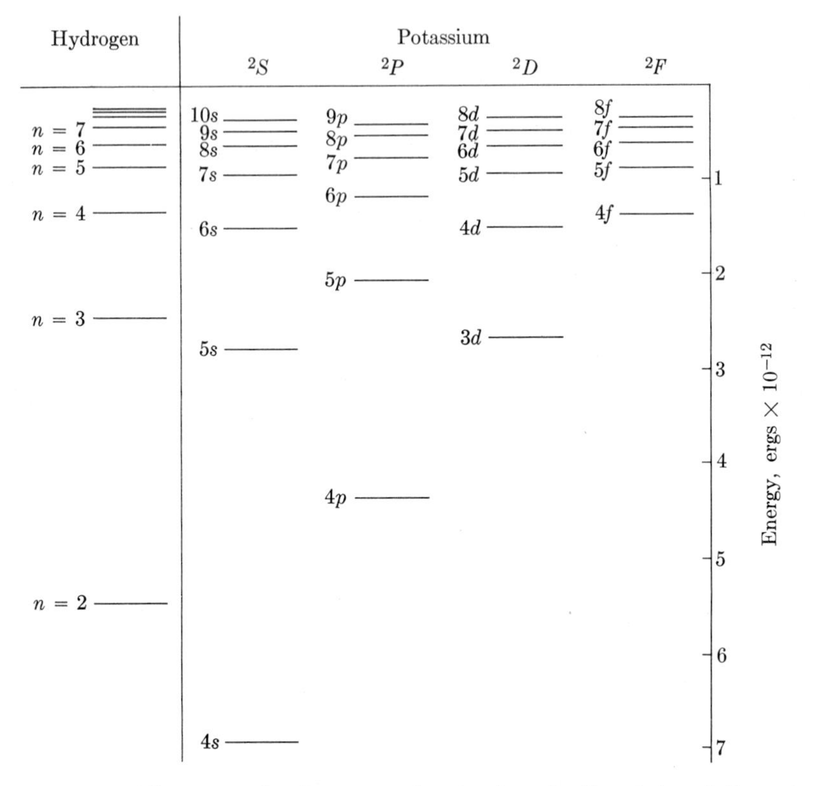

Fig. 17–1. The energy-level system of potassium for the states of the outer (valence) electron. The inner eighteen electrons are assumed to be in their normal atomic orbitals. Spectroscopic notation for the energy levels is shown at the top. The corresponding hydrogen spectrum, with the values of the principal quantum number n, is shown at the left for comparison.

nuclear positive charge is greater for the $3S$-states than for the $3P$-states. The effective charge acting on the $3D$-state electrons is even smaller. Thus the $3S$-states lie below the $3P$-states in energy, and these in turn lie below the $3D$-states. Hence in filling the $(n = 3)$-shell, the first eight electrons go into the $3S$- and $3P$-states. However, the last (valence electron) does not go into the $3D$-shell, but into the $4S$-state, as the orbit-penetration effect is sufficient to cause the $4S$-state to be lower than the $3D$-states.

The energy levels playing a role in optical spectroscopy all correspond to a change in state of the valence electron. The motion of the valence electron is best considered first from the standpoint of another simple approximation. Assume that all electrons but the valence electron are pulled in close to the nucleus in such a way as to reduce its effective charge to $Z = 1$. The valence electron then moves in the hydrogenic orbits $3D$, $4S$, $4P$, $4D$, etc. The larger and less penetrating the orbit, the better is this approximation. Thus for large n and l, the energies are nearly the corresponding hydrogen values. The orbit-penetration effect causes the $4S$-state to lie below the $3D$-state. However, the $4S$-, $4P$-, and $4D$-levels form a family (see Fig. 17–1). In similar fashion, the $5S$-, $5P$-, $5D$-, and $5F$-levels form another family, a regular sequence with the S-state lowest. Note the positions of these families of levels relative to the corresponding hydrogen state, also shown in Fig. 17–1.

17–3 The spin-independent Hamiltonian. The discussion of the effect of particle symmetry on the state of the system is somewhat simplified if it can be assumed that the Hamiltonian is independent of the spins of the particles. Under these conditions, the spin operators for the various particles commute with the Hamiltonian:

$$[\mathrm{S}_j, \mathrm{H}] = 0. \tag{17-9}$$

It is sometimes convenient to introduce the particle-spin exchange operator S_{12}, which operates only on the spin coordinates of the particles. For two particles, the operators for the z-components of the spin angular momentum of the individual particles commute with the Hamiltonian, but they do not commute with the interchange operators P_{12} and S_{12}, inasmuch as the effect of the operator P_{12} or S_{12} on S_{1z} would be that of changing the 1 into a 2. Hence these two spin operators in the Hamiltonian are not suitable commuting operators to describe the states of definite symmetry. On the other hand, the total z-component of the spin angular momentum of the particle does commute with the Hamiltonian and also with the interchange operators, since S_z is symmetric in the subscripts 1 and 2:

$$\mathrm{S}_z = \mathrm{S}_{1z} + \mathrm{S}_{2z}. \tag{17-10}$$

The square of the total spin angular momentum also is symmetric in the subscripts 1 and 2 and also commutes with the Hamiltonian and the interchange operators. This can be seen from

$$\mathrm{S}^2 = (\mathbf{S}_1 + \mathbf{S}_2)^2. \tag{17-11}$$

Thus the five operators S^2, S_z, H, P_{12}, and S_{12} form a mutually commuting set of operators, and to this approximation the energy states of any two-(identical) particle system can be characterized by the quantum numbers of the total spin angular momentum, the z-component of the total spin angular momentum, the energy, the (total) symmetry of the particle, and the spin symmetry.

Next, we will compute the form of the wave functions which are eigenfunctions of S^2 and S_z, assuming that the particles have spin-one-half Fermi statistics. The formalism thus applies to electrons; it also applies to protons and neutrons, which are also particles of spin one-half satisfying Fermi statistics. Two particles of spin one-half can have parallel spins, leading to a total angular momentum of $\hbar$ in the direction of the spin, or they can have antiparallel spins, in which case the two angular momenta cancel each other, giving a total spin of zero for the system. The wave functions will be characterized by subscripts designating the orientation of the spin axis of each of the two particles relative to the z-axis.

A wave function will thus be written in the form

$$\psi = \psi_{+-}, \tag{17-12}$$

for example, where the subscript $+$ indicates that the first particle has its spin pointing in the positive z-direction and the minus subscript indicates that the spin orientation of the second particle is in the negative z-direction. There are four possible different spin states of this form, characterized by the four possible different combinations of subscripts, $++$, $+-$, $-+$, and $--$. Four independent spin states would be expected, inasmuch as there are three possible orientations for the triplet electronic state with a total spin of 1 but only one orientation for the singlet state of spin zero, also leading to a total of four possible independent states.

We can compute the wave functions which are eigenfunctions of S^2 and S_z in terms of the functions of the type given in Eq. (17–12). The $(++)$-function is one in which both particles have their spin axes pointing in the positive z-direction; it is also an eigenfunction of S^2 and S_z, as can be seen directly by applying these operators:

$$\begin{aligned} S^2\psi_{++} &= 2\hbar^2\psi_{++}, \\ S_z\psi_{++} &= \hbar\psi_{++}. \end{aligned} \tag{17-13}$$

This $(++)$-wave function is the first of the series of three functions characterized by a total spin quantum number $s = 1$; the others can be generated by applying the ladder operator $S_- = S_x - iS_y$:

$$S_- = S_{1-} + S_{2-}. \tag{17-14}$$

Each of the two components of this ladder operator, in acting on a wave function of the type of Eq. (17–12), gives a result of the form

$$S_{1-}\psi_{m_{s1}m_{s2}} = [(s_1 + m_{s1})(s_1 - m_{s1} + 1)]^{1/2}\hbar\psi_{m_{s1}-1,m_{s2}}. \tag{17-15}$$

This results directly from Eq. (9–59). Making use of this equation, one has, for the operator S_{1-} applied to the (++)-state,

$$S_{1-}\psi_{++} = \hbar\psi_{-+}. \tag{17–16}$$

For the total ladder operator of Eq. (17–14), we find

$$S_{-}\psi_{++} = \hbar(\psi_{-+} + \psi_{+-}) = \sqrt{2}\hbar \frac{1}{\sqrt{2}} (\psi_{+-} + \psi_{-+}). \tag{17–17}$$

The second expression is written in a way that emphasizes the normalization of the wave function. Applying S_{-}^2 to the original function gives

$$S_{-}^2\psi_{++} = 2\hbar^2\psi_{--}. \tag{17–18}$$

By introducing another set of subscripts for the wave functions characterized by the eigenvalues s and m_s, we can write

$$\psi_{++} \equiv \psi_{11} = \psi_{s=1,m_s=1}. \tag{17–19}$$

For this particular function, the quantum numbers can be chosen to be either the z-components of the two spins of the particles separately or the total spin angular momentum and the z-component of the total spin angular momentum. The two functions are identical for each set of quantum numbers. Equation (17–14) applied to the general state ψ_{s,m_s} gives

$$S_{-}\psi_{s,m_s} = [(s + m_s)(s - m_s + 1)]^{1/2}\hbar\psi_{s,m_s-1}. \tag{17–20}$$

This, applied to the first wave function of the series, Eq. (17–19), yields

$$S_{-}\psi_{11} = \sqrt{2}\hbar\psi_{10}. \tag{17–21}$$

Comparing this with Eq. (17–17), we see that we can write

$$\psi_{10} = \frac{1}{\sqrt{2}} (\psi_{+-} + \psi_{-+}). \tag{17–22}$$

This represents an expansion of the wave function having quantum numbers s and m_s in terms of the wave functions labeled by the quantum numbers m_s of each of the two particles. It is a simple example of the representation transformations discussed in Chapter 13. In similar fashion, applying the operator S_{-} again yields

$$\psi_{1,-1} = \psi_{--}. \tag{17–23}$$

Inasmuch as the wave function for which the total spin angular momentum is zero must be orthogonal to the other functions for which the spin angular momentum is 1, and in particular must be orthogonal to the function ψ_{10}, the function must have the form

$$\psi_{00} = \frac{1}{\sqrt{2}} (\psi_{+-} - \psi_{-+}). \tag{17–24}$$

This function clearly has the correct total spin angular momentum in the z-direction and is orthogonal to the functions ψ_{11}, ψ_{10}, and $\psi_{1,-1}$.

A word may be said here about terminology. When two electrons or other particles of spin one-half have their spins antiparallel to each other, they are said to be in a *singlet* state; when they are in a state for which their spins are parallel, they are said to be in a *triplet* state.

17–4 Effect of spin symmetry on the energy of a state. The spin-interchange operator S_{12} is an operator of the type given in Eq. (17–1) except that it acts only on the subscripts of the spin variables in the wave function. Consequently, the spin-interchange operator, when applied to a wave function of the type given by Eq. (17–12), has the effect of interchanging the first and second subscripts in the wave function. If a spin-interchange operator is applied to any of the functions given by Eqs. (17–19), (17–22), or (17–23), it can be seen by inspection that the function is left unchanged. Consequently, the three triplet states are symmetric under a spin-interchange operator. On the other hand, when the spin-interchange operator is applied to Eq. (17–24), it changes the sign of the function; the singlet state is odd under spin interchange.

Assuming again that the system of interest is composed of two Fermi particles and that the total spin operator S^2, the z-component of the total spin S_z, the Hamiltonian, and the two interchange operators all commute with one another, the wave functions may be chosen to be eigenfunctions of all five operators. The general form of the wave function is consequently

$$\psi_{nsm_s} = u_{ns}(r_1, r_2)v_{sm_s}. \tag{17–25}$$

The space dependence of the function is given only by the first term on the right, and the spin dependence is contained in the second term. Because the Hamiltonian is independent of the spin orientations for the two particles, the spin function can always be separated off in this manner. In other words, the position part, the first term in Eq. (17–25), should be independent of the spin variables. This, however, is not completely correct. The total function ψ_{nsm_s} must be antisymmetric under an interchange of both spins and positions of the particles. As a result, there are important spin-dependent effects.

As has been seen, the spin function v_{sm_s} is symmetric if the spins are parallel and antisymmetric if the spins are antiparallel; that is, it is symmetric under a spin interchange if $s = 1$ and it is antisymmetric if the quantum number $s = 0$. The position part of the function, $u_{ns}(r_1, r_2)$, is antisymmetric or symmetric depending on whether the second term is symmetric or antisymmetric: if the spin function is symmetric under spin interchange, then the position part of the wave function must be antisymmetric for the whole function to be antisymmetric under an interchange of both spin and position coordinates. For this reason, the term $u_{ns}(r_1, r_2)$ contains both the subscripts n and s, and the energy of the system does depend on the spin quantum number s in spite of the Hamiltonian's independence of the spin variables. This somewhat paradoxical effect comes about only because of the symmetry properties.

As we shall see shortly, the symmetry effects can be quite large; for example, the energy levels in the helium atom for which the spins are parallel to each other are quite different from the corresponding levels for which they are antiparallel. The effect on the energy of the system as a result of the symmetry properties of the term under a position interchange of the two particles can be seen qualitatively in the following way. When the function u is antisymmetric under an interchange of the positions of the two particles, the function will vanish whenever the particles occupy the same point. In other words, particles will move under these conditions in such a way as to tend to stay away from each other. On the other hand, when the function u is symmetric, the particles tend to be found near each other. Since there is an electrostatic repulsive force between the two electrons, we would usually expect states which are symmetric to be states of higher energy than those for which the wave function is antisymmetric under position interchange.

To examine these ideas a little more closely, consider as an example the case of the helium atom mentioned above. If we neglect the spin-orbit coupling terms and the spin-spin interaction terms between the two electrons, we can write the Hamiltonian for the helium atom as if the atom were a two-particle system with

$$\mathrm{H} = \frac{1}{2m}\,(\mathrm{P}_1^2 + \mathrm{P}_2^2) - \left(\frac{2e^2}{r_1} + \frac{2e^2}{r_2}\right) + \frac{e^2}{r_{12}}. \tag{17–26}$$

As a first very crude approximation, we can neglect the interaction between the two electrons, the last term in this equation, in which case the energy levels are characterized by the two quantum numbers n_1 and n_2 for each of the two electrons taken separately, and the energy can be written as

$$E_{n_1,n_2} = -2mc^2\alpha^2\left(\frac{1}{n_1^2} + \frac{1}{n_2^2}\right). \tag{17–27}$$

The wave function is obtained from products of the coulomb (hydrogenic) wave functions for the individual electrons.

A system of quantum numbers that designates the energy states of the system in this approximation is $n_1, n_2; l_1, l_2; m_{l1}, m_{l2}; m_{s1}, m_{s2}$. However, these quantum numbers are not suitable if the wave function is to be properly symmetrized.

Note that the Hamiltonian of Eq. (17–26) does not contain spin operators. Hence, as discussed above, properly symmetrized states can always be chosen to be the product of separate space and spin functions. The spin and space functions are each separately symmetric or antisymmetric under particle interchange. As seen above, only one of the four spin functions for a two-electron system is antisymmetric. This is the singlet state, for which the total spin angular momentum is zero. Consequently, the space part of this wave function must be symmetric. Similarly, the three triplet spin states are symmetric, and the corresponding space parts of the wave functions must be antisymmetric.

The particle-interchange operator does not commute with the separate spin or orbital angular-momentum operators, although it does commute with the total spin and total orbital angular-momentum operators. Also, whereas the orbital angular-momentum operators of the two particles taken separately do not commute with the last term in the Hamiltonian of Eq. (17–26), the total **L** does. The operators H, P_{12}, L^2, S^2, L_z, and S_z [where $L^2 = (\mathbf{L}_1 + \mathbf{L}_2)^2$ and $S^2 = (\mathbf{S}_1 + \mathbf{S}_2)^2$] form a mutually commuting set. The simultaneous eigenfunctions can be divided into two classes corresponding to singlet and triplet states. If the coupling term e^2/r_{12} is omitted from the Hamiltonian, these eigenfunctions are

$$\psi_{1nlsm_lm_s} = \frac{1}{\sqrt{2}}\,[u_{100}(1)u_{nlm_l}(2) \pm u_{100}(2)u_{nlm_l}(1)]v_{sm_s}, \qquad (17\text{–}28)$$

where the subscripts refer to the quantum numbers n_1, n_2, l, s, m_l, and m_s for the total system, and to n, l, and m_l for the one-electron states. For simplicity, one electron is assumed to be in the hydrogenic ground state with $n = 1$. The functions u_{nlm_l} refer to hydrogenic wave functions. The positive sign corresponds to the singlet state $s = 0$, and the negative sign to the three triplet states $s = 1$. It is evident that for a given n, l, and m_l, the four spin states (both singlet and triplet) are degenerate.

The coupling term e^2/r_{12} can be included as a first-order perturbation. Although the unperturbed energy states are degenerate, the matrix of the perturbation is already diagonal in the chosen representation. The (diagonal) elements of e^2/r_{12} are

$$\left(1nlsm_lm_s\left|\frac{e^2}{r_{12}}\right|1nlsm_lm_s\right) \equiv A \pm B, \qquad (17\text{–}29)$$

where A is the *screening interaction energy* and B is the *exchange interaction energy:*

$$A \equiv \left(u_{100}(1)u_{nlm_l}(2), \frac{e^2}{r_{12}}\, u_{100}(1)u_{nlm_l}(2)\right),$$
$$B \equiv \left(u_{100}(1)u_{nlm_l}(2), \frac{e^2}{r_{12}}\, u_{100}(2)u_{nlm_l}(1)\right). \tag{17–30}$$

The exchange energy is usually positive. As a result, the singlet states have a higher energy than the triplet.

The screening interaction energy is actually too large for a first-order perturbation calculation to be very significant. However, in an exact instead of a perturbation treatment, the quantum numbers l, m_l, s, and m_s are still valid, for the interaction term commutes with the corresponding operators. (This is merely another way of stating that the matrix of the interaction in this representation is diagonal.)

The experimentally observed energy levels for the helium atom are shown in Fig. 17–2, in comparison with the one-electron levels for $Z = 1$. The helium levels are characterized as being either singlet or triplet. This is customarily indicated, as shown in the figure, by a superscript prefix to the term designation S, P, D, ... Note that for each singlet level except the lowest, there is a group of triplet levels with nearly the same energy. There can be no triplet state corresponding to the lowest singlet level, by the Pauli principle, since in this state the two electrons have the same orbital wave function. Note also that the triplet energy states lie somewhat below the corresponding singlet energy states. When the electrons are in a triplet spin state, the state being symmetric under spin interchange, the position part of the wave function is antisymmetric under particle interchange. Consequently, as discussed above, the electrons avoid each other when they are in a triplet state. Since they avoid each other, the electrostatic repulsion energy between the two electrons is, on the average, less than when they are in a singlet state, and this positive contribution to the energy is smaller in the triplet state than it is in the singlet state. *This causes the singlet energy states to lie above the corresponding triplet energy states.* This is very similar to what we would expect if the magnetic moments of the two electrons were to interact with each other in such a way as to lower their energy when the electrons are antisymmetric and to increase the energy when the spins of the two electrons are parallel. However, as has been pointed out above, the effect on the energy has nothing to do with magnetic fields, but arises only from the electrostatic interaction between the electrons.

Several other things may be noted about the positions of the energy levels in this system. First of all, the ground state lies very much below

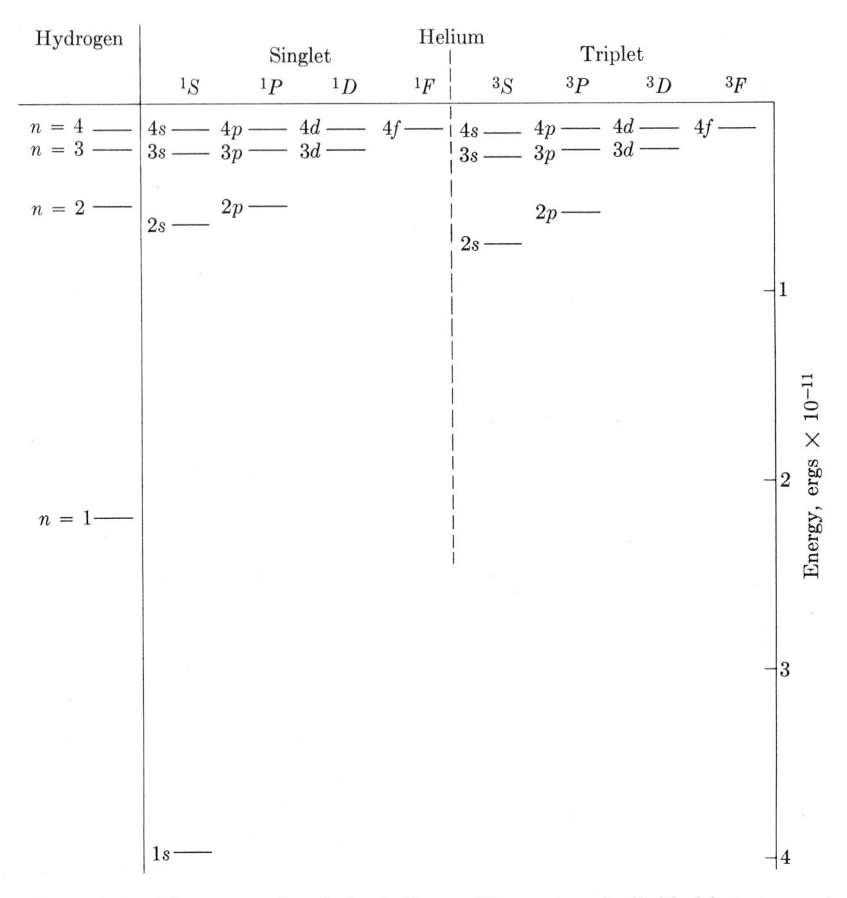

FIG. 17–2. The energy levels for helium. The system is divided into two sets of terms, corresponding to *singlet* and *triplet* helium. The energy levels for hydrogen are shown at the left.

the other energy levels. This can be expected because both electrons in the innermost orbit are attracted strongly by the nucleus. However, for all the other states, one electron exists in a higher (approximately hydrogenlike) orbit, which falls largely outside the electron cloud of the other (inner) electron. Consequently, the innermost electron moves in a nearly hydrogenlike orbit in the field of the doubly-charged helium nucleus, whereas the outer electron in the higher excited state moves in a hydrogenlike orbit for which the inner electron neutralizes one of the charges on the nucleus. In this approximation, we can think of the innermost electron as being bound very tightly to the nucleus, and the less tightly bound electron sees what looks like a singly-charged nucleus. This means that the energies of the higher excited states of the helium atom should be approximately those of an electron moving in the field of a singly-charged nucleus. As mentioned, the hydrogen energy levels are also indicated in Fig. 17-2. It is seen that the helium levels for excited states agree closely with the energy levels of a hydrogen atom. It may also be noted in general that the higher the l-value of a helium energy level, the more nearly it agrees with an energy level of the hydrogen atom. This is because for large l the outer electron does not appreciably penetrate the space-charge cloud of the inner electron surrounding the nucleus. Stated another way, the S-states lie substantially below the $Z = 1$ hydrogenic values because the S-orbitals penetrate the electron charge cloud and "see" a larger effective positive charge at the nucleus.

In the electric dipole approximation, transitions involving radiation cannot occur between the triplet system of levels in the helium atom and the singlet system. This can be seen by considering the electric dipole operator of Chapter 15 which determines the (first-order) interaction with the electromagnetic field. This operator, which involves only the positions of the particles, is independent of the spin; hence the matrix elements of this operator will be zero unless they join singlet states with other singlet states, or triplet with triplet. There are no intercombination transitions in which an atom jumps from a purely triplet to a purely singlet state.

In the case of very heavy elements with two outer electrons, where the spin-orbit interaction term in the Hamiltonian is not negligible, the systems are not purely singlet and purely triplet, since the spin-orbit interaction is sufficiently strong so that the total spin angular momentum is not a good quantum number of the system; that is, **S** does not commute with H. For such heavy elements, e.g., mercury, there are intercombination transitions between the "triplet" and "singlet" systems. (In such a heavy element, the two outer electrons can again be considered to be moving in a common field, now created by the inner electrons, which provide an effective central field of force in which the outer electrons move.)

If desired, the spin-orbit and spin-spin interaction energies between the electrons in the helium atom can be included in the above treatment as perturbations. Because of the degeneracy of the energy levels it is necessary that the unperturbed energy states be chosen so as to give a diagonal matrix for these perturbing terms. The quantum numbers m_l and m_s are no longer appropriate, since the spin-orbit interaction leads to spin and orbital precession. From very fundamental symmetry grounds, however, the total angular momentum **J** and its projection J_z must be constants of the motion. Consequently, an appropriate representation for discussing these spin interactions has quantum numbers n_1, n_2, l, s, j, and m_j. For singlet states, j takes on the value $j = l$, and for triplet states,

$$j = l + 1, l, l - 1 \geq 0.$$

For triplet states with $l > 0$, the level is split into groups of three levels (triplets) having different values of j.

Note that, strictly speaking, with a spin-orbit term present, **L** and **S** are not constants of the motion. However, the spin interactions are weak, and to a good approximation l and s are suitable quantum numbers.

It has been seen that the strong electrostatic interaction between the electrons, in conjunction with the Pauli principle, is equivalent to strong spin-spin interactions which separate the singlet from the triplet states. The Pauli principle thus effectively couples the two electron spins to each other as well as coupling the two orbital motions together. Because of the spin-orbit interaction, different values of j have slightly different energies. This type of angular-momentum coupling system in which the individual **L**'s are rather tightly coupled into a resultant **L** and the individual **S**'s into a resultant **S**, which are then weakly coupled to give **J**, is known as *Russell-Saunders* or *L-S coupling.* It can be generalized to more than two electrons and is the usual coupling found among the lighter elements.

When the spin-orbit energies are large, as is the case in the heavy elements of high Z, it may happen that the spin-orbit (i.e., multiplet) splittings are larger than the exchange-energy splittings. In this case, a better approximation is obtained by first taking into account the spin-orbit interaction which couples the spin and orbital angular momenta to give a resultant $\mathbf{J}_1, \mathbf{J}_2, \ldots$ for each of the electrons. The individual **J**'s are then coupled through the exchange interaction considered as a relatively weak perturbation. This coupling scheme is known as *j-j coupling.*

17–5 Valence binding in the hydrogen molecule. As another example of the effect of statistics on the behavior of a system of particles, consider two hydrogen atoms interacting with each other and, in particular, the valence forces which tend to hold the two atoms together in a molecule. This can be considered as a two-electron problem by treating the two protons and their coulombic fields as relatively fixed so far as the rapid motions of the electrons are concerned.

The Hamiltonian can be written as

$$\mathrm{H} = \frac{1}{2m}\,(\mathrm{P}_1^2 + \mathrm{P}_2^2) - \left(\frac{e^2}{r_{1A}} + \frac{e^2}{r_{2A}} + \frac{e^2}{r_{1B}} + \frac{e^2}{r_{2B}}\right) + \frac{e^2}{r_{AB}} + \frac{e^2}{r_{12}}. \tag{17–31}$$

The subscripts A and B refer to the two nuclei, and the subscripts 1 and 2 refer to the two electrons. Considering only the space part of the wave function, and again assuming that spin forces are negligible, we can choose the wave functions to be either symmetric or antisymmetric under a position interchange, the symmetric function being associated with a singlet spin system for the two electrons and the antisymmetric space state being associated with the triplet spin system. Consequently, when the two hydrogen atoms are sufficiently far apart that their electronic wave functions are only slightly disturbed by interaction with each other, the total wave function can be written as

$$\psi_{\pm} = \frac{1}{\sqrt{2}} [u_A(r_1)u_B(r_2) \pm u_A(r_2)u_B(r_1)], \tag{17-32}$$

where the plus sign applies to the singlet (antisymmetric spin) state and the minus to the triplet (symmetric spin) state.

As a first approximation, assume that for this type of wave function, the orbits of the electrons are only slightly disturbed by the presence of the other hydrogen atom, that is, that $u_A(r_1)$ and $u_B(r_2)$ are wave functions for individual hydrogen atoms. Further assume that this form of the wave function will hold even when the atoms are relatively close to each other. With these assumptions, it is possible to calculate the expectation value of the Hamiltonian of Eq. (17-31). If we do this, we obtain the energy curves of Fig. 17-3 as functions of the separation between the protons. In this figure, the zero of energy is taken to be the energy of the

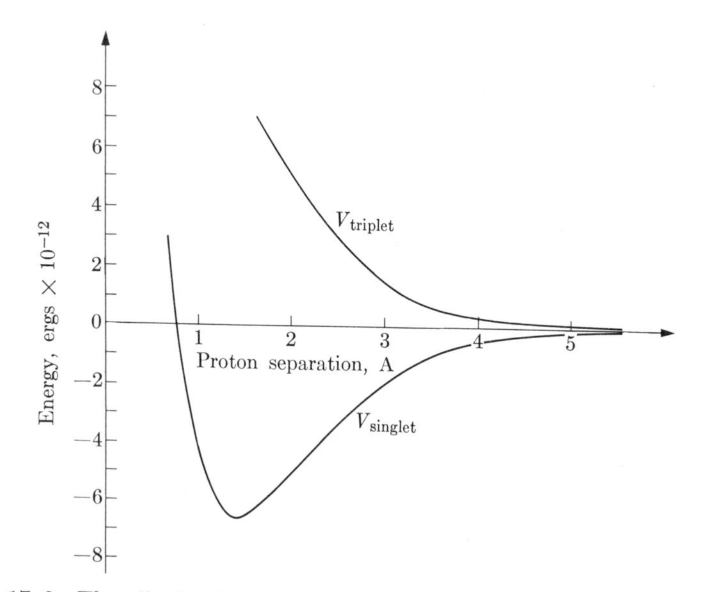

FIG. 17-3. The effective interaction potentials for two hydrogen atoms in the *singlet* and *triplet* electronic states, as a function of internuclear separation. It is seen that only the singlet spin system permits a bound state (hydrogen molecule) to be formed.

hydrogen atoms when they are far apart, and the change in energy that results from the interaction of the two atoms as they move together is plotted against proton separation. Note that when the atoms are in a singlet state, the energy first decreases as the atoms approach each other and then increases, whereas in a triplet state the energy increases continuously. Consequently, hydrogen atoms with parallel spins are always repelled upon collision with each other, whereas if they collide with each other in a singlet state, they are attracted.

The reasons for the form of the energy curves of Fig. 17–3 can be seen qualitatively by considering the wave functions of Eq. (17–32). As has been seen, the electrons tend to be found in the same place when the plus sign applies and tend to be found apart when the minus sign applies. The only region in which we would expect the electrons to occupy the same point with any probability is in a region between the two protons. Hence, for the plus (singlet) state, the electrons are found preferably between the two protons. In this position, they are able to interact with each of the protons. It is true that there is some repulsive energy between the two electrons, but this is more than overcome by the attraction of the neighboring protons. Consequently, such states are states of low electrostatic energy, accounting for the dip in the curve as the two atoms move together. The rise in this curve as the proton separation decreases beyond a certain point results from interpenetration of the electronic clouds by the two protons so that they strongly repel each other, and it is thus to be associated with the repulsive energy between the two protons.

On the other hand, for the triplet ($s = 1$) state, the electrons tend to avoid each other and hence are not found in the region between the two protons, which is the region in which they strongly cement the two protons together. Hence the energy rises monotonically as the two atoms move together. The bound state of the hydrogen molecule corresponds to the two atoms' being bound in the potential well of the lower curve of Fig. 17–3, corresponding to a total spin angular momentum of the electrons of zero. This type of molecular binding is known as *exchange binding.*

The energy difference between the space symmetric and antisymmetric states of a pair of hydrogen atoms can result in a periodic interchange of the two electrons between the two nuclei. This can be seen by noting that a state for which initially the spin of the electron on one atom is plus while the other is minus is a superposition of states of different energy ($s = 1$ and $s = 0$). It is consequently nonstationary, with the electron spins interchanging at a frequency given by the energy difference between the singlet and triplet states. If the atoms are widely separated, there is no energy difference and each electron can be considered as associated with its own nucleus.

17-6 Para- and ortho-hydrogen. As a final example of the effect of statistics on the motion of particles, again consider the hydrogen molecule. Now the molecule will be treated as a two-particle system by noting that the electrons move very rapidly compared with the speed of the nuclei, producing an effective field of force in which the nuclei move. (This is the force which produces the potential of Fig. 17-3.) Thus the hydrogen molecule will now be considered as a two-particle system with the nuclei as the particles. The Hamiltonian of this system can be written as

$$\mathrm{H} = \frac{1}{2m}(\mathrm{P}_A^2 + \mathrm{P}_B^2) + V(r_{AB}). \tag{17-33}$$

The potential-energy term involves not only the electrostatic repulsion between the two protons but also the effective potential arising from the field of the electrons in their motions around the two protons. By introducing the center-of-mass coordinates and the position of the one proton relative to the other, we can write the Hamiltonian in the form

$$\mathrm{H} = \frac{1}{2M}\mathrm{P}^2 + \frac{1}{2\mu}\mathrm{p}^2 + V(r), \tag{17-34}$$

where M is the total mass of the system, μ is the reduced mass for the relative motion of the protons, $\mathbf{P}$ is the momentum of the center of mass, $\mathbf{p}$ is the momentum associated with the relative motion, and V is the effective potential for the relative motion.

Energy eigenfunctions of this Hamiltonian can be written as

$$\psi_{lm_lsm_s} = \exp(i\boldsymbol{k}\cdot\boldsymbol{R})g(r)Y_{lm}(\theta,\phi)v_{sm_s}. \tag{17-35}$$

The total orbital angular momentum of the nuclei, the z-component of their orbital angular momentum, the total nuclear-spin angular momentum, and the z-component of total nuclear-spin angular momentum all commute with the Hamiltonian, and use is made of the commutation relations to arrive at Eq. (17-35). (We have seen that the total *electronic* spin is zero in the bound molecules.) The last term in the equation represents the spin function describing the spin orientation of the two protons.

The energy eigenvalue associated with the internal energy of the molecule can be written as

$$E_{lm_l} = \frac{1}{2I}l(l+1)\hbar^2. \tag{17-36}$$

The constant I, which can be interpreted as the moment of inertia of the molecule, is determined by the proton separation characterizing the minimum in the potential-energy function. It is assumed that the so-called "centrifugal stretching effect" is negligible, so that I can be regarded as a constant in the denominator of Eq. (17–36).

So far, nothing has been said about symmetrizing the wave function. The two protons satisfy Fermi statistics; consequently, the wave function must be so chosen as to be antisymmetric under an interchange of the two particles. Since the coordinate r represents the position of one proton relative to the other, an interchange of the two particles merely changes the direction of this vector, introducing a transformation of the spherical harmonic of Eq. (17–35) given by

$$\mathrm{P}_{AB} Y_{lm}(\theta, \phi) = Y_{lm}(\pi - \theta, \phi + \pi). \tag{17–37}$$

The spherical harmonics are even under such transformations if l is even and are odd if l is odd. Consequently, the position part of the wave function in Eq. (17–35) is even under particle interchange if the quantum number l is even and is odd if the quantum number l is odd. The spin part of the wave function must be odd if the position part is even, and vice versa. Therefore, even l must be associated with singlet nuclear-spin states, and odd l must be associated with triplet states. For example, if the molecule is in its lowest rotational state, for which l is zero, it must be in a state for which $s = 0$ or, in other words, the spins of the two protons must be antiparallel.

This relationship between the evenness or oddness of l and the nuclear spins has an important consequence. For the two proton spins parallel, there are three possible orientations of the total spin angular momentum; consequently, the states of odd l have a statistical weight which is three times as great as they would have if the protons had no spin. On the other hand, the statistical weight of each state for which l is even has the normal value for particles without spin. As a result, in thermal equilibrium at moderate and high temperatures, the states of odd l are populated by three times as many molecules as those with even l.

A further interesting effect occurs at very low temperatures under the influence of suitable catalysts. At very low temperatures, all the atoms settle into the state of lowest rotational energy, namely $l = 0$. This is a state in which the spins are all antiparallel. States for which the spins are antiparallel are called *para*-states of hydrogen. *Ortho*-hydrogen, on the other hand, is composed of molecules in triplet nuclear-spin states ($s = 1$). Now at a very low temperature (below 20°K, for example), after all the molecules are in the para-state, the catalyst can be removed and the hydrogen warmed. The interactions between the magnetic dipole moments of the various hydrogen nuclei are so weak that para-hydrogen can exist for a very long time at high temperatures without reconversion to the high-temperature equilibrium ortho:para ratio of 3:1. This nonequilibrium form of hydrogen can be distinguished from the normal equilibrium form because there are slight differences in the properties of para- and ortho-hydrogen. For example, the specific heats of the two forms of hydrogen gas are different because the spacings of the rotational energy levels for states of even l are different from those of odd l.

17-7 Systems of more than two particles. The discussion of the effect of particle identity upon quantum mechanics was limited in this chapter to systems of two particles. This was done for simplicity and because the main physical ideas can be presented without going to more complex systems where the physics tends to become submerged in the mathematical formulation. Nonetheless, the formalism can be generalized. For an n-particle system there are $\frac{1}{2}n(n - 1)$ particle interchange operators. These may be taken in combination in various sequences to form $n!$ permutation operators, which together constitute a group. When the Hamiltonian does not depend upon the spin operators of the individual particles, the total spin angular momentum commutes with all members of the permutation group and with the Hamiltonian. The effects of electrostatic interactions between particles and of particle statistics then lead to a removal of degeneracy for states of different total s, just as for the case of the helium atom. Thus the L-S coupling scheme is generally valid for all atoms for which the spin-orbit interaction is small.

17-8 Summary. In this chapter, we have considered the effect on quantum formalism of the general indistinguishability of atomic particles. This indistinguishability led to the concept of Fermi particles, whose wave function is antisymmetric under particle exchange, and Bose particles, whose wave function is symmetric under particle interchange. Fermi particles were then studied in more detail because the common elementary particles (electrons, protons, neutrons) obey Fermi statistics. The nomenclature of singlet and triplet states was introduced. The effects of spin symmetry on the electrostatic interaction energies of two Fermi particles were discussed and illustrated by the case of the helium atom. These effects were then used to explain the binding of the hydrogen molecule. The role of nuclear spin statistics in creating two different forms of hydrogen, ortho- and para-hydrogen, was considered and a brief mention was made of the way in which the formalism we developed can be extended to systems of more than two particles.

Problems

17–1. Two particles of mass m are placed in a rectangular box of sides $a \neq b \neq c$ in the lowest energy state of the system compatible with the conditions below. Assuming that the particles interact with each other according to the potential $V = V_0\,\delta(r_1 - r_2)$, use first-order perturbation theory to calculate the energy of the system under the following conditions: (a) Particles not identical. (b) Identical particles of spin zero. (c) Identical particles of spin one-half with spins parallel.

17–2. Calculate the cross section, including its spin dependence, for the scattering of thermal neutrons by neutrons. Assume that the interaction between neutrons is spin-independent and is of the form of a potential well of radius r_0 and depth V_0.

17–3. (a) State the Pauli exclusion principle and discuss its application. (b) Show in detail how with its aid one can order the elements in the periodic table according to their chemical properties. (c) Why do the rare-earth elements have similar chemical properties? (d) Why are the alkali metals similar?

17–4. Discuss the energy-level structure of the helium atom.

17–5. Calculate the differential scattering cross section for the mutual scattering of two identical hard spheres with spin one-half and radius $a \ll \lambda$. Include the effects of S-, P-, and D-waves but neglect higher partial waves.

17–6. (a) Show that the spin-exchange operator can be written as

$$\mathrm{S}_{12} = \frac{1}{\hbar^2}\left[\mathrm{S}_{1+}\mathrm{S}_{2-} + \mathrm{S}_{1-}\mathrm{S}_{2+} + (2\mathrm{S}_{1z}\mathrm{S}_{2z} + \tfrac{1}{2}\hbar^2)\right].$$

[*Hint:* Show that the first term in the brackets changes the spin state $-+$ into $+-$ and gives zero for the remaining three spin states of the form of Eq. (17–12). What operations do the remaining two terms in the brackets perform?] (b) Show that the above spin-exchange operator can be expressed as

$$\mathrm{S}_{12} = \frac{1}{\hbar^2}\left(2\mathbf{S}_1 \cdot \mathbf{S}_2 + \tfrac{1}{2}\hbar^2\right).$$

(c) Show that it can also be written as

$$\mathrm{S}_{12} = \frac{1}{\hbar^2}\left(\mathrm{S}^2 - \hbar^2\right).$$

CHAPTER 18

QUANTUM-STATISTICAL MECHANICS

18–1 Introduction. Our development of quantum mechanics so far has concerned the description of systems that are in *pure* states, that is, in states for which the wave function is known. This chapter will consider systems for which only incomplete knowledge of the state of the systems is available. Such systems will be said to be in *mixed* states. These must be handled by suitable statistical techniques. The classical analogue of quantum statistics is classical statistical mechanics, developed by Boltzmann, Gibbs, and others. Because of the intrinsically statistical character of quantum mechanics, quantum statistics involves statistical considerations at two separate levels. The one concerning the statistical distribution of measurements on systems having *identical* wave functions has been dealt with already. The second deals with the statistical distribution of systems among the various wave functions compatible with the (incomplete) knowledge of the state of the system of interest.

As in many statistical problems, it is helpful to introduce the idea of an ensemble of similar systems. Consider such an ensemble with possible wave functions $\psi_1, \psi_2, \psi_3, \ldots$ A complete description of the ensemble is then given by the specification of the numbers $n_1, n_2, n_3, \ldots$, each representing the number of systems n_j described by the wave function ψ_j. However, the set of numbers n_j may contain information that is of no physical significance. For example, as emphasized previously, two systems with wave functions differing only in phase cannot be distinguished. Clearly, including functions differing only in phase in the set of ψ_j is neither necessary nor desirable. There may also be other redundancies which should be eliminated.

The only physically significant properties of an ensemble are the distribution functions for each of the possible measurements which can be made on the ensemble of systems. Thus, if $P(q)$ represents the probability per unit q that a measurement of the observable Q performed on a member of the ensemble will give q as the result, then the distribution function $P(q)$ gives all the physically significant information about the ensemble that is obtainable from measurements of Q.

The distribution function $P(q)$ determines the average values of all powers of Q, through

$$[Q^n] = \int P(q)q^n \, dq. \tag{18–1}$$

Here and in the remainder of this chapter, brackets will be used to indicate an average over the ensemble. Conversely, these average values or *moments* determine the distribution function, as can readily be shown for well-behaved, i.e., square-integrable, distribution functions by introducing a variable k, multiplying Eq. (18–1) through by $i^n k^n/n!$ and summing over n:

$$\begin{aligned} W(k) &\equiv \sum_n \frac{1}{n!} i^n k^n [Q^n] \\ &= \int P(q) \exp(ikq)\, dq. \end{aligned} \tag{18–2}$$

The function $W(k)$, defined as the sum above, is the Fourier transform of $P(q)$; $P(q)$ can therefore be determined from

$$\begin{aligned} P(q) &= \frac{1}{2\pi} \int_{-\infty}^{\infty} W(k) \exp(-ikq)\, dk \\ &= \frac{1}{2\pi} \int_{-\infty}^{\infty} \sum_n \frac{1}{n!} i^n k^n [Q^n] \exp(-ikq)\, dk, \end{aligned} \tag{18–3}$$

from which it is seen that under these conditions a *complete* physical description of an ensemble of similar systems is given by the average values of all observables of the system. (Here the various powers of a given observable are regarded as separate observables.)

The expectation value $\langle Q \rangle$ of an observable Q gives the average of the observable when the system has some definite wave function. To obtain the ensemble average, $\langle Q \rangle$ must then be averaged over the ensemble:

$$[Q] = [\langle Q \rangle] = [(\psi, \mathrm{Q}\psi)]. \tag{18–4}$$

18–2 The density matrix. In dealing with the behavior of statistical ensembles, it is convenient to introduce a *density function* ρ defined by

$$\rho(x, x') \equiv [\psi(x)\bar{\psi}(x')]. \tag{18–5}$$

In terms of the density function, Eq. (18–4) can be written as

$$[Q] = \int \delta(x - x')\mathrm{Q}\rho(x, x')\, dx\, dx'. \tag{18–6}$$

The operator Q operates only on the x-variable in ρ. Since Q is a Hermitian operator,

$$\begin{aligned} [Q] &= \int \overline{\mathrm{Q}\, \delta(x - x')} \rho(x, x')\, dx\, dx' \\ &= \int \mathrm{Q}'\, \delta(x' - x)\rho(x, x')\, dx\, dx'. \end{aligned} \tag{18–7}$$

Now Q′ operates only on the primed variable in $\delta(x' - x)$. The function

$$Q(x', x) \equiv \mathrm{Q}' \, \delta(x' - x) \tag{18–8}$$

will be recognized as the matrix element of the operator $\mathbf{Q}$ interpreted as a matrix in a position-diagonal representation. (See Chapter 11.) This suggests that the density function be interpreted as a *density matrix,* defined by

$$\boldsymbol{\rho} \equiv [\psi\psi^*], \tag{18–9}$$

where ψ is a column vector and ψ^* is its Hermitian adjoint. This equation thus defines a square matrix, with elements given by Eq. (18–5). In matrix form, Eq. (18–7) can be written as

$$\begin{aligned}[Q] &= \operatorname{tr} \mathbf{Q}\boldsymbol{\rho} = \int Q(x', x)\rho(x, x') \, dx \, dx' \\ &= \operatorname{tr} \boldsymbol{\rho}\mathbf{Q};\end{aligned} \tag{18–10}$$

the ensemble average of Q is obtained by taking the trace of the matrix product of $\mathbf{Q}$ and $\boldsymbol{\rho}$. The product may be taken in either order. This is a general property of a trace of the product of two matrices.

Equation (18–10) is invariant under a similarity transformation, as was mentioned in the discussion of Eq. (13–34). To see this in another way, form

$$\begin{aligned}\operatorname{tr} \mathbf{Q}\boldsymbol{\rho} &= \operatorname{tr} \mathbf{T}^{-1}\mathbf{T}\mathbf{Q}\mathbf{T}^{-1}\mathbf{T}\boldsymbol{\rho} \\ &= \operatorname{tr} \mathbf{T}\mathbf{Q}\mathbf{T}^{-1}\mathbf{T}\boldsymbol{\rho}\mathbf{T}^{-1} \\ &= \operatorname{tr} \mathbf{Q}^{\dagger}\boldsymbol{\rho}^{\dagger}.\end{aligned} \tag{18–11}$$

Here use is made of the fact that the trace is left unchanged by a change in order of the factor $\mathbf{T}^{-1}$. Equation (18–10) is thus valid for any matrix representation of the matrices. (See also Chapter 13.)

Since Eq. (18–10) can be used to obtain the average values of all observables, *the density matrix* $\boldsymbol{\rho}$ *must contain all the physically significant information that is known about the ensemble.* This is usually less information than is contained in an enumeration of the relative frequencies of all possible wave functions. This situation is without a classical analogue and leads to interesting paradoxes, some of which will be discussed later.

Some of the properties of the density matrix will now be considered briefly. First, it is Hermitian. This can be seen by forming the Hermitian adjoint of Eq. (18–9) or, equivalently, by interchanging x and x' and taking the complex conjugate of Eq. (18–5). Second, the trace of $\boldsymbol{\rho}$ is unity. This follows from the normalization of the wave functions:

$$\int \rho(x, x) \, dx = 1. \tag{18–12}$$

While density-matrix formalism is particularly useful for the description of mixed states, it is also applicable to pure states. In such a case, the ensemble averages of Eqs. (18–5) and (18–9) reduce to the single terms corresponding to the pure state. Then the eigenvalues of $\boldsymbol{\rho}$ are 0 and 1, with the value 1 being nondegenerate. To see this, square Eq. (18–9), omitting the brackets:

$$\begin{aligned} \boldsymbol{\rho}^2 &= \psi\psi^*\psi\psi^* = \psi\psi^* = \boldsymbol{\rho}, \\ \boldsymbol{\rho}(\boldsymbol{\rho} - \mathbf{I}) &= 0. \end{aligned} \tag{18–13}$$

The eigenvalue 1 must be nondegenerate, since the trace of $\boldsymbol{\rho}$, which is the sum of the eigenvalues, is unity.

Note that the diagonal elements of $\boldsymbol{\rho}$ represent the probability per unit x of finding a system in the ensemble with the coordinates x. In similar fashion, if the stationary states are enumerated by an index n representing energy eigenstates, the density matrix in a representation with energy diagonal will have discrete elements $\rho_{nn'}$, and ρ_{nn} will represent the probability of finding a system in the ensemble in the nth energy state. If the corresponding wave function is designated as $u_n(x)$, then, as was shown in Chapter 13, the $u_n(x)$ may be interpreted as the elements of a unitary matrix which can be used to transform $\boldsymbol{\rho}$ into the representation with energy diagonal:

$$\rho_{nn'} = \int \overline{u_n}(x)\rho(x, x')u_{n'}(x')\, dx\, dx'. \tag{18–14}$$

Note that if the system is definitely in the nth energy state,

$$\begin{aligned} \rho(x, x') &= u_n(x)\overline{u_n}(x'), \\ \rho_{nn'} &= \delta_{nn'}. \end{aligned} \tag{18–15}$$

In similar fashion, other representations can be used to make the probability-distribution functions of the other observables appear on the diagonal of the density matrix.

As an elementary application of density-matrix formalism, consider the density matrix for an ensemble of unpolarized electrons, i.e., electrons in completely random spin states. Employ a representation with the z-component of an electron spin diagonal. The density matrix in this case is one-half times the identity matrix:

$$\boldsymbol{\rho} = \begin{bmatrix} \frac{1}{2} & 0 \\ 0 & \frac{1}{2} \end{bmatrix}. \tag{18–16}$$

This can be seen as follows. First note that the two spin orientations (with respect to the z-axis) have equal probability. Also, the average value of any spin component is obtained from

$$[\boldsymbol{\sigma}] = \operatorname{tr} \boldsymbol{\sigma\rho} = \tfrac{1}{2} \operatorname{tr} \boldsymbol{\sigma} = 0, \tag{18–17}$$

since the trace of any component of $\boldsymbol{\sigma}$ is equal to the sum of the two spin eigenvalues. Thus the density matrix in Eq. (18–16) describes what is commonly meant by an ensemble of unpolarized electrons, namely, electrons without a preferred spin orientation. We can see that Eq. (18–16) is a unique description (in this representation) of an ensemble of unpolarized electrons because any other matrix would have unequal elements on the diagonal after the diagonalizing transformation. Such a diagonal density matrix with unequal elements corresponds to a net spin alignment along the z-axis in the transformed coordinate system.

It is convenient to extend the notion of a *completely random state* to all systems having a finite number (N) of states. The density matrix of such a completely random state is

$$\boldsymbol{\rho} = \frac{1}{N} \mathbf{I}. \tag{18–18}$$

It is interesting and significant that a completely unpolarized ensemble of electrons can, *for any orientation of z*, be considered to consist of electrons every one of which is oriented in either the positive or negative z-direction. Thus a beam of unpolarized electrons can be passed through a device which measures, for example, the z-component of spin for each electron in the ensemble. If the device does not separate or "label" the electrons in any way, the ensemble is unaffected by the measurement. *It is still completely random.*

This interpretation of a random ensemble as a mixture of systems in appropriate pure states is equivalent to a decomposition of a density matrix into two or more parts each of which describes a pure state. For example, referring again to a system of electron spins, the density matrix

$$\boldsymbol{\rho} = \begin{bmatrix} \frac{3}{4} & \frac{1}{4} \\ \frac{1}{4} & \frac{1}{4} \end{bmatrix} \tag{18–19}$$

can be decomposed as

$$\boldsymbol{\rho} = \tfrac{1}{2}\boldsymbol{\rho}_1 + \tfrac{1}{2}\boldsymbol{\rho}_2, \tag{18–20}$$

where

$$\boldsymbol{\rho}_1 = \begin{bmatrix} \frac{1}{2} & \frac{1}{2} \\ \frac{1}{2} & \frac{1}{2} \end{bmatrix} \quad \text{and} \quad \boldsymbol{\rho}_2 = \begin{bmatrix} 1 & 0 \\ 0 & 0 \end{bmatrix} \tag{18–21}$$

are the density matrices representing electrons oriented in the $+x$-direction and in the $+z$-direction, respectively. This decomposition signifies that the ensemble is equivalent to a mixture of equal numbers of electrons oriented in these two directions. This decomposition is not unique, however. For example, another possible decomposition is

$$\boldsymbol{\rho} = \frac{\sqrt{2}+1}{2\sqrt{2}}\boldsymbol{\rho}_3 + \frac{\sqrt{2}-1}{2\sqrt{2}}\boldsymbol{\rho}_4, \tag{18–22}$$

where

$$\boldsymbol{\rho}_3 = \frac{1}{2\sqrt{2}}\begin{bmatrix}\sqrt{2}+1 & 1\\ 1 & \sqrt{2}-1\end{bmatrix} \quad \text{and} \quad \boldsymbol{\rho}_4 = \frac{1}{2\sqrt{2}}\begin{bmatrix}\sqrt{2}-1 & -1\\ -1 & \sqrt{2}+1\end{bmatrix} \tag{18–23}$$

respectively represent an ensemble with spins oriented in the xz-plane at an angle of 45° with both the positive x- and z-axes and an ensemble with spins oriented in the opposite direction. The decomposition of Eq. (18–22) thus represents a mixture of electrons with fractions $(\sqrt{2}+1)/2\sqrt{2}$ and $(\sqrt{2}-1)/2\sqrt{2}$ in these two orientations.

Confusion sometimes arises because, for a mixed state, a given density matrix can be decomposed in more than one way, and consequently there is an ambiguity in the ensemble representation of the mixed state. An interesting example is provided by some of the theoretical papers on electron physics, particularly on electron interference. In these electron-interference experiments, electrons are emitted by a hot cathode; they are accelerated to form an electron beam, which is then used to bombard scattering foils. It was the feeling of some of the investigators in the field that the electrons are emitted by the cathode in the form of wave packets having an energy spread equal to the observed energy spread of the electron beam. Electron-interference effects were then calculated, with these wave packets used as electron-wave functions.

However, the density matrix describing the state of electrons emitted by the cathode has a form such that it can be decomposed into either monoenergetic pure states or wave-packet pure states. Hence the ensemble representation of the mixed state is ambiguous. Although the electrons may be thought of as emitted in the form of wave packets, this need not be done. Since interference calculations are more easily carried out using monoenergetic wave functions, it is much more convenient to consider each electron as having a definite energy. The two descriptions are physically equivalent.

To show the equivalence of the two representations, we will for convenience ignore the transverse motion of the electron relative to the surface of the cathode (considered plane) and use a position-diagonal representation for the wave functions and density matrix. With the assumption that an electron is emitted as a wave packet, we can write its wave function after emission as

$$\psi = \int_{-\infty}^{\infty} A(k) \exp \{i[kx - \omega(t - t_0)]\} \, dk, \tag{18–24}$$

with

$$\omega = \frac{\hbar k^2}{2m}, \tag{18–25}$$

where t_0 is the time of emission and $A(k)$ gives the form of the wave packet. Various electrons are emitted at various times t_0, which may be considered to be random. The density function is obtained by averaging over t_0:

$$\rho(x, x', t) = [\psi(x, t)\overline{\psi(x', t)}]_{t_0}. \tag{18–26}$$

In the average over t_0, nonvanishing cross terms in Eq. (18–24) are obtained only when the two frequencies are equal, implying equal k. Hence

$$\rho(x, x', t) = \int |A|^2 \exp [ik(x - x')] \, dk. \tag{18–27}$$

Note that the time dependence has disappeared.

This ensemble can equally well be considered to be an ensemble of plane-wave or monoenergetic states having wave functions

$$\psi_k = \exp [i(kx - \omega t + \delta_k)]. \tag{18–28}$$

The density matrix can be written as a decomposition in density matrices, each representing such a plane-wave state:

$$\rho(x, x') = \int |A(k)|^2 \psi_k \overline{\psi_k} \, dk. \tag{18–29}$$

Note that the probability that an electron will have the momentum k (per unit k) is $|A(k)|^2$ for both ensembles.

18–3 The equation of motion of the density matrix. The equation of motion of the density matrix is easily obtained from the Schrödinger equation, which can be written in matrix form as

$$\mathsf{H}\psi = i\hbar \frac{\partial \psi}{\partial t}. \tag{18–30}$$

If we multiply on the right by the Hermitian adjoint ψ^*, we find

$$\mathsf{H}\psi\psi^* = i\hbar \frac{\partial \psi}{\partial t} \psi^*. \tag{18–31}$$

Note that, being a matrix, H operates only on ψ, and not on ψ^*. Taking the adjoint of Eq. (18–30) and multiplying on the left by ψ yields

$$\psi\psi^*\mathsf{H} = -i\hbar\psi\frac{\partial\psi^*}{\partial t}\cdot \tag{18–32}$$

Subtracting this from Eq. (18–31) gives

$$\mathsf{H}\psi\psi^* - \psi\psi^*\mathsf{H} = i\hbar\frac{\partial}{\partial t}(\psi\psi^*). \tag{18–33}$$

If we now form the ensemble average and use Eq. (18–9), we find

$$\mathsf{H}\boldsymbol{\rho} - \boldsymbol{\rho}\mathsf{H} = [\mathsf{H}, \boldsymbol{\rho}] = i\hbar\frac{\partial}{\partial t}\boldsymbol{\rho}. \tag{18–34}$$

(Here the brackets denote a commutator, rather than an ensemble average.) Note that this differs in sign from the equation of motion of an *observable* in a Heisenberg representation. Note also that in a Heisenberg representation, $\boldsymbol{\rho}$ is a constant and Eq. (18–34) does not hold. Written in component form, this equation is, in position representation,

$$\int [H(x, x'')\rho(x'', x') - \rho(x, x'')H(x'', x')]\, dx'' = i\hbar\frac{\partial}{\partial t}\rho(x, x'). \tag{18–35}$$

Equation (18–34) gives the correct equation of motion for the average value of an observable. This can be seen by computing

$$\begin{aligned}\frac{d}{dt}\operatorname{tr}\mathsf{Q}\boldsymbol{\rho} &= \operatorname{tr}\mathsf{Q}\frac{\partial}{\partial t}\boldsymbol{\rho} = -\frac{i}{\hbar}\operatorname{tr}\mathsf{Q}[\mathsf{H}, \boldsymbol{\rho}] \\ &= -\frac{i}{\hbar}\operatorname{tr}[\mathsf{QH}\boldsymbol{\rho} - \mathsf{Q}\boldsymbol{\rho}\mathsf{H}] = -\frac{i}{\hbar}\operatorname{tr}[(\mathsf{QH} - \mathsf{HQ})\boldsymbol{\rho}] \\ &= \operatorname{tr}\{\mathsf{Q}, \mathsf{H}\}\boldsymbol{\rho},\end{aligned} \tag{18–36}$$

where $\{\mathsf{Q}, \mathsf{H}\}$ signifies the Poisson bracket of Q and H. In the second line of the above equation, use is again made of the invariance of the trace of a product to the order in which the product is taken.

18–4 Ordered and disordered ensembles. In the discussion of many important statistical problems, a measure of the *order* or the *disorder* of an ensemble is needed. A suitable quantitative measure is provided by

$$\sigma \equiv -\operatorname{tr}\boldsymbol{\rho}\ln\boldsymbol{\rho}. \tag{18–37}$$

An ensemble is in its most highly ordered state when all its members are in the same pure state, i.e., when Eq. (18–13) is satisfied. In this case, it is readily seen that $\sigma = 0$. On the other hand, for the completely random state of Eq. (18–18),

$$\sigma = -\ln\left(\frac{1}{N}\right) = +\ln N, \tag{18–38}$$

where N is the number of possible quantum states, and the density matrix has dimensions $N \times N$. As will be shown later, this constitutes an upper bound on σ. For any reasonable definition of order, the completely random state must be regarded as the state of maximum disorder. Since any departure of the ensemble from the completely random state can only decrease σ, σ as defined in Eq. (18–37) is a suitable quantitative measure of the order of an ensemble.

If all the members of an ensemble are subjected to the same disturbance, σ remains unaffected. For example, assume that the forces given by a time-independent Hamiltonian H act on the member systems of the ensemble for a time τ. From Eq. (13–56), the wave function $\psi(0)$ of each system is transformed into

$$\psi(\tau) = \exp\left(-\frac{i\mathrm{H}\tau}{\hbar}\right)\psi(0) \tag{18–39}$$

by the interaction. If this expression is substituted into Eq. (18–9), it is seen that the interaction transforms the density matrix into

$$\rho(\tau) = \exp\left(-\frac{i\mathrm{H}\tau}{\hbar}\right)\rho(0)\exp\left(\frac{i\mathrm{H}\tau}{\hbar}\right). \tag{18–40}$$

This constitutes a unitary transformation on ρ. If the Hamiltonian is time-dependent, it can be decomposed into an (infinite) sequence of time-independent segments. The over-all transformation is the product of these unitary transformations, and is also unitary. However, as was discussed in Chapter 13, the trace of a matrix is invariant under a unitary transformation. As a result, σ is unaffected by a disturbance that is applied to all members of the ensemble. Consequently, it is impossible to introduce either order or disorder into an ensemble by acting on each member of the ensemble with the same force field.

If the members of an ensemble are acted on by different forces, however, there is usually a trend toward more disorder in the ensemble. We can see this if we first consider the special case of an ensemble represented in an energy representation by the stationary density matrix

$$\begin{aligned} \rho_{nn} &= 1, \\ \rho_{lm} &= 0, \qquad l \neq m \quad \text{or} \quad l = m \neq n. \end{aligned} \tag{18–41}$$

This ensemble has all its members in the nth energy state. We now consider the effect of an instantaneous disturbance at the time $t = t_0$ on all members of the ensemble. This disturbance can be represented in its effect on the ensemble by the unitary transformation

$$\mathbf{U}\boldsymbol{\rho}(t_0)\mathbf{U}^{-1} = \mathbf{U}\boldsymbol{\rho}(t_0)\mathbf{U}^{*} = \boldsymbol{\rho}'(t_0). \tag{18–42}$$

If the nth column of $\mathbf{U}$ has elements $a_1, a_2, \ldots$, then $\boldsymbol{\rho}'$ has the form

$$\boldsymbol{\rho}'(t_0) = \begin{bmatrix} |a_1|^2 & a_1\overline{a_2} & a_1\overline{a_3} & \cdots \\ a_2\overline{a_1} & |a_2|^2 & a_2\overline{a_3} & \cdots \\ a_3\overline{a_1} & a_3\overline{a_2} & |a_3|^2 & \cdots \\ \vdots & & & \end{bmatrix}, \tag{18–43}$$

where

$$\sum_j |a_j|^2 = 1. \tag{18–44}$$

Equation (18–43) represents the density matrix at $t = t_0$ after the disturbance has occurred. At some later time, the density matrix has elements

$$\rho'_{ij}(t) = a_i\overline{a_j}\exp\left[i\omega_{ij}(t - t_0)\right], \tag{18–45}$$

where

$$\omega_{ij} \equiv \frac{E_i - E_j}{\hbar}. \tag{18–46}$$

Imagine now that different members of the ensemble are disturbed at different times, and that the disturbances are randomly distributed in time. Such a disturbance will be said to be random. The resulting density-matrix elements are obtained from Eq. (18–45) by averaging over t_0. With nondegenerate energy states, all off-diagonal elements average to zero. If there are degeneracies, these degeneracies may be split by other disturbances; these will in general lead to the same conclusions.

A random disturbance acting on the various members of the ensemble produces a new stationary ensemble characterized by a diagonal matrix in an energy representation. Individual members of the ensemble may thus be considered to be in definite energy states. It can be said that such random disturbances produce transitions between the various energy levels, inasmuch as the density matrices are completely described by the populations of the various energy levels.

If the original density matrix $\boldsymbol{\rho}$ characterizing the system is diagonal in an energy representation, it may be decomposed into matrices of the form of Eq. (18–41). We see from Eq. (18–43) that after a series of random disturbances, $\boldsymbol{\rho}$ becomes $\boldsymbol{\rho}'$, with elements

$$\rho'_{kk} = \rho_{kk} + \sum_l C_{kl}(\rho_{ll} - \rho_{kk}). \tag{18–47}$$

Here $C_{kl} = C_{lk}$ represents the (positive) transition probability between states k and l due to the disturbance. Note that each term in the sum in this equation serves to increase ρ_{kk} if $\rho_{ll} > \rho_{kk}$. Also, ρ_{ll} is then decreased by the same amount by the corresponding term in its sum. Note also that the sum

$$\sigma_k + \sigma_l \equiv -(\rho_{kk} \ln \rho_{kk} + \rho_{ll} \ln \rho_{ll}) \tag{18–48}$$

is increased by a transfer of population from state l to state k (when $\rho_{ll} > \rho_{kk}$). Consequently, we can see by an iteration of the above argument that the order parameter σ is increased by random disturbances; that is, after random disturbances,

$$\sigma' = -\operatorname{tr} \boldsymbol{\rho}' \ln \boldsymbol{\rho}' \geq \sigma; \tag{18–49}$$

random disturbances introduce disorder into an ensemble. It is reasonable to assume that the interactions occurring between any system and a heat bath constitute such random disturbances which increase σ.

If an individual random disturbance produces only a small change in $\boldsymbol{\rho}$, Eq. (18–47) can be written as the differential equation

$$\frac{d\rho_{kk}}{dt} = \sum_l B_{kl}(\rho_{ll} - \rho_{kk}). \tag{18–50}$$

This may be recognized as a diffusion equation. Its solution shows that a "diffusion" of the members of the ensembles between the various energy levels takes place until all energy levels which can be coupled by the disturbances (for which $B_{kl} \neq 0$) are equally populated. [It is only under this condition that the time derivatives of Eq. (18–50) vanish.] Thus, systems for which Eq. (18–50) is valid tend to approach the random distribution of Eq. (18–18) when acted on by a series of random disturbances.

It is clear from the behavior of the order parameter σ discussed above that it is related to the thermodynamical-state variable *entropy*. In fact, it can be shown* that a suitable quantum-mechanical definition of entropy is

$$S \equiv k\sigma, \tag{18–51}$$

where k is Boltzmann's constant.

---

* R. C. Tolman, *Principles of Statistical Mechanics*, Oxford University Press, Oxford, 1st ed., 1938, Chapter 13.

18–5 Stationary ensembles. The density matrix for a completely random ensemble, Eq. (18–18), is proportional to the identity matrix. It therefore has the unique property that it commutes with *every* Hamiltonian and hence is *always stationary*. This means, as mentioned earlier, that there is no way in which the same force field acting on all members of such a random ensemble can introduce order into the system. A system characterized by a stationary density matrix is in an *equilibrium* state or condition. A necessary and sufficient condition for a state to be stationary is the commutation of $\boldsymbol{\rho}$ with the Hamiltonian. A sufficient condition is that $\boldsymbol{\rho}$ be some function of H:

$$\boldsymbol{\rho} = \boldsymbol{\rho}(\mathsf{H}). \tag{18–52}$$

Stationary ensembles are of particular importance for systems interacting with a heat bath. Such systems approach a stationary state characterized by the temperature of the bath. Another important application of a stationary ensemble is in the representation of a system for which only the energy is known. If there are many states of the same energy, it is reasonable to give to each such state the same *a priori* probability. The density matrix then has equal nonzero elements on the diagonal for these energy states only. In a similar manner, a system for which there is no information can be assumed to be in the completely random state described previously. All these ensembles are characterized by density matrices which commute with the Hamiltonian and are stationary.

The type of stationary ensembles which is of chief interest here is the maximum-disorder ensemble. Various classes of such ensembles, completely random, microcanonical, canonical, and grand canonical, will be considered.

As discussed previously, the *completely random ensemble* is defined as one for which all energy states are equally probable. Alternatively, it may be defined as the state for which σ is maximized without any physical auxiliary conditions. Thus it is determined by the requirement that the variation $\delta\sigma$ vanish:

$$\delta\sigma = \delta\,(\operatorname{tr}\boldsymbol{\rho}\ln\boldsymbol{\rho}) = 0. \tag{18–53}$$

The only auxiliary condition on the variation is

$$\operatorname{tr}\boldsymbol{\rho} = 1. \tag{18–54}$$

For the diagonal density matrices under consideration,

$$\delta\sigma = \delta\sum_j \rho_{jj}\ln\rho_{jj} = \sum_j \delta\rho_{jj}\,(\ln\rho_{jj} + 1) = 0. \tag{18–55}$$

The variations $\delta\rho_{jj}$ are arbitrary, subject only to the condition that

$$\sum_j \delta\rho_{jj} = 0. \tag{18–56}$$

This auxiliary condition can be introduced by the method of Lagrangian multipliers. If Eq. (18–56) is multiplied by a constant λ and added to Eq. (18–55), the result, for any λ, is

$$\sum_j \delta\rho_{jj}\,[\ln\rho_{jj} + 1 + \lambda] = 0. \tag{18–57}$$

We may choose λ so as to make any one of the bracketed terms in this equation vanish. All the other bracketed terms must vanish, since the remaining $\delta\rho_{jj}$ may be independently varied. Therefore

$$\ln\rho_{jj} = \text{constant}, \tag{18–58}$$

which leads immediately to the density matrix for a completely random ensemble, given by Eq. (18–18).

The *microcanonical ensemble* is defined to be one for which σ is a maximum subject to the condition that all members of the ensemble have energies lying in a narrow energy range. Such an ensemble can be used to describe the state of a gas for which only the total energy of the gas is known. Formally, the microcanonical ensemble is one for which σ is maximized subject to the condition that the only nonzero elements of $\boldsymbol{\rho}$ lie in the prescribed energy range. Equations (18–53) through (18–58) are valid provided the sums are interpreted as being only over the prescribed energy range. Consequently, from Eq. (18–58), a microcanonical ensemble is one for which all energy levels in the prescribed energy range are equally populated.

The *canonical ensemble* is defined to be one for which σ is maximized subject to the condition that the mean energy of the ensemble takes on some previously assigned value. The canonical ensemble is useful in describing an ensemble whose members have been allowed to interact with a heat bath at some definite temperature T. The mean energy of the ensemble, after equilibrium has been established, is determined by this temperature. Consequently

$$\delta\sigma = \delta\,\mathrm{tr}\,\boldsymbol{\rho}\ln\boldsymbol{\rho} = 0, \tag{18–59}$$

subject to the conditions that

$$\mathrm{tr}\,\boldsymbol{\rho} = 1, \qquad \mathrm{tr}\,\mathsf{H}\boldsymbol{\rho} = [E]. \tag{18–60}$$

These two auxiliary conditions can again be taken into account by the technique of multipliers. The resulting expression is

$$\sum_j \delta\rho_{jj} [\ln \rho_{jj} + 1 - \ln A + \lambda E_j] = 0, \tag{18–61}$$

where A and λ are constants. Again the bracketed terms all vanish and

$$\rho_{jj} = A \exp(-\lambda E_j). \tag{18–62}$$

The constants must be chosen so as to satisfy Eq. (18–60). In addition, the average energy can be related to the temperature of the heat bath. To do this, consider an ensemble of one-dimensional oscillators. Their average energy is

$$\begin{aligned}
[E] = \operatorname{tr} \mathsf{H}\boldsymbol{\rho} &= \sum_j E_j \rho_{jj} = \sum_j (j + \tfrac{1}{2})\hbar\omega A \exp[-\lambda(j + \tfrac{1}{2})\hbar\omega] \\
&= -\hbar\omega A \frac{d}{d(\lambda\hbar\omega)} \sum_{j=0}^{\infty} \exp[-(j + \tfrac{1}{2})\lambda\hbar\omega] \\
&= -\hbar\omega A \frac{d}{d(\lambda\hbar\omega)} \frac{\exp(-\lambda\hbar\omega/2)}{1 - \exp(-\lambda\hbar\omega)} \\
&= \frac{\hbar\omega}{2} A \frac{\exp(\lambda\hbar\omega/2) + \exp(-\lambda\hbar\omega/2)}{[\exp(\lambda\hbar\omega/2) - \exp(-\lambda\hbar\omega/2)]^2} \cdot
\end{aligned} \tag{18–63}$$

For an ensemble of one-dimensional oscillators, the first of equations (18–60) can be written as

$$1 = \sum_j A \exp[-(j + \tfrac{1}{2})\lambda\hbar\omega] = A \frac{\exp(-\lambda\hbar\omega/2)}{1 - \exp(-\lambda\hbar\omega)} \cdot \tag{18–64}$$

If we substitute this into Eq. (18–63), we find that

$$\begin{aligned}
[E] &= \tfrac{1}{2}\hbar\omega \frac{\exp(\lambda\hbar\omega/2) + \exp(-\lambda\hbar\omega/2)}{\exp(\lambda\hbar\omega/2) - \exp(-\lambda\hbar\omega/2)} \\
&= \tfrac{1}{2}\hbar\omega + \frac{\hbar\omega}{\exp(\lambda\hbar\omega) - 1} \cdot
\end{aligned} \tag{18–65}$$

In the limit of very low frequencies, this becomes

$$[E] \xrightarrow[\omega \to 0]{} \frac{1}{\lambda} \cdot \tag{18–66}$$

However, classical results apply in this limit, and from classical statistics,

$$[E] = kT. \tag{18–67}$$

Therefore

$$\lambda = \frac{1}{kT} \cdot \tag{18–68}$$

At first glance, this result appears to be highly restricted in its validity, being limited to low-frequency harmonic oscillators, but it may easily be seen to be quite general. Consider a system composed of two noninteracting subsystems. Let one of these subsystems be a low-frequency linear oscillator. The combined system may be considered to be either a single system or two independent systems. In either case, the results of Eqs. (18–67) and (18–68) are valid for the oscillator. Considered as a combined system, however, there is but one λ, determined by Eq. (18–68), for the combined system.

To summarize, a canonical ensemble is one for which the population of an energy state is proportional to the Boltzmann factor $\exp(-E_j/kT)$. If this result is substituted into Eq. (18–60), the average energy at a temperature T may be calculated for any system.

Often the total number of particles in the system is unknown, for example, in the case of a gas. Consequently, it is sometimes convenient to consider still another kind of stationary ensemble, one in which the members vary in the total number of particles. If the total number of particles in the system is introduced formally as a dynamical variable with an operator N having eigenvalues 0, 1, 2, 3, . . . , it is seen that for the nonrelativistic systems which are being considered, the total number of particles is a constant of the motion. N therefore commutes with the Hamiltonian and the density matrix may be taken to be simultaneously diagonal in H and N. In a manner similar to that for the canonical ensemble, the disorder parameter may be maximized subject to the conditions that both the energy and the particle number assume some prescribed average value:

$$\delta\sigma = \delta\,(\mathrm{tr}\,\boldsymbol{\rho}\ln\boldsymbol{\rho}) = 0, \tag{18–69}$$

subject to

$$\mathrm{tr}\,\mathbf{H}\boldsymbol{\rho} = [E], \qquad \mathrm{tr}\,\mathbf{N}\boldsymbol{\rho} = [N], \qquad \mathrm{tr}\,\boldsymbol{\rho} = 1. \tag{18–70}$$

Thus

$$0 = \mathrm{tr}\,[\ln\boldsymbol{\rho} + \lambda\mathbf{H} + \nu\mathbf{N} - \ln A]\,\delta\boldsymbol{\rho}, \tag{18–71}$$

and

$$\boldsymbol{\rho} = A\exp(-\lambda\mathbf{H} - \nu\mathbf{N}), \tag{18–72}$$

where A, λ, and ν are constants. For a representation with $\mathbf{H}$ and $\mathbf{N}$ simultaneously diagonal, $\boldsymbol{\rho}$ is also diagonal. An ensemble represented by a density matrix of the form of Eq. (18–72) is known as a *grand canonical ensemble.*

18–6 Systems of noninteracting particles. As discussed in Chapter 17, there are important, sizable effects arising from the symmetry requirements imposed when a system is composed of particles which cannot be distinguished. In this section, a system of noninteracting particles will be treated under the varying assumptions that the particles can be distinguished, that they are Bose particles, and that they are Fermi particles.

First we will consider the particles to be distinguishable. A system composed of otherwise equivalent but distinguishable particles is known as a *Boltzmann system* or a system obeying Boltzmann statistics. We will designate the single-particle energy levels of the system by the nondegenerate energies E_i. The total energy of the system is then

$$E = \sum_i n_i E_i, \tag{18–73}$$

where n_i is the number of particles with energy E_i. The energy E is an energy level of the gas treated as a single system. It has a degeneracy

$$g_E = \frac{N!}{\prod_i n_i!}, \tag{18–74}$$

where

$$N = \sum_i n_i. \tag{18–75}$$

This degeneracy follows because all the $N!$ permutations of the N particles lead to different energy states for the whole gas, except those which interchange particles only in the same single-particle state E_i.

To calculate the average value of n_i, we can use the canonical ensemble. The average value of n_i can then be written, using Eqs. (18–62), (18–68), and (18–74), as

$$[n_i] = \frac{1}{Z} \sum \frac{N!}{\prod_j n_j!}\, n_i \exp\left(-\frac{E}{kT}\right), \tag{18–76}$$

where the sum is over all possible sets of values of n_j, subject to the condition of Eq. (18–75). The quantity Z, known as the *sum-over-states*, or *partition function*, is given by

$$Z \equiv \sum \frac{N!}{\prod_j n_j!} \exp\left(-\frac{E}{kT}\right), \tag{18–77}$$

again with the condition of Eq. (18–75) on the sum. Note that Eq. (18–76) is simply a sum over all possible values of n_i, each value being multiplied by the probability of that particular value occurring. Because of the degeneracy of the energy level with energy

$$E = \sum_i n_i E_i, \tag{18–78}$$

the Boltzmann factor of Eq. (18–62) must be multiplied by the degeneracy factor of Eq. (18–74) if it is to represent a sum over all the states represented by a particular choice of the occupation numbers $n_1, n_2, \ldots$

The partition function Z can be evaluated explicitly by noting that a polynomial expansion gives

$$Z = \left[\exp\left(-\frac{E_1}{kT}\right) + \exp\left(-\frac{E_2}{kT}\right) + \cdots\right]^N. \tag{18–79}$$

It may also be noted that Eq. (18–76) can be written as

$$\begin{aligned}[n_i] &= -\frac{1}{Z}\frac{\partial Z}{\partial(E_i/kT)} = -\frac{\partial\,(\ln Z)}{\partial(E_i/kT)} \\ &= N\frac{\exp\,(-E_i/kT)}{\sum_j \exp\,(-E_j/kT)}.\end{aligned} \tag{18–80}$$

This result is identical to that obtained by considering the system as composed of N noninteracting single-particle systems and applying Eq. (18–62) directly to the single-particle systems. Thus it is apparent that a complicated formalism has been used to obtain a simple result. The real value of this technique appears only after the indistinguishability of the particles is taken into account.

Next let us consider the case of indistinguishable particles that satisfy Bose statistics. Any permutation of the particles leads to no change in the wave function; the stationary state is specified completely by the quantum numbers n_i, and the state is nondegenerate. Hence for Bose particles, the degeneracy factor of Eq. (18–74) must be replaced by unity. Again the average value $[n_i]$ will be calculated. However, it is inconvenient to use the canonical ensemble because the resulting sum is difficult to evaluate. Hence we use the grand canonical ensemble, Eq. (18–72). This gives, in place of Eq. (18–76),

$$[n_i] = \frac{1}{Z}\sum_{n_1=0}^{\infty}\sum_{n_2=0}^{\infty}\cdots n_i \exp\left(-\frac{E}{kT} - \nu N\right), \tag{18–81}$$

with

$$\begin{aligned}Z &\equiv \sum_{n_1=0}^{\infty}\sum_{n_2=0}^{\infty}\cdots \exp\left(-\frac{E}{kT} - \nu N\right), \\ E &\equiv \sum_i n_i E_i, \\ N &\equiv \sum_i n_i.\end{aligned} \tag{18–82}$$

The partition function can be written as

$$Z = \prod_i \sum_{n_i=0}^{\infty} \exp\left(-\frac{n_i E_i}{kT} - \nu n_i\right)$$

$$= \prod_i \frac{1}{1 - \exp\left[-(E_i/kT) - \nu\right]}. \tag{18-83}$$

Again,

$$[n_i] = -\frac{\partial \ln Z}{\partial(E_i/kT)} = \frac{1}{\exp\left[(E_i/kT) + \nu\right] - 1}. \tag{18-84}$$

The constant ν is determined from the requirement that

$$[N] = \sum_i [n_i] = \sum_i \frac{1}{\exp\left[(E_i/kT) + \nu\right] - 1}. \tag{18-85}$$

With Fermi statistics, the Pauli exclusion principle holds; i.e., the wave function changes sign under any odd permutation, and the occupation numbers n_i can only be either zero or unity. Once again these occupation numbers completely specify the state, and the degeneracy is unity. If we employ the grand canonical ensemble, we find that

$$[n_i] = \frac{1}{Z} \sum_{n_1=0}^{1} \sum_{n_2=0}^{1} \cdots n_i \exp\left(-\frac{E}{kT} - \nu N\right), \tag{18-86}$$

with

$$Z \equiv \sum_{n_1=0}^{1} \sum_{n_2=0}^{1} \cdots \exp\left(-\frac{E}{kT} - \nu N\right). \tag{18-87}$$

The partition function can be written as

$$Z = \prod_i \left[1 + \exp\left(-\frac{E_i}{kT} - \nu\right)\right]. \tag{18-88}$$

Then

$$[n_i] = -\frac{\partial \ln Z}{\partial(E_i/kT)} = \frac{1}{\exp\left[(E_i/kT) + \nu\right] + 1}. \tag{18-89}$$

As for the case of the Bose system, the constant ν is evaluated by the condition that

$$\sum_i [n_i] = [N]. \tag{18-90}$$

In the case of Fermi statistics, ν (which is dimensionless) is usually written in the form

$$\nu = -\frac{E_F}{kT}, \tag{18-91}$$

where E_F is known as the *Fermi energy* (or *level*) of the system. Equations (18-80), (18-84), and (18-89) can all be written in the form

$$[n_i] = \frac{1}{\exp[(E_i/kT) + \nu] + \beta}, \tag{18-92}$$

with $\beta = 0$, -1, and $+1$ for Boltzmann, Bose, and Fermi statistics respectively.

18-7 Ideal gas. As an example of the application of the three kinds of statistics, Boltzmann, Bose, and Fermi, to a system of noninteracting particles, we will consider the classic example of an ideal gas. A Boltzmann gas may seem of no physical significance because molecules of any gas are in fact indistinguishable. However, it is possible to have systems for which the individual molecules possess internal states with large degeneracy, e.g., molecules with large spins associated with one or more of their constituents; such molecules are approximately distinguishable by virtue of possessing different spin orientations. A gas of such molecules approximates, therefore, a Boltzmann system.

Equation (18-92) is immediately applicable to the case of an ideal gas. However, it can be written in a more convenient form if the degeneracy of one-particle energy states for a box are included explicitly. The case of a particle in a one-dimensional box was treated in Chapter 3. If the results obtained there are generalized to three dimensions and the origin is moved from the center of the box to one corner, the wave function for a (spinless) particle in a cubical box of side a becomes

$$\psi_{qrs} = \left(\frac{8}{a^3}\right)^{1/2} \sin\frac{\pi qx}{a} \sin\frac{\pi ry}{a} \sin\frac{\pi sz}{a}, \qquad q, r, s = 1, 2, 3, \ldots \tag{18-93}$$

The corresponding energy of the particle is

$$E = \frac{\pi^2\hbar^2}{2ma^2}(q^2 + r^2 + s^2). \tag{18-94}$$

Since the energy spacings between levels are so small for any reasonable values of particle mass m and box size a, it is convenient to assume that the energy levels are distributed continuously and to consider the number of energy states $dn(E)$ in an energy range dE about E. This distribution function can be found by considering the (integral) parameters q, r, and s as the components of a vector in momentum space. Equation (18–94) is the equation for a sphere in this space, and the volume dV of one octant of the spherical shell of radius $R = (a/\pi\hbar)(2mE)^{1/2}$ and thickness $dR = (a/\pi\hbar)(m/2E)^{1/2}\,dE$ is the number of energy states $dn(E)$ in the energy range dE. Thus

$$dn(E) = \frac{1}{8} \times 4\pi R^2\,dR = \frac{m}{2\pi^2}\left(\frac{a}{\hbar}\right)^3 (2mE)^{1/2}\,dE. \tag{18–95}$$

If the particles have a spin s, there are $2s + 1$ possible spin orientations for each of these translational states. The state density is then given by Eq. (18–95) multiplied by the factor $(2s + 1)$. The number of particles dN in the gas in the energy range dE about E is obtained from Eqs. (18–92) and (18–95):

$$dN = \frac{m}{2\pi^2}\left(\frac{a}{\hbar}\right)^3 (2mE)^{1/2} \frac{dE}{\exp\,[(E/kT) + \nu] + \beta}, \tag{18–96}$$

where $\beta = 0$, -1, or $+1$, depending on the statistics. If spin degeneracy is included and the particles have spin s, the number of particles in the gas per unit volume and energy is

$$W(E) = \frac{m(2mE)^{1/2}}{2\pi^2\hbar^3} \frac{2s + 1}{\exp\,[(E/kT) + \nu] + \beta}. \tag{18–97}$$

As discussed previously, the constant ν must be chosen so as to give the correct particle density.

One point should be noted in connection with Eq. (18–97). It is clear that for the case of Bose statistics, ν cannot be negative or else, from Eq. (18–84), $[n_i]$ could become negative. The highest particle density therefore corresponds to $\nu = 0$. However, if ν is set equal to zero and Eq. (18–97) is integrated over all possible energies, a *finite* particle density is obtained. It would thus appear that the formalism developed is unable to account properly for high-density Bose gases. This is not the case, however. The confusion arises from considering the particle density distribution function $W(E)$ as associated with a *continuum* of states. Considering ideal gas states as discrete, however, Eq. (18–84) shows that it is possible to have an infinite particle density associated with just the lowest energy state, $E_i = 0$.*

It is clear from Eq. (18–97) that ν approaches infinity as the particle density goes to zero. Under this condition, all three distribution functions

* For a more detailed discussion, see E. Schrödinger, *Statistical Thermodynamics*, Cambridge University Press, 1952, Chapter 8.

corresponding to different values of β reduce to the same form. Consequently, the effects of particle indistinguishability become important only at high particle densities. Note from Eq. (18–92) that when ν is sufficiently great to give substantially the same distribution functions for all three types of statistics, i.e., when $\exp \nu \gg 1$, then $[n_i] \ll 1$ for all values of i. Stated in physical terms, it is only when the particle density is sufficiently great to give an appreciable probability of finding more than one particle in the same state that any important effect results from the identity of particles.

To show the effect of statistics on the distribution of molecules of an ideal gas among the possible particle-in-a-box energy states, we have plotted Eq. (18–92) in Figs. 18–1 through 18–3 for the three different statistics for three different particle densities. The values of ν have been chosen so that each figure corresponds to the same total particle density. The average numbers of particles in the lowest energy state ($E = 0$) are given in Table 18–1 for the three statistics. Figure 18–1 corresponds to a low particle density. We see that except for the very lowest energies, the effects of particle indistinguishability are negligible.

Figure 18–2 corresponds to a case where the particle density has been increased by a factor of 10. We see that at this density the effects of particle identity are already becoming pronounced. Two features should be noted: in the Bose gas, there is a definite tendency for the lowest energy states to be populated relative to the higher energy states, and in the Fermi gas, the low-energy states have a tendency toward an abnormally low population. The first of these effects is known as the *Bose condensation*. Under conditions of high density (small ν), for which there is a noticeable Bose condensation, an increase in the particle density merely results in a higher concentration of low-energy particles. The gas pressure does not

TABLE 18–1

AVERAGE POPULATION $[n_0]$ OF THE GROUND-ENERGY STATE FOR THE THREE PARTICLE DENSITIES SHOWN IN FIGS. 18–1 THROUGH 18–3.

Figure	Statistics		
	Maxwell-Boltzmann	Bose-Einstein	Fermi-Dirac
18–1	0.181	0.220	0.153
18–2	1.81	15.88	0.77
18–3	27.1	$\sim 0.81N$*	1.0

* Valid for reasonably high particle densities. This huge number is typical of the Bose condensation.

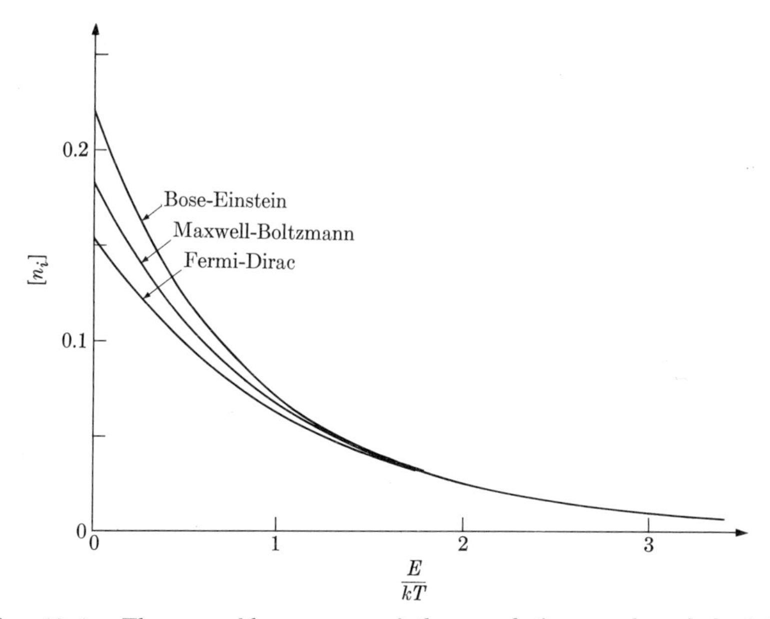

FIG. 18–1. The ensemble averages of the population numbers $[n_i]$ of the various energy states of a free particle in a box, for an ideal gas obeying the three statistics: Maxwell-Boltzmann, Bose-Einstein, and Fermi-Dirac.

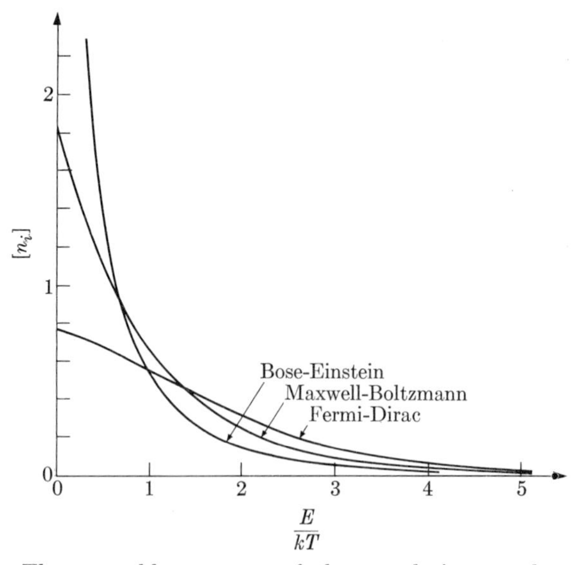

FIG. 18–2. The ensemble averages of the population numbers $[n_i]$ of the various energy states of a free particle in a box, for an ideal gas obeying the three statistics. The density of the gas represented in this figure is 10 times that of the gas represented in Fig. 18–1. Note the change of scales. The Bose gas is beginning to show a condensation in the lower energy states.

increase appreciably. In this sense, a Bose gas behaves something like a saturated vapor: increasing the amount of the substance merely increases the amount in the "condensed" phase without materially increasing the pressure. This condensation is shown in more striking form in Fig. 18–3, which corresponds to a further increase in the particle density by a factor of 15.

Note that the parameter ν is not only a function of the particle density, but also of the temperature. Figures 18–1 through 18–3 have been drawn to show the effect of increasing the particle density while holding the temperature constant. Qualitatively, the general shape of the curves also corresponds to the effect of *lowering* the temperature at constant particle density, but of course this cannot hold quantitatively.

As a further illustration of the effects of particle indistinguishability, Eq. (18–97) is plotted in Fig. 18–4 for the case of Fermi particles of spin one-half for the three values of ν illustrated in Figs. 18–1, 18–2, and 18–3.

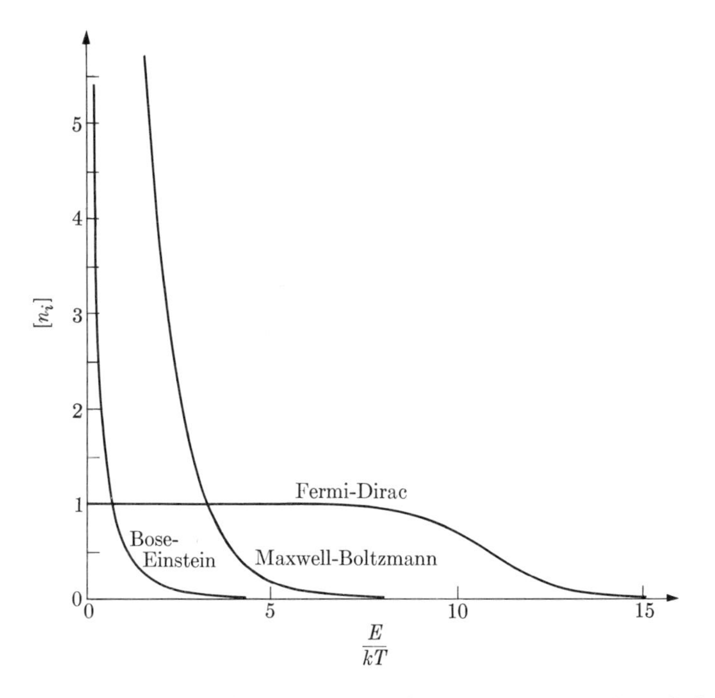

FIG. 18–3. The ensemble averages of the population numbers $[n_i]$ of the various energy states of a free particle in a box for an ideal gas obeying the three statistics. The density of the gas represented in this figure is 150 times that of the gas represented in Fig. 18–1. Extreme degeneration effects are seen in both the Fermi and Bose systems. (See also Table 18–1.)

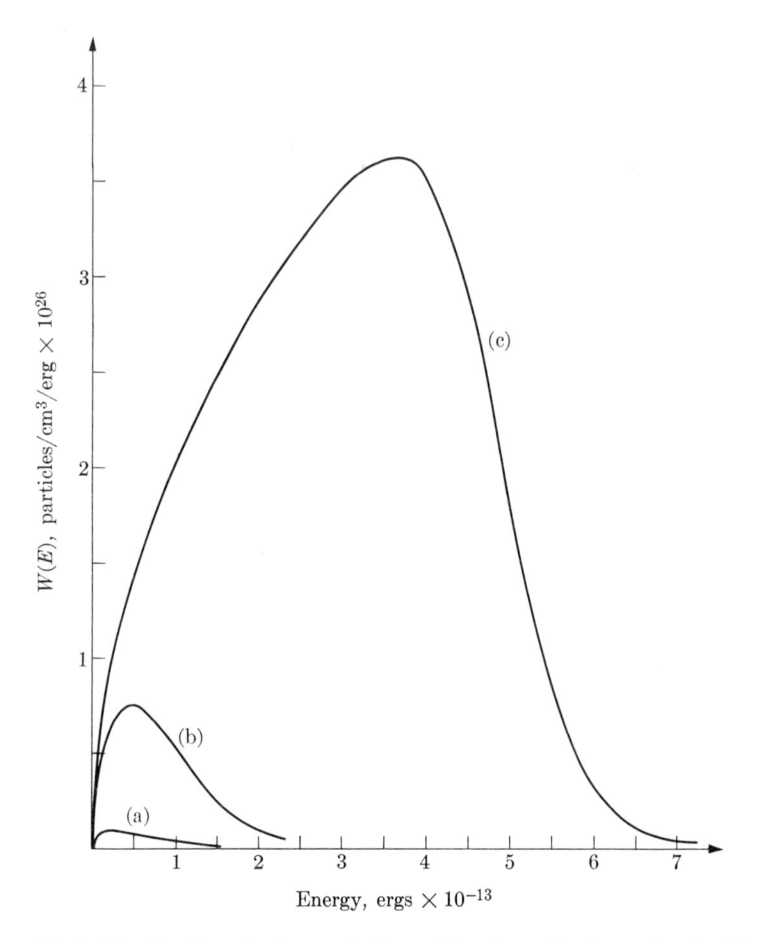

FIG. 18–4. The density of spin one-half particles in an ideal gas obeying Fermi statistics, per unit energy range, plotted against energy, for the three particle densities illustrated in Figs. 18–1 through 18–3. The curves are drawn for particles of mass $m = 9.11 \times 10^{-28}$ gm at room temperature ($T = 293$°K). Curve (a) corresponds to Fig. 18–1 and a particle density of $N = 8.78 \times 10^{11}/\text{cm}^3$. Curve (b) corresponds to Fig. 18–2 and $N = 8.78 \times 10^{12}/\text{cm}^3$. Curve (c) corresponds to Fig. 18–3 and $N = 1.32 \times 10^{14}/\text{cm}^3$.

18–8 Summary. This introduction to quantum mechanics has concluded with a discussion of quantum-statistical mechanics. The idea of mixed states, corresponding to incomplete knowledge of the system, was introduced, and distribution functions were shown to provide a complete physical description of an ensemble of similar systems. The density matrix was introduced and was shown to be Hermitian with unity trace. The case of spin orientations in an ensemble of spin-one-half particles was considered as an elementary application of density matrices. The concept of a random system was introduced. Electron-interference experiments were discussed briefly in terms of density matrices.

The equation of motion of the density matrix was derived, and an expression for the equation of motion of an observable was found in terms of the density matrix. Ordered and disordered ensembles were discussed, and a quantum definition of entropy was given. Next, various stationary ensembles—random, microcanonical, canonical, and grand canonical—were considered. The question of distinguishability of particles in systems of noninteracting particles was examined, and some properties of systems of Maxwell-Boltzmann, Bose-Einstein, and Fermi-Dirac particles were developed. These results were applied to an ideal gas confined in a box, and some physical differences associated with the gases corresponding to the different statistics were used as illustrative examples.

Problems

18–1. The state of polarization of a photon can be described by a wave function in the form of a two-component column vector. [As has been seen, the photon behaves like a particle with spin $s = 1$, but the component of spin $m_s = 0$ never appears when the axis of quantization is chosen to coincide with the direction of propagation of the light. The polarization state is then characterized by the amplitudes of the ($m_s = \pm 1$) substates.] The polarization state of an ensemble of photons (a partially polarized light beam) can then be characterized by the density matrix

$$\rho_{ij} = \langle a_i \overline{a_j} \rangle_{\text{avg}},$$

where $a_{\pm 1}$ are the two amplitudes of the circular polarization states $m_s = \pm 1$. Show that the state of polarization of a light beam usually requires three real numbers for its description.

18–2. In terms of the representation described in Problem 18–1, the circular polarization of a photon has as its operator the Pauli two-component spin operator σ_z. In similar fashion, σ_x and σ_y are operators for measurements of plane polarization. (More generally, linear combinations of σ_x and σ_y represent arbitrary sets of orthogonal plane-polarization states.) (a) By analogy with the discussion of particle spin states with $s = \frac{1}{2}$, find the density matrix of a completely unpolarized light beam. (b) What is the average value of each of the three polarization operators σ_x, σ_y, and σ_z for such an unpolarized light beam? (c) Compute the disorder parameter $\sigma = -\text{tr}\, \boldsymbol{\rho} \ln \boldsymbol{\rho}$ for an unpolarized light beam. (d) What is σ for a completely polarized light beam?

18–3. (a) Show that a light beam of arbitrary polarization can always be considered to be a mixture of a beam of completely polarized light and a beam of unpolarized light. (b) Show that the disorder parameter σ is determined completely by the amount of unpolarized light in the mixture.

18–4. Show that a completely unpolarized light beam may be considered to be a mixture of two completely polarized light beams of equal intensity but opposite polarization. The polarization of these polarized beams may be plane, circular, or elliptical.

18–5. In a solid, in addition to the "core" electrons which are tightly bound to individual atoms in the crystal lattice, there are "valence" electrons which contribute to the chemical forces holding the crystal together. These valence electrons cannot be associated uniquely with individual atoms, but must be associated with the crystal as a whole. The allowed energy states for these electrons form continua, or *bands*. In many materials, certain of these bands are separated by *energy gaps* in which no allowed electron states exist. (See Fig. 18–5.) If the valence electrons only partially fill the uppermost (*conduction*) band, the electrons are easily excited into the unfilled energy states, and the crystal exhibits metallic conduction. In an insulator, the electrons just fill the so-called *valence* band of allowed states and are not free to conduct electricity unless they are highly excited across the energy gap into the higher-lying conduction band.

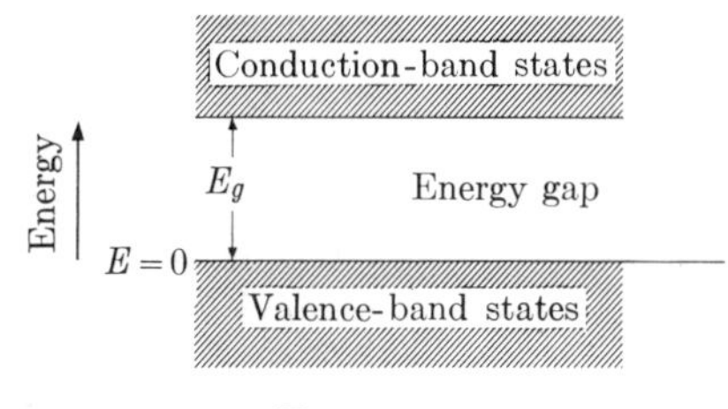

FIGURE 18–5

In a semiconductor at absolute zero temperature, the valence-band states are filled and the conduction-band states are empty; i.e., the semiconductor is an insulator. As the temperature is raised, however, the electrons can be thermally excited across the energy gap. It is, in general, a reasonable approximation to assume that the electrons excited to the conduction band behave much as if they were free. Measuring the electron energies from the *top of the valence band*, the density of conduction band states is then

$$g(E)\,dE = \frac{1}{2\pi^2}\left(\frac{2m_e}{\hbar^2}\right)^{3/2}(E - E_g)^{1/2}\,dE.$$

Because the electrons in a crystal are not really free, the actual electron mass must be replaced by an "effective mass" m_e in the crystal. (a) Assuming that $(E - E_F) \gg kT$, compute the number of electrons excited thermally into the conduction band at temperature T, in terms of the energy gap E_g and the Fermi energy E_F.

Whenever an electron is excited into the conduction band, it leaves behind it in the valence band a "hole." This hole behaves like a free particle of charge $+e$ and (effective) mass m_h. (b) Assuming that the density of hole states is given by

$$g(E)\,dE = \frac{1}{2\pi^2}\left(\frac{2m_h}{\hbar^2}\right)^{3/2}(-E)^{1/2}\,dE$$

(zero energy at the top of the valence band) and that $(E_F - E) \gg kT$ for states in the valence band, find the equilibrium number of holes at temperature T in terms of E_g and E_F.

In a pure semiconductor, the number of conduction-band electrons equals the number of valence-band holes. (c) Use this condition and the above results to determine the Fermi energy E_F as a function of T. (d) Show that for $m_e = m_h$, the Fermi energy is in the middle of the band gap, that is, $E_F = \frac{1}{2}E_g$.

18–6. Photons may be considered as particles obeying Bose-Einstein statistics. Using the expression derived in the text for the average number of particles (photons) in any energy state, together with the expression of Chapter 1 for the density of modes of electromagnetic vibration per unit volume in an enclosure, obtain the Planck radiation law, Eq. (1–4). [*Note:* In deriving the expression for $[n_i]$ in the text, the Lagrangian multiplier ν was introduced to impose the constraint that the total number of particles $\sum_i [n_i] = N$ be a constant. In the case of radiation, however, photons are created and destroyed, and the total number need not be conserved. The removal of this constraint for the case of photons is obtained by setting $\nu = 0$.]

18–7. Use density-matrix formalism to compute the expectation value of the magnetic moment of an ensemble of spin-one-half particles located in a large static field when a small oscillating field near resonance acts perpendicular to the static field. The weak oscillating field can be described by matrix elements $H_{12} = H_{21} = -\mu\mathcal{B}\cos\omega t$, where subscripts 1 and 2 refer respectively to the higher- and lower-energy spin states of (unperturbed) energies $E_1 = \mu\mathcal{B}_0$ and $E_2 = -\mu\mathcal{B}_0$. Here μ is the magnetic moment of each spin, $\mathcal{B}$ is the magnitude of the oscillating field, $\mathcal{B}_0$ is that of the static field, and ω is the (circular) frequency of the oscillating field.

In considering the equations of motion of the individual density-matrix components, remember that relaxation mechanisms are operative. The above perturbation elements include only the effects of the electromagnetic fields acting on the ensemble; the relaxation-effect terms have not been given. These will produce changes in the density matrix tending to restore it to the form characterizing thermal equilibrium. The effect of relaxation processes is to maintain ρ_{11} and ρ_{22} constant (at values which may be altered from those of thermal equilibrium). Thus $\partial\rho_{11}/\partial t$ and $\partial\rho_{22}/\partial t$ may be taken equal to zero. Also, in evaluating ρ_{12}, neglect the nonresonant term $1/(\omega + \omega_0)$ and the transient term of the form $A\exp(-i\omega_0 t)$, where $\omega_0 = (E_1 - E_2)/\hbar$. (a) Show that, with these approximations, the density matrix has the form

$$\boldsymbol{\rho} = \begin{bmatrix} \rho_{11} & \dfrac{1}{2}\dfrac{\mu\mathcal{B}}{\hbar}\dfrac{(\rho_{11} - \rho_{22})}{\omega_0 - \omega}\exp(-i\omega t) \\ \dfrac{1}{2}\dfrac{\mu\mathcal{B}}{\hbar}\dfrac{(\rho_{11} - \rho_{22})}{\omega_0 - \omega}\exp(i\omega t) & \rho_{22} \end{bmatrix}.$$

(Because of the approximations made, the off-diagonal terms are singular on resonance. A more exact treatment would lead to finite terms on resonance.) (b) From this density matrix and the Pauli spin matrices, evaluate the expectation values of the three components of the net magnetic moment of the ensemble.

18–8. Show that the trace of the product of two matrices is independent of the order of the product.

18–9. Use the density-matrix formalism to compute the spin paramagnetic susceptibility of an ideal electron gas. (Neglect interactions between the electrons.)

18–10. In an electron gas, one-half of the electrons have had their z-spin component measured. Compute the maximum possible value of $[\sigma_x]$.

18–11. A low-density plasma has each electron spin polarized in the x-direction at $t = 0$. (a) Write a density matrix for the electron spins, assuming that a uniform magnetic field in the z-direction acts on the plasma. (b) Assuming a collision relaxation mechanism, how does the density matrix vary with time? (c) How does the disorder parameter (Eq. 18–37) vary with time? [*Hint:* With collision relaxation, each electron suffering a collision is depolarized.]

18–12. Calculate the density matrix representing an ensemble of particles for which the mean value of the square of the x-coordinate is a^2. [*Note:* It should be assumed that the ensemble has only as much *order* as is implied by the above statement. Hence, the disorder parameter (Eq. 18–37) should be maximized subject to this condition.]

18–13. (a) Calculate the density matrix representing an ensemble of particles for which the mean values of x^2 and p_x^2 are a^2 and b^2 respectively. (See Problem 18–12.) (b) Show that the product ab must exceed some lower bound. (c) What is this bound? (d) What is Eq. (18–37) at the lower bound? (e) Compute σ as a function of ab.

18–14. As discussed in Problem 15–7, the ground state of atomic hydrogen is split by the hyperfine interaction into two states of total angular momentum $F = 1$ and $F = 0$. Here the total angular momentum is

$$\mathbf{F} \equiv \mathbf{S} + \mathbf{I},$$

where $\mathbf{I}$ is the proton spin angular momentum and $\mathbf{S}$ is the spin of the electron. ($I = \frac{1}{2}$, $s = \frac{1}{2}$.) The spin-spin interaction term in the Hamiltonian which leads to this hyperfine splitting can be written for the ground state as $\Delta E(\mathrm{F}^2 - \frac{3}{2}\hbar^2)/2\hbar^2$, with $\Delta E = h\nu$ and $\nu = 1420$ Mc/sec.

Collisions between hydrogen atoms in a gas of atomic hydrogen lead generally to electron exchange effects which serve to transfer energy freely between the translational and spin degrees of freedom of the gas. In such electron interchanges the total spin angular momentum of the gas is left unchanged. (a) Compute the density matrix for the internal spin states of a hydrogen gas assumed to be initially polarized by a magnetic field which is then suddenly switched off. [*Hint:* The individual hydrogen atoms may be treated approximately as independent dynamical systems interacting with a heat bath at a temperature T. The resulting statistical equilibrium is such that the mean angular momentum $[\boldsymbol{F}]$ takes on the value given by the initial polarization. The density matrix then takes on the canonical form but is modified by the additional condition that the mean value of $\mathbf{F}$ is predetermined.] (b) Compute the following average values: $[S_z]$, $[I_z]$, $[F^2]$. (c) How does the internal spin energy of the gas depend upon $[\boldsymbol{F}]^2$?

TABLE OF ATOMIC CONSTANTS

Electron charge:

$e = 4.80294 \pm 0.00008 \times 10^{-10}$ esu

Electron mass:

$m = 9.1086 \pm 0.0003 \times 10^{-28}$ grams

Proton mass:

$M_p = 1.67245 \pm 0.00005 \times 10^{-24}$ grams

Velocity of light:

$c = 2.997928 \pm 0.000004 \times 10^{10}$ cm/sec

Planck's constant:

$h = 6.6254 \pm 0.0002 \times 10^{-27}$ erg-sec

Avogadro's number:

$N_0 = 6.0247 \pm 0.0002 \times 10^{23}$/mol

Fine-structure constant:

$\alpha = 7.29729 \pm 0.00003 \times 10^{-3}$

$\alpha^{-1} = 137.0371 \pm 0.0005$

Boltzmann constant:

$k = 1.38049 \pm 0.00005 \times 10^{-16}$ erg/°K

Bohr magneton:

$\mu_0 = 9.2733 \pm 0.0002 \times 10^{-21}$ erg/oersted

Rydberg constant:

$R_\infty = 13.6050$ ev

Stefan-Boltzmann constant:

$\sigma = 5.6696 \pm 0.0004 \times 10^{-5}$ erg/cm^2-sec-°K^4

Bohr radius (hydrogen atom):

$a_0 = 5.29173 \pm 0.00002 \times 10^{-9}$ cm

Electron Compton wavelength:

$\lambda\!\!\!^{-}_c = \hbar/mc = \alpha a_0 = 3.86153 \pm 0.00004 \times 10^{-11}$ cm

"Classical" electron radius:

$r_0 = e^2/mc^2 = \alpha \lambda\!\!\!^{-}_c = 2.8179 \pm 0.0002 \times 10^{-13}$ cm

Rest energy of electron:

$mc^2 = 0.511$ Mev

Rest energy of proton:

$M_pc^2 = 931$ Mev

Ionization energy (hydrogen atom):

$I_0(\mathrm{H}) = 13.55$ ev

INDEX